# A GUIDE TO BRITISH BREWERS

# A GUIDE
# TO
# BRITISH BREWERS
## Their Beers and Pubs

Peter Tombs

Illustrations by Emma Tombs

SIDGWICK & JACKSON

LONDON

# *Acknowledgments*

With thanks to all the brewers, without whose help this guide could not have been compiled, and to Bill Yeomans, the greatest ale-taster and chauffeur of them all.

First published in Great Britain in 1990 by
Sidgwick & Jackson Limited

Text copyright π 1990 by Peter Tombs
Illustrations copyright π 1990 by Emma Tombs

ISBN 0 283 99996 9

Typeset by Macmillan Production Limited
Printed by Billings Ltd of Worcester
for Sidgwick & Jackson Limited
1 Tavistock Chambers, Bloomsbury Way,
London WC1A 2SG

# Contents

# CHAPTER ONE

# A Brief History of Breweries

The earliest evidence of an alcoholic beverage being brewed in Britain comes from Bronze Age burial sites dating to around 3000 BC. This is by no means the earliest evidence in the world (the Ancient Egyptians were very fond of beer). No doubt an accidental soaking of barley, or perhaps a chance fermentation of honey, led to the first British hangover more than five thousand years ago.

By the first century AD British coins were depicting ears of barley and it is known that the Romans, on landing in Kent, discovered to their disgust that instead of wine the locals drank a form of ale. The historian of the times, Pliny the Elder, recorded that scenes of drunkenness among the natives were observed wherever the invaders went. Certainly we know that over the next few centuries the brewing and drinking of beer became interwoven into the fabric of social life.

So widespread was the habit after the Romans had gone that by the sixth and seventh centuries officialdom was forced to intervene with the first laws relating to beer. Ina, King of Wessex, established alehouses by law and penalties were fixed for bad brewing. By 965 AD King Edgar found it necessary to close down many of those taverns, allowing only one alehouse per village to remain. To combat disreputable inn-keepers the Magna Carta of 1215 decreed that there should be a standard measure for ale.

Those early ales were likely to have been cloyingly sweet and liable to rapid deterioration. Quality would have varied from one alehouse to another and from one brew to the next. Brewing was carried out at home as well as in the taverns, but as stability returned to Britain after the Norman Invasion and transport facilities improved, the significance of the roadside tavern increased.

The beers were sometimes flavoured with herbs but the introduction of hops from the Low Countries was a comparatively late development in the history of British beer. The British, preferring their strong sweet ales, resisted the use of hops, despite their obvious advantages of flavour and preservative value. Consequently, the fifteenth century was underway before Continental hops began to make an appearance in British beers.

By this time taxes and controls on beers had become familiar. As early as 1188 Henry II had raised the Saladin Tithe, a tax on beer, and the price had been regulated by the Assize of Bread and Ale in 1267. The Assize appointed ale-tasters to exercise some control over brewers. In Alcester, Warwickshire, for example, there is to this day an annual tour of pubs by the officially appointed ale-tasters. For about four hundred years beer was mainly brewed on the premises and thus each publican produced his own ale. Some of them abused their position and it was the job of the ale-tasters to keep a check.

The first hint of licensing public houses came in 1495. Henry VII gave justices the power to close taverns if they thought it necessary. Quite a number of brewers found that permission to sell liquor was withdrawn. Since that date the control of licensed premises and licensing hours has gradually tightened.

As an inevitable result of the controls on beer quality, a new breed began to emerge in the sixteenth century – the common brewers. It had been only a question of time before the demand for the products of the better brewers enabled them to produce beers for more than one outlet. Besides the obvious economies of scale of brewing in greater quantities, a more consistent type of ale could be provided and more attention could be given to maturing the beers.

The process which would inevitably lead to the establishment of the large breweries had begun. First these common brewers, who gradually spread around the country from their beginnings in London, eroded the home-brew house market and then even more substantial companies began to take large portions of the trade. The first of the major brewing companies was set up in the eighteenth century: the brewery which was to become Devenish in Weymouth was founded in 1742. Two years later Worthington of Burton upon Trent began brewing. Hartley's of Ulverston, Cumbria, was founded

THE OLDEST
LICENSED HOUSE
IN GREAT BRITAIN

LICENSED OVER 510 YEARS

Seven Stars, Manchester

in 1754. Many others were established around the same time.

The steady trend away from the publican brewer continued as the numbers of common brewers increased, a process which was accelerated by the Industrial Revolution. As many of the population moved from a rural to an urban way of life, so the concentration of beer drinkers in the towns and cities provided the ideal market for large-scale breweries. The family firms which had become established during the eighteenth century were able to expand production and build up large estates of their own public houses.

New technology improved brewing. Steam was used to mechanise processes which had previously been undertaken by men or horses. Scientific advances were made – the two essential tools of the brewer, the hydrometer and the thermometer, became widely available. More was being learned about what actually happened in the mash tun and fermentation vessel and this new detailed understanding of the brewing process helped to improve beer quality.

From about 24,000 breweries in Britain at the start of the nineteenth century, the next 100 years saw a steady decrease to slightly over 6,000. The publican brewer had largely been replaced by the common brewer and the common brewers had become large companies. This trend continued apace during the first half of the twentieth century. The pike were gobbling up the minnows, and mergers made sizeable companies even stronger. The total number of breweries dropped below 1,000 for the first time just before the Second World War.

The tied-house system enabled the ambitious to buy up smaller breweries and so acquire the victims' estates of public houses as new outlets for their own beers. And the companies were beginning to dictate taste. The introduction of canned beers by Felinfoel in 1935 may not have been a disaster, but the dreaded keg beer was another matter. Pressurised beers began to take hold as the brewers started to exploit the manipulative influence of modern advertising.

During the 1960s the 'Big Six' emerged as the power of British brewing – Allied, Bass, Courage, Scottish and Newcastle, Watney's and Whitbread, as they were then known. These monsters continued to grow, feeding on regional brewers. Long-established family breweries disappeared at an alarming rate.

But the consumer objected. The concentration of brewing into such a few companies had reduced choice and enabled those companies to dictate what should and should not be drunk. Suddenly in the 1970s the drinkers began to form a movement. After a few splutterings, the Campaign for Real Ale (CAMRA) emerged to champion the cause. Keg beer was the enemy, particularly the symbolic Watney's Red Barrel. So effective was the uprising that Watneys took refuge and even had to re-paint its pubs. If you walk into the gents' lavatory of the Flamingo and Firkin in Derby today, you will see a barrel of Watney's Red with its tube hanging down into the urinal as a silent testimony to that famous victory.

The new awareness of quality in ale caused the emergence of a number of home-brew enterprises (there had been just four publican brewers left in existence before CAMRA) and small-scale common brewers. Free houses looked to expand their range of beers. Choice became the new priority and keg beers were on the retreat. Even John Smith (part of Courage) and keg stalwarts Mansfield were forced to produce a real ale.

From a low of just over 150 breweries (and bear in mind that about 25 per cent of these were in the hands of the Big Six) there began a modest increase. But there have been numerous casualties along the way. In the euphoria of an increasing demand for real ales many optimistic ventures were established only to collapse within a few years. Only the better brewers with sound marketing techniques were able to survive. The tied-house system meant that they were battling all the time to find outlets for their beers. A small brewery could not offer the inducements (particularly in the form of loans) to the free trader in order to encourage him to sell its ales.

At the same time the Big Six were still determined to change the public's taste. Lager was being promoted at the expense of beer. Advertising campaigns, aimed particularly at the young, tried to push traditional ale into the minority obsession of the T-shirt and beer-belly brigade. 'Lager louts' became the new blight on society, probably sent a little silly by all that injected carbon dioxide. The brewers decided to take pity and add low-alcohol beers and lagers to the shelves so that someone could stay sober enough to drive those fellows home!

In 1988 permitted opening hours were extended. The real-ale revolution had contributed much towards improving the elements of choice for drinkers and certainly the major brewers had been forced to provide traditional beers for their tied houses, but the dominance of the few had not been broken. Of the national beer market, 83 per cent remained the province of just six combines:

| Company | Percentage of market |
| --- | --- |
| Bass | 22 |
| Allied Breweries | 14 |
| Whitbread | 13 |
| Grand Metropolitan | 13 |
| Scottish and Newcastle | 11 |
| Elders IXL | 10 |

Drinkers had been questioning this imbalance of supply for years but it was 1989 before the Government decided to intervene. The Monopolies Report in March of that year had made two main recommendations: that no brewer should hold more than 2,000 public houses, and that the 'tie' should be relaxed so that tenants could stock a guest beer. At first the prospects for small brewers seemed likely to improve. However, after much lobbying and an extravagant advertising campaign by the larger members of the industry, the Government backed down and reduced its assault on pub ownership. It decided that by 1 November 1991 the Big Six must release all product ties on half of their numbers of pubs exceeding 2,000.

It remains to be seen how much opportunity such a relaxation will offer to small brewers through the 1990s, but it must be said that few of them responded to the watered-down proposals with much optimism. However, it is fortunate that such proposals have coincided with an improved stability among the new-wave brewers. In 1989 there was a noticeable drop in the number of annual failures within the mini-sector. It seems certain that the revival of the publican and common brewer will not be a short-lived phenomenon.

CHAPTER TWO

# The Brewing Process

There is no particular secret about the brewing process. The ingredients are familiar ones and the equipment may vary in detail from one brewery to another, but is essentially of standard form. Why then is there such a variation between one company's beers and those of another, or from one region to another? The answer lies in the brewer's choice and blending of the ingredients and in his individual skill. The essence of the subtle art of brewing is to produce a distinctive and yet consistent beer. It is part of our heritage that we have the talented brewers and range of sizes and types of brewery in Britain to provide us with such an outstanding choice of real ales.

## THE RAW MATERIALS OF BREWING

*Malt*  Water may be the first ingredient of the national drink, but malted barley is the most important. The grain from those waving fields of barley, after malting (described on page 9) and milling, provides the basic body of our ales. Long before hops were introduced, soggy fermenting cakes of barley created that foul-smelling ale which the Romans found so disgusting.

Barley is very versatile. Pale malt is the fundamental ingredient of brewing, but a longer period in the kiln or a higher temperature will produce, from the same grain, crystal malt (for a golden colour), dark malt (for milds) or roasted malt (for stouts). There are a number of specialist maltsters around the country whose products have a very individual flavour and provide choice and blending potential for the brewer.

*Hops*  The hop cone used in British brewing is the female flower of the plant. Although only one species of hop is grown in Britain, there are many varieties available, each with its own particular flavour. Hop gardens or yards can be seen in several counties, the main ones being Kent and Hereford and Worcester. The fields are unmistakable with their rows of poles and strings supporting the vines. These days much of the hop harvest from these farms is compressed into pellets and delivered to the breweries in this less bulky, concentrated form.

The advantages of hops to the brewer are three-fold. They import that bitterness and aroma which so characterise British beer; they have a preservative value; and they provide a valuable filter bed for the removal of unwanted material before the wort (sugar-laden liquor) is passed to the fermenting vessels.

*Sugars* Sometimes cane or other sugar is added to increase the gravity of beers. Strict traditional brewers frown on this practice and declare proudly that theirs is an all-malt brew. When sugar is used, and it is quite common even in the larger breweries, it is mixed into the wort for the hop-boil and can make a contribution to the strength, flavour and colour of the end product. It is normally dissolved and added in syrup form.

*Liquor* Water for brewing is known as liquor. The siting of many old breweries was based upon the availability of local well or spring water. A great deal of importance has always been placed on the properties of that water. Burton upon Trent's fame as a brewing centre arose from the presence of gypsum, which is particularly well suited to bitters, in the waters there.

These days fewer and fewer breweries rely upon local waters. The public supplies can be adjusted by chemical treatment to suit whichever type of beer is being brewed. Well water is more likely to be used for cleaning and cooling purposes.

*Yeast* The fermentation of traditional beers is carried out by a top-fermenting beer yeast, which feeds upon the simple sugars of the wort and produces alcohol and carbon dioxide as by-products of its activities. Many breweries can truthfully claim that they are using the same yeast that they were using thirty or forty years ago. At the conclusion of fermentation there will be about six times the amount of yeast originally introduced a week earlier. The surplus is pressed and sold off (it is no accident that Marmite is made in Burton upon Trent), while sufficient is retained for the brewer's future needs.

# THE BREWING PROCESS

*Malting* Ripe barley from the fields is made into a raw material for brewing in maltings. Few breweries these days have their own facilities for the process and the job is left to specialist maltsters. Traditional floor maltings still exist but have largely been replaced by more modern systems.

The grain is steeped in water for around forty-eight hours so that it absorbs sufficient moisture to be ready to grow. It is then allowed seven days of controlled growth. A shoot and rootlets emerge from each grain and the chemical changes that accompany this germination begin to convert the starch in the barley into the sugars which the brewer wants.

At precisely the correct time the 'green' barley is placed in the kiln and dried so as to halt the chemical changes without destroying the enzymes. It can then be cooled, bagged and stored for future use. Although pale malt, after removal of the rootlets, looks much like the original ripened barley from the field, the grains are now ready to complete the process of converting the starch to sugar.

*Milling* When the malt is delivered to the brewery, it is in a whole-grain state. Cracking is necessary in order to release its potential sugars. It is screened and then tipped into a mill to be ground to the right consistency for the mash. Without making the husk disintegrate, the malt is reduced to a coarse powder (known as grist).

*The Mash* The mash tun is the heart of the operation. Grist from a hopper or grist case is mixed in batches with pre-heated liquor – at 150–160°F (65.5–71°C) – by the use of a masher and this enables the essential character of the beer to begin to be created. With the critical temperature under careful control, the mixture (known as the goods) is allowed to stand for around one and a half hours. During this period the reactivated enzymes do their work and the conversion of the starch to sugar is completed.

*Sparging* The sugar-laden liquor (which is called the wort) is drained off and the remaining sugars which are trapped in the goods are washed out by a process known as sparging. A fine spray of hot water, usually from a rotating sparge-arm, coaxes the remainder of the goodness down from the false bottom of the mash tun.

# THE BREWING PROCESS

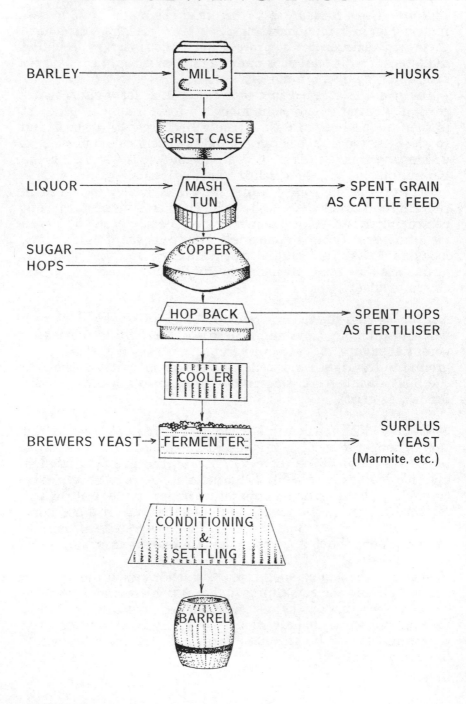

A Brewery Copper

*Boiling* The wort is transferred to a copper and the hops are added. A hop-boil, usually of one hour's duration, blends the flavours of the essential ingredients. The bitterness is extracted from the hops, the wort is thoroughly sterilised and unwanted protein matter is coagulated. That delightful smell of a brewery town, often on a Monday, emanates mainly from the coppers.

*Hop Back*    After boiling, the hops need to be removed and this is achieved in a vessel known as a hop-back. Before being discarded (or, more likely, being sold as fertiliser), they are allowed to settle and act as a filter. In this way unwanted protein matter can be eliminated from the wort.

*Cooling*    An essential part of the brewing process is a rapid cooling of the hot wort. In a tower brewery the liquid will be pumped back to the top of the building to a wort receiver in readiness for the cooling process. It will then be fed through a heat-exchange cooler to reduce its temperature to 60-62°F (15.5-16.5°C). In many breweries a sophisticated Paraflow cooler is used. During the rapid cooling a 'cold break' is induced which is important to the eventual taste and clarity of the beer. A cold break is the point when a reaction between the protein matter and the tannins of malt and hops creates the potential for clarity and a sound fermentation.

*Fermentation*    After cooling the wort may be passed to collecting vessels where the yeast is added and the wort is held for around sixteen hours. Otherwise it may be transferred directly to fermenting vessels and the yeast pitched there. The advantage of using collecting vessels is that the second transfer allows the liquid to be aerated as it is poured into the fermenting vessels and the oxygen absorbed will help the yeast in its work.

A thick creamy head is soon created by the top fermentation and this is usually skimmed off after two days and the temperature in the tank then reduced to around 50°F (10°C). A further five days at this temperature will normally have completed the fermentation.

*Processing*    The young beer is passed to racking squares (collection vessels) where finings and primings – and sometimes colouring agents – are added. For draught beers which are destined for casks the brewer requires the twin potentials of clarity and a slight secondary fermentation in the barrel. Finings will provide the clarity. A milky liquid made from isinglas is added in a measured dose to the beer – these finings will collect any solids in suspension and deposit them on the bottom of the vessel. Primings are merely a light dose of sugar syrup which will induce a secondary fermentation.

*Maturing* Filled casks are normally kept in the brewery for one to three days to ensure a degree of maturation. It may be necessary to add more finings at the end of this period. Dry-hopping – the introduction to each barrel of a small amount of fresh hops – may be effected at this stage, a treatment which gives a distinctive 'tang' to bitter beer when it is eventually drawn off by the publican.

When the draymen have rolled the barrels down to the pub cellar, a further period of maturing is necessary in that cool environment. A good cellarman will 'soft-peg' the barrel (using a special type of wooden peg in a shive to facilitate control of conditions) and make sure that it is otherwise left undisturbed on the thrall (shelf or platform) until the necessary maturation is complete and the beer is ready to be pulled into a pint glass.

## SPECIAL BREWING METHODS

*Burton Union System* A unique brewing method was evolved in Burton upon Trent and its premium bitters have had a distinctive Burton taste because of it. Rather than conducting the whole fermentation in an open tank, the Burton brewers developed a system of rows of oak casks linked by open pipes ('swans' necks') to a trough which ran over the barrels. In the nineteenth century this was a box-shaped wooden trough but it was replaced in later years by stainless steel.

The Union Room at the Bass Brewery was like a cathedral for the real-ale lover. Yeast foamed from each barrel through the swan's neck into the overhead channel and then circulated round as fermentation continued. The oak and the unique system produced a remarkable 'winy' taste in a well-matured beer. Sadly, Bass have abandoned the system. However, about a mile away Marston's still has a Union Room. Locals will tell you, with some justification, that Marston's Pedigree is the finest of all traditional bitters because it is fermented in this special way.

*Malt Extract* At the other end of the brewing spectrum, one of the phenomena of the revival of the publican and small common brewer has been the introduction of malt extract. Home brewers have been buying beer kits based upon this extract of malt for many years, of course, but no major brewer would consider it an adequate substitute for the wort from his mash tun.

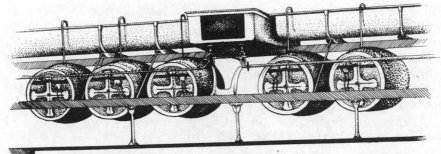

# The Burton Union System

The use of malt extract produces very distinctive, full-flavoured beers and its advantages to the brewer are that it is quick and cheap. The extract can go directly to the boiling stage of the brewing process with added sugar and the hops (the hops may in fact have been pre-boiled in the liquor) and thus the equipment needed in the brewery is considerably less than for a full mash. However, the quality of the end product can be rather variable.

## STRENGTH OF BEERS

*Original Gravity* The strength of beers used to be something of a mystery to the drinker. Only the Customs and Excise seemed very interested. These days brewers indicate the original gravity (OG) of their products. Before the invention of the hydrometer brewers always referred to the extracted malt in terms of brewer's pounds per quarter – they could only check the product of the mash by comparing the weight of a barrel of wort against that of a barrel of water. The malt sugars weigh more than water and it is this increased density which the hydrometer measures in giving us the original gravity of the brew.

This OG reading is a reasonable guide for customers of the strength of the beer they are drinking. It does not quite tell the full story, because a beer which has finished 'sweet' may not have been fermented out to the same extent as one which has finished 'dry', but the difference in strength between them will be marginal.

Water has an OG of 1000 and the OG of a beer will, if we ignore very strong ales, be in the range of 1030-60. A mild or bitter of 1030-5 will be a light, lunchtime or 'session' drink, one of 1035-40 a beer of average strength and one of 1040-50 a premium ale of good strength. Anything above 1050 comes into the cautionary strong-ale class.

## TYPES OF TRADITIONAL BEER

*Bitter* Britain has become famous for its bitter, the most popular traditional beer enjoyed here, and the type of drink which the definition covers is quite remarkable in its variety. Some bitters are dry and hoppy, others sweet and luscious. It is difficult to believe that the sharp Boddington's or Robinson's brews from around Manchester, for instance, should be classified as the same type of beer as the much more soft and malty offerings of Ruddle's or Sam Smith's.

Besides the draught versions there are a few self-conditioned bottled beers which satisfy the real ale drinker's idea of a true bitter. Worthington White Shield still sells well and is widely available. Pour it carefully so that the tiny film of yeast is left in the bottle.

*Mild* Sadly, mild has become a regional drink. In the Midlands and North West there are plenty of pubs where a simple request for 'a pint' will bring forth a pint of mild. Normally mild is darker than bitter and of relatively modest strength. However, there are exceptions. Many Lancashire milds are light in colour, almost like a pale ale. Some dark milds are strong – Sarah Hughes' mild has an OG of 1058. Certainly the West Midlands is the home of smooth, nutty, dark beers.

The difference in the brewing method is that darker malts are used for milds in most cases. In addition the drink tends to be sweeter, because of the use of added caramel or sugar, and to have less bitterness as a result of the presence of hop varieties such as Fuggles (which do not carry the same 'bite' as the hops used in bitters). When bottled, mild is called 'brown ale', but it is almost always in a pasteurised gassy form.

*Old Ale* In its true sense an old ale is a stronger and richer form of mild. Robinson's Old Tom (OG 1080) and Wadworth's Old Timer (OG 1055) are examples of this dark warming drink.

It is normally brewed in the winter months and is often drawn straight from a barrel on the bar.

*Porter*  Porter was brewed for 200 years until it faded out of fashion in the early 1970s. Fortunately several of the new breweries have revived the tradition – the Bridge Brewery in Staffordshire produces a particularly fine example of this unusual beer.

Porter originated in London, where the porters were apt to purchase a combination of different beers (a pint of 'mixed'). One enterprising brewer created what he called 'entire' – a beer which combined the entire range of the drinks which the porters were mixing. Not surprisingly the beer came to be known as porter. It is a dark fruity beer, not as nutty or black as a stout but stronger and more full-bodied than a mild.

*Stout*  Guinness at one time brewed porter but the company opted for a stronger and more inky 'extra stout'. Originally the word stout referred merely to the strength of the beer. The bottled version, which is as popular as ever, is self-conditioned and is truly a real ale, whereas Draught Guinness is dispensed under pressure in most places except its homeland.

It is the body and colour of stout which makes it so distinctive – a heavy and contemplative beer which is often 'prescribed' for anaemics. If Guinness is good, Imperial Russian Stout is excellent. With an original gravity of over 1100, this splendid Courage beer is brewed every three or four years by John Smith's of Yorkshire.

*Strong Ale and Barley Wine*  The distinction between premium bitters, strong ales, barley wines and old ales is not always a precise one. Some breweries market a so-called strong ale which carries little more alcohol than Director's Bitter. On the other hand some strong ales which are sold by the pint are akin to a barley wine.

The common factor among the strong beers is that they are rich and almost always sweet on the palate. Some are dark and some quite light. All of them warrant a degree of respect. If you want a unique experience in beer drinking, try a bottle of Eldridge Pope's Thomas Hardy's Ale (OG 1125) – it has a higher alcohol content than many wines.

# CHAPTER THREE

# Southern Counties

### Archers Ales Limited
Local and Free-Trade Brewers
London Street, Swindon, Wiltshire

Since its establishment in 1979 Archer's has become an increasingly popular source of real ales in the South and South West. Swindon is better known for building fine steam engines and railway carriages than for the brewing of beer and it is appropriate that Archer's occupies one of the old Great Western Railway sheds on what is now an industrial estate.

Mark Wallington began with a twelve-barrel plant but he was soon expanding into adjoining premises to increase capacity. He will tell you that the high vaulted ceilings and cool interior of these old buildings are ideal for brewing and his beers prove his point. Up to eighty-five barrels a week are produced for the company's own public houses and for the free trade.

A traditional full-mash system is employed to brew the four beers, using only English malted barley, a blend of Kentish hops and water from springs at the head of the Thames. The only concession to modern methods is the use of stainless steel for the brewing vessels, which facilitates cleaning and sterilisation.

The strong ale, well named Headbanger, has three times won prizes at the Great Western Beer Festival. 'Try it and see why!' says Mark with justifiable pride.

REAL ALES
Village Bitter (OG 1035) – a clean-tasting light bitter
Best Bitter (OG 1040) – full-flavoured and well-hopped
A.S.B. (OG 1048) – a fruity and powerful bitter
Headbanger (OG 1065) – a rich and dark strong ale

TIED HOUSES
Although the majority of the barrels leaving Archer's brewery find their way to free houses within a 30-mile radius of Swindon, the company now owns three public houses:

*Gloucestershire*
Cheltenham: Kemble Brewery     Cirencester: Drillman's Arms

*Wiltshire*
Swindon: Glue Pot Inn


## J. Arkell and Sons Limited
Independent Regional Brewers
Kingsdown Brewery, Swindon, Wiltshire

Local boy John Arkell, who came to be known as 'Honest John', founded the business in 1843 on his return from a trip to Canada. The Kingsdown Brewery has been the home of this famous family firm since that date, steadfastly resisting outside interference. The present chairman is the great-grandson of 'Honest John'.

The company has always placed the emphasis of its operation not just upon the quality of its fine ales but also upon the serving of those beers and the surroundings in which they are enjoyed. Soon after the brewery had opened, the first Arkell's pubs appeared in Swindon. 'Good beers, good pubs, good landlords' was the family's watchword then and it remains so to this day. Now you can find Arkell's beers many miles from Swindon, the hub of the estate, but the company can still boast that the genuine 'pub atmosphere' and congenial surroundings are present in every one of its tied houses.

There is a flourishing wine merchants which contributes to the uniqueness of these pubs. John Arkell Vintners imports directly from France. The customer can enjoy quality wines rather than the nameless red or white plonk which is so prevalent on the shelves of the licensed trade.

The Arkell family employs over 1,000 full- and part-time workers and pays in excess of £2 million a year in beer duty and company taxes. These facts, proudly stated by the company, derive from the success of its beers, which are brewed from only British barley and British hops with no chemicals or additives of any kind. Arkell's is a traditional brewery in the true sense.

Arkell's Brewery

REAL ALES
Brewer's Bitter (OG 1031-5) – a well-flavoured session beer
3B (OG 1036-40) – a full-bodied satisfying bitter
Kingdsown Ale (OG 1050-4) – an award-winning strong ale

TIED HOUSES
Arkell and Sons has an estate of sixty-nine public houses and a few off-licences. You should have little difficulty in finding the beers in Wiltshire (there are twenty-five pubs in and around Swindon alone), but the following will help in locating Arkell's in neighbouring counties:

*Berkshire*
Lambourn: George Hotel
Stockcross: Lord Lyon
Woodside (near Ascot): Duke of Edinburgh

*Gloucestershire*
Cirencester: Brewer's Arms, Golden Cross, Plume of Feathers, Talbot
Eastleach Turville: Victoria
Elkstone: Highwayman
Fairford: Bull Hotel, Plough
Kemble: Tavern
Kempsford: George Inn
Lechlade: Red Lion, Royal Oak

*Oxfordshire*
Faringdon: Baker's Arms

**Ballards' Brewery Limited**
Free-Trade Brewers
Nyewood, Rogate, Petersfield, Hampshire

Bruce and Nancy Ballard first began brewing in the cowhouse of a remote Sussex farm over thirty years ago. In June 1985 their daughter Carola and her husband Mike Brown opened the Ballards' pub at Elsted Marsh, near Midhurst. It was only a matter of months before the brewing equipment was installed in the stable block behind the family pub.

The rural characteristics of the small business were not to last much longer, however. In October 1988 the need for greater capacity brought about another move. This time the mash tun was set up in a unit on an industrial estate, just over the county boundary.

Ballards' is a modern brewery to delight the purist. The ales are brewed from just the basic ingredients – no additives are used. As a result the ales from Nyewood are some of the very few British beers to satisfy the exacting German purity laws. As well as Best Bitter and Wassail, Ballards produce limited quantities of very strong beers which are usually sold in bottles. The original gravity is pitched to match the year. In 1988 Ballards' Old Bounder had an OG of 1088. Although brewing is now in a different setting, the link with the countryside is not forgotten, for the annual strong ale is a legacy of the old rural practice of brewing a strong ale for harvest-time.

REAL ALES
Best Bitter (OG 1042) – a nutty, well-balanced premium bitter
Wassail (OG 1060) – a malty and very tasty strong ale

REGULAR FREE-TRADE OUTLETS
*Hampshire*
Charlton: Fox Goes Free
Hawkley: Hawkley Inn
Passfield: Passfield Oak
Petersfield: Good Intent

Portsmouth: Brewery Tap
Priors Dean: White Horse
Rogate: White Horse
Southsea: Wine Vaults

*West Sussex*
Byworth: Black Horse
Chidham: Old House at Home
Cocking: Richard Cobden

Donnington: Blacksmith's Arms
Eastbourne: Holly Tree

Elsted: Elsted Inn, Three
  Horseshoes
Felpham: Old Barn
Heyshott: Unicorn
Lavant: Earl of March
Lodsworth: Halfway Bridge,
  Hollist Arms

Midhurst: Royal Oak, Spread
  Eagle
Petworth: Paddington's Wine
Trotton: Keeper's Arms,
  Southdown Hotel
West Ashing: Richmond Arms
Westergate: Labour in Vain
Wittering: Lamb

## Bunce's Brewery
Free-Trade Brewers
The Old Mill, Netheravon, Wiltshire

'The happy small brewer is one who sells enough to be able to carry on doing what he likes best – brewing beers that people want to drink.' This is the cheerful philosophy of Tony and Robin Bunce, who have established a successful operation not far from Stonehenge.

The Old Mill at Netheravon is a listed building. It was built on the site of an old corn mill in 1914 to house an electricity-generating station for a nearby airfield. Subsequently it was used for several purposes, including as a silent cinema and as a hall for boxing bouts, until it was sold by the Ministry of Defence. Tony Bunce, who had taken early retirement at the age of fifty-five, had been looking for suitable premises for a small brewery for some time. The Old Mill was filthy and rat-infested when he found it and decided to buy. Together the happy couple cleaned it and adapted it. Within a year the cold shell had been transformed into a traditional brewery with a flat above. They were able in 1984 to revive Netheravon's long-forgotten history of brewing – T. W. Hussey, the town's previous brewer, had sold out to Strong and Co. in 1913.

At first sight a casual observer might question the suitability of the attractive Old Mill as a brewhouse. In fact it has proved to be almost ideal. The height has enabled a miniature 'tower brewery' system to be installed, so that gravity is the prime mover. The only pump necessary in the brewing process is for conveying the hot wort through a plate cooler to the fermentation vessel. The plant has a twenty-barrel brew-length and these days operates close to its maximum capacity.

Beers are transported directly to the free trade in oak and sterilised steel casks over a radius of up to 50 miles

from the brewery and via agents to more distant outlets. In late 1988 Old Smokey was introduced to complete the splendid range of bitters from the brewery which places its emphasis on traditional quality rather than on mere quantity.

REAL ALES
Benchmark (OG 1035) – a session bitter of full flavour
Best Bitter (OG 1042) – a rounded bitter with good hop content
Old Smokey (OG 1050) – a dark hoppy bitter which is not
    too sweet

FREE TRADE
Try any of the following regular outlets:

*Hampshire*
Thruxton: White Horse          Whitsbury: Cart Wheel

*Somerset*
Nunney: George

*Sussex*
West Wittering: Lamb

*Wiltshire*
Corsham: Two Pigs              Hamptworth: Cuckoo

## Burt
Independent Regional Brewers
The Ventnor Brewery, Ventnor, Isle of Wight

Burt's is an independent regional brewery in miniature. Situated in the popular holiday resort of Ventnor, it has provided ales for the island for many years. The spate of takeovers and mergers simply passed it by and it survived happily as a traditional family business.

The brewery was built on its present site in 1840, attracted by the abundant supplies of fresh spring water. When the Phillips family acquired the business in 1906, they decided to retain the name of the original owner.

During the Second World War the buildings were bombed and were put out of action for a year. Temporary repairs in 1944 enabled the beer to flow again and put a smile back on the faces of the island's drinkers. The full rebuilding programme was not completed until 1953, but the redesigned brewhouse brought a spate of awards at National Brewers' Exhibitions.

Burt is a totally independent affair, seemingly untouched by the many changes on the mainland. The family own eleven pubs on the island and supply many free houses. In the words of the company's own publicity material: 'Our endeavour is to produce a drink of quality which will appeal to the majority of our customers.'

REAL ALES
Mild (OG 1030) – a dark mild of delicate flavour
Bitter (OG 1030) – one of the lightest bitters brewed
VPA (OG 1040) – a full-flavoured bitter
4X (OG 1040) – an old ale which is not quite in the 'strong ale' category

TIED HOUSES
Arreton Downs: Hare and Hounds
Freshwater: Standard Hotel
Lake: Stag Inn
Shanklin: Chine Inn
Ventnor: Central Hotel, Central Tap, Terminus Hotel, Millbay Hotel, Walmer Castle, Volunteer Inn
Wroxall: Star Inn

## Eldridge, Pope and Company Limited
Independent Regional Brewers
Dorchester Brewery, Dorchester, Dorset

'The masses worshipped it, the gentry loved it more than wine, and by the most illustrious country families it was not despised. Anybody brought up for being drunk and disorderly in the streets of its natal borough had only to prove that he was a stranger to the place and its liquor to be honourably dismissed by the magistrates, as one overtaken in a fault that no man could guard against who entered the town unawares.' In this way Thomas Hardy described Dorchester's strong ale in his novel *The Trumpet Major*.

The story of Huntsman Ales began in 1833 when Charles and Sarah Eldridge took over the Antelope Hotel in Dorchester. Having adapted remarkably quickly to the trade, they opened the Green Dragon Brewery a mere four years later. When Charles died in 1846, his wife continued the business, employing Alfred Mason as her brewer.

Edwin Pope entered the scene in 1870 by purchasing the retiring brewer's share of the company. Within a few years Edwin and his brother Alfred had taken full control of the enterprise and the name of Eldridge Pope had been created. The firm prospered and the brothers built the present brewery in 1880.

Eldridge Pope is rightly very proud of its products. The bottled Hardy Ale, which is naturally conditioned, is a famous drink of exceptional character. It is one of the strongest ales produced in Britain. Of rather less weight, the flagship draught ale Royal Oak owes its existence to a stroke of luck. When the Dorchester brewery was gutted by fire in 1922, among the few things to be rescued from the disaster were the brewing books. During the conflagration an enterprising employee threw them down from the brewer's office, which was near the top floor. From those records it has been possible to brew a beer very similar in quality and strength to the old pale ale of 1896. The brewing books are now proudly displayed in the company's museum.

The brewery nowadays owns around 200 public houses, mainly on the south coast but extending as far as London, Bristol and Exeter. The business is still run by the descendants of Alfred Pope. In the recent history of the firm they have diversified into lager production and into the promotion of the Huntsman Family Pub and 'Tuck Inn' eating houses. The draught beers remain as good as ever.

REAL ALES

Dorchester Bitter (OG 1030-4) – a light beer with a clean bitterness

EP Best Bitter (OG 1037-9) – a session bitter introduced in 1989

Dorset Original IPA (OG 1039-43) – stronger with a dry-hopped flavour

Royal Oak (OG 1046-50) – the 1896-style strong ale

TIED HOUSES

There is an abundant supply of Huntsman Ales in Dorset (thirteen pubs serve them in Dorchester, fifteen in Weymouth and sixteen in the Poole area) and in Hampshire (twenty-two in and around Bournemouth, eleven in the Southampton area and ten in Winchester). Outside these two counties you can choose from:

*Avon*

Bath: Broadley's Wine Vaults, Crystal Palace, Huntsman, Rummer, Smith Bros

Bristol: Bush, Murphy's City Bar, Mr Pope's, Quadrant

*Devon*

Exeter: Hole in the Wall

*London*

Knightrider Street: Horn Tavern

*Somerset*

Charlton Hawthorns: King's Arms

Crewkerne: White Hart

East Chinnock: Portman Arms

Lydford-on-Fosse: Lydford Hotel

Marston Magna: Red Lion

Milbourne Port: Gainsborough Arms, King's Head

North Cadbury: Catash Inn

Stoke-sub-Hamdon: Fleur de Lys

Yeovil: Green Dragon, Greyhound Hotel, Nelson Inn, Royal Marine Inn, Three Choughs, Westfield Hotel, Yew Tree

*West Sussex*

Rake: Flying Bull

*Wiltshire*

Downton: White Horse

Salisbury: Avon Brewery Inn, Bird in Hand, Butt of Ale, Devizes Road Hotel, Engineer's Arms, Huntsman's Tavern

Swallowcliffe: Royal Oak

Tisbury: Boot Inn

**Frog and Frigate**
Home-brew Pub
Canute Road, Southampton, Hampshire

If you are young (or just young at heart) and 'fancy a piece of the action', get along to the Frog and Frigate. It is opposite the yacht marina (Ocean Village) and not far from

Itchen Bridge. Most nights there is a vibrant atmosphere there with live music featuring regularly. You will probably end up dancing on the table.

The Frog and Frigate was opened in 1981, complete with sawdust on the floor and a full-mash brewery in the cellar. Ninety gallons of Croaker and Frog's Original are produced from the small Peter Austin stainless-steel plant and at appropriate times a winter special, Captain Frigate, occupies the third fermenting vessel. For a while the beers were sold at other pubs in Southampton and Portsmouth, but these days you will have to travel to Canute Road to sample them. If you enjoy a boisterous night out, you will not be disappointed at the Frog and Frigate.

REAL ALES
Frog's Original (OG 1038) – a hoppy session bitter
Croaker (OG 1050) – stronger and well-rounded
Captain Frigate (OG 1078) – a powerful winter warmer


**George Gale and Company Limited**
Independent Regional Brewers
Horndean, Portsmouth, Hampshire

The village of Horndean straddles the Portsmouth to London Road and the Ship and Bell Inn there was a regular stopping point during the coaching era. To accommodate travellers, beer was brewed there with water drawn from a well beneath the inn. Smugglers from Hayling Island often called in, hiding their horses and contraband in the woods, before journeying on to Liphook.

In the middle of the eighteenth century a larger brewery was built on the opposite side of the main road (now the A3) by an enterprising common brewer. Those buildings survived for a hundred years before a fire destroyed most of them – only the old blacksmith's shop and the cooper's shop exist today. The remainder of the site was redeveloped with a new Victorian-style brewery in 1869, adjacent to the Ship and Bell. In fact the saloon bar of the pub became the brewery house and the current sugar store used to be the bar.

In June 1847 Richard Gale had acquired the Ship and Bell and George Gale and Son (operated by Richard's son) became established after the rebuilding work. By the early twentieth century expansion was evident. Homewell Brewery, Havant, Square Brewery, Petersfield, and the Angel Brewery, Midhurst, were all acquired together with their public houses. Six generations of the Gale family have been involved in running the company to the present day.

Through the years the approach to brewing has deliberately encompassed traditional processes and the brewery is a mixture of the old and new. The malt screen in use was manufactured in 1898 and some of the wooden fermenting vessels are over fifty years old. The existing copper was installed about forty years ago when its predecessor blew up (the underback had to be used for brewing for three weeks). This traditional equipment has been married with modern technology and the brewery can boast an extensive laboratory and very modern plant.

One of the secrets of Gale's success can be found in the fact that there has been an infrequent change in the head brewership over the years. This has enabled the character and quality of the products to be maintained with little variation. Only four men have held the post since the turn of the century and the medallions from various brewer's exhibitions which hang in the brewery office testify to their skill.

Two beers are worthy of particular mention. Horndean Special Bitter is generally considered the best of the high-gravity bitters brewed in the South of England. It was created by Major E.T. Argyle in 1959. The other is a bottle-conditioned barley wine, Prize Old Ale, with a breath-taking original gravity of 1094, which is sold in corked bottles and is much cherished by the strong-ale lover. The Old Ale is matured for many months before being hand-filled into half-pint bottles. It is then matured for a further six months before being released to its adoring public.

REAL ALES
XXX(L) (OG 1030) – a refreshing light mild
XXX(D) (OG 1032) – a lush, tasty dark mild
Buster Brew Bitter (OG 1037) – a balanced session bitter
XXXXX (OG 1044) – a dark, full-bodied winter ale
Horndean Special Bitter (OG 1051) – a distinctive premium
   bitter

TIED HOUSES
There are sixty-two Gale's pubs on 'mainland' Hampshire and plenty more in the adjoining counties and on the islands for you to choose from:

*Hayling Island*
Kittiwake, Lifeboat Inn,
   Maypole Inn

*Isle of Wight*
Ryde: Castle, Simeon Arms
Sandown: Commercial

*Oxfordshire*
Cane End: Fox Inn
Mapledurham: Pack Horse,
   Pack Saddle
Woodcote: Black Lion

*Surrey*
Farnham: Queen's Head           Normandy: Anchor
Haslemere: Prince of Wales      Shalford: Sea Horse
Hindhead: Woodcock Inn          Thursley: Three Horseshoes
Milford: Red Lion               Tilford: Duke of Cambridge

*Sussex*
Bepton: Shamrock Inn            Lagness: Royal Oak
Binstead: Black Horse           Middleton-on-Sea: Elmer
Chichester: Cattle Market Inn,  Midhurst: Angel Hotel,
   Eastgate Inn, New Inn,          Three Horseshoes
   Park Tavern, Wickham Arms    Milland: Rising Sun
Cocking: Greyhound Inn          Rake: Sun Inn
Elsted: Railway Inn             Sompting: Ball Tree Inn
Fernhurst: King's Arms          Stedham: Hamilton Arms


**Gibbs Mew Plc**
Independent Regional Brewers
Anchor Brewery, Salisbury, Wiltshire


Salisbury's family brewery was formed in 1898 to take over
the businesses of Bridger Gibbs and Sons and Herbert Mew
and Company. It is believed that the Gibbs family had been
brewing since the middle of the eighteenth century. The
current chairman's great-great-grandfather is known to have
been brewing at the Swan, Haslemere, around that time. His
brother, George Bridger Gibbs, was a partner in a brewery in
Endless Street, Salisbury in 1838. Twenty years later he moved
to the site of the present Anchor Brewery to form Bridger Gibbs
and Sons.

The company has continued the tradition of using the water from its own well (the deepest in the district) together with finest English malt and hops and its own special strain of yeast to brew beers for the local palate. Not only is the method of production steeped in history, but transporting of the beers is still made in the vicinity of the brewery by horse-drawn dray. The dray trundling through the historic centre of Salisbury is a splendid sight.

Both the tied estate and many free houses are supplied with a range of the company's beers, of which the renowned strong ale Bishop's Tipple is probably the most famous. Gibbs Mew has gained a string of prizes for its brews. A few years ago the Gold Medal for the Quality Export Category at the British Beer Bottlers' Institute was awarded to Bishop's Tipple.

The company has shown ambition and foresight over the last decade. It has a specialised production unit dealing with many well-known lagers for distribution to the trade and its subsidiary, Seymour's, has built up a leading reputation for its range of Gold Medal Soft Drinks.

The years of 1987 and 1988 witnessed a remarkable upsurge in the fortunes of the company. When Godson's brewery closed in 1987, Gibbs Mew began brewing Godson's beers under licence. In the same year a deal was struck with a German brewery which saw Gibbs Mew International Beer launched in that country – a major *coup* for a British brewer. In early 1988 a half-share in Cooper's of Wessex was purchased, giving access to a large sector of the free trade, and then the company outbid all of its rivals to acquire 105 tenanted pubs for £13.3 million from Grand Metropolitan (Watneys). More recently Gibbs Mew has been disposing of some of its own outlets which do not suit its changing portfolio.

There is no doubt that the company will consolidate its position as one of the major small brewers in the South of England. In 1989 a 5.8-acre site on the outskirts of Salisbury was purchased to relieve pressure on the rather cramped Anchor Brewery in the city centre. It is probable that future development on the new site will include a company headquarters.

REAL ALES
Wiltshire Traditional Bitter (OG 1036) – a well-hopped session
    bitter

Chudley Local Line (OG 1036) – a rounded refreshing bitter
Salisbury Best (OG 1042) – a distinctive premium bitter
Premium Bitter (OG 1042) – malty and full of flavour
GBH (OG 1047) – full-bodied and dark
Bishop's Tipple (OG 1066) – the famous strong ale

TIED HOUSES
With all of the acquisitions and disposals over recent years,
Gibbs Mew has had a changing and temporarily unstable
estate of public houses. Nevertheless, if you are in or around
Wiltshire you will not require a guide to find the beers. The
following are just a few examples of Gibbs Mew houses in four
counties:

*Dorset*
Portland: Eight Kings, Pulpit
Weymouth: Globe, Waterloo

*Hampshire*
Bognor Regis: Richmond Arms
Chichester: Victoria
Fareham: Traveller's Rest
Portsmouth: Compass Rose
Southampton: Crown and
  Sceptre
Winchester: Littleton,
  Running Horse

*Somerset*
Frome: First and Last
Sampford: Haywain

*Wiltshire*
Donhead: Rising Sun
Downton: King's Arms
Salisbury: Anchor, Cloisters,
  Greyfisher, Railway Inn,
  Yew Tree
Shrewton: Plume of Feathers
Steeple Ashton: Long's Arms
Tisbury: Crown Inn
West Lavington: Bridge Inn


**Goldfinch Brewery**
Single-pub and Free-trade Brewers
Tom Brown's, 47 High Street East, Dorchester, Dorset

People will tell you that Alan Finch's brewery is the second
biggest in Dorchester. Although this is true, it is rather mislead-
ing. His tiny plant comes a poor second to the might of Eldridge

Pope and there is no third contender. However, Goldfinch is a precious miniature and the success of its beers is a tribute to Alan's determination and skill.

He changed the name of his pub from the Buffers Inn to Tom Brown's in 1987. There are illustrations of the famous schoolboy and a few canes on the wall. The fine painting of Tom on the pub sign suffered from the carelessness of a lorry driver in 1989 but it has been repaired. It is a terraced pub with plenty of timber on the front elevation and one sizeable bar.

A tiny one-barrel full-mash plant was installed on the first floor so that Alan could start brewing his Tom Brown's Best and the cleverly named Flashman's Clout, using Golding hops in both cases. Despite this meagre capacity he has been able to make some incursions in the free trade. The chances are that if a free house takes Goldfinch ales, the proprietor will soon be asking for more on a regular basis. For this reason Alan is installing a new five-barrel plant, using adapted cellar tanks, in an outbuilding at the rear of the pub. This will enable him to increase production and ease his back, after two years of humping barrels up and down stairs.

The Tom Brown beers are likely to become more common in Dorset and beyond, including in London. Alan is looking to buy another pub, preferably in the capital. His beers are certainly good enough to encourage expansion.

REAL ALES
Tom Brown's Best (OG 1039) – a hoppy, fresh bitter
Flashman's Clout (OG 1043) – a malty premium bitter

FREE TRADE
Outlets for the beers are limited and rather infrequent at present but the situation is likely to improve. The most regular sources are:

*Dorset*
North Wootton: Three Elms

*Hampshire*
Portsmouth: Tap

*Greater London*
Hampton High Road: White
Hart

Badger Brewery

## Hall and Woodhouse Limited
Independent Regional Brewers
Blandford Forum, Dorset

'Badger Country' is good drinking territory. Hall and Woodhouse have been perfecting their art in Dorset for over 200 years. It is a true family firm with a justified pride in its beers.

The first brewer to be recorded in the company's history was Charles Hall, who, branching out from his farming background, founded the Ansty Brewery in 1777. To his great fortune a military encampment was soon established near Weymouth (England was at war with France at the time) and Charles cleverly secured a Government contract to supply his beers to the camp. From that point there was no looking back.

Steady growth was maintained by Charles' son Robert who in 1847 took G.E.I. Woodhouse into partnership. When Mr Woodhouse married one of founder Charles Hall's grand-daughters, the names were linked in the company's title. Although Hall and Woodhouse has remained the name of the firm since that date, Robert was the last of the Halls to represent the family on the board.

The business expanded gradually, acquiring small breweries with their public houses, and became a limited company at the

turn of the century. It moved to the present brewery at Blandford
St Mary shortly afterwards – it is a sobering thought that the
splendid buildings cost only £28,000.

In more recent years Hall and Woodhouse has developed
by diversifying its interests in liquid products. A Southampton-
based off-licence chain was purchased in 1953, Palmers (Wine
and Spirits Merchants) of Bournemouth was acquired in 1970
and five years later a shipping firm (to import those wines and
spirits) was added. The Panda Soft Drinks factory, managed by
one of the Woodhouse family, stands next to the brewery.

Badger beers are an example of a distinctive regional product which local drinkers love. The ales have the uniqueness of
flavour which make them part of the character of the area. A
man who sits behind a pint of Badger will tell you that he has
been 'weaned on it'.

REAL ALES
Badger Best Bitter (OG 1041) – a full-drinking well-hopped
  bitter
Tanglefoot (OG 1048) – a well-rounded premium ale/strong
  ale

TIED HOUSES
There is no problem in finding the beers in Dorset (try the King's
Arms at Thornford or the Cock and Bottle, Morden) or in nearby
Hampshire. Hall and Woodhouse have thirty-two tied houses in
the Blandford area and twenty-one around Wimbourne. Further
afield you may have to search a little more thoroughly and the
following list may help:

*Somerset*
Clevedon: Regent Hotel
Nunney Catch: Theobald Arms
Templecombe: Royal Hotel
West Coker: Royal George

Weston-super-Mare: The
  Clipper
Wincanton: Miller's Inn, Nog
  Inn, Railway Inn

*Wiltshire*
Mere: Ship Hotel, Talbot Hotel,
  Walnut Tree
Salisbury area: Bear Inn, Bull
  Hotel, Catherine Wheel Inn,
  Green Dragon, New Inn,
  Oddfellow's Arms, Pelican,

Pembroke Arms, Radnor
  Arms, Talbot Inn, Toll Gate,
  Wheatsheaf (Wilton),
  Wheatsheaf (Lower
  Woodford)
Swindon: Swindon Hotel

The Kings Arms, Thornford

## Hop-Back Brewery
Home-brew Pub with Free-trade Outlets
Wyndham Arms, Escourt Road, Salisbury, Wiltshire

The Wyndham Arms is a compact Victorian corner pub in a residential area of Salisbury. John Gilbert, a former food scientist with plenty of experience in brewing, began his own small brewery in the cellars there in 1987. He constructed a full-mash plant with a four-to-six-barrel capacity, using converted cellar tanks. The success of his beers has been quite remarkable.

'Gilbo', as he is known, was encouraged to brew a special beer for the 1989 Great British Beer Festival in Leeds. The result was Summer Lightning, a pale, strong best bitter, and his reward was the prize for the best entry in the New Brewery category. By introducing this new ale, John has increased his range of beers to four. His output is normally around twelve barrels per week.

Fortunately some of the beers are sold in the free trade, providing greater opportunity for locals to locate and enjoy them. The Wyndham Arms does most of its trade in the evenings and is usually closed at lunchtime on Monday to Thursday.

REAL ALES
GFB (OG 1035) – a dry and bitter session beer
Hop-Back Stout (OG 1040) – a dry, black stout

Hop-Back Special (OG 1042) – a full-flavoured premium bitter
Summer Lightning (OG 1050) – a dryish, strong bitter of
  character

FREE TRADE
  *Wiltshire*
Enford: Swan
Pitton: Silver Plough


## Mole's Brewery (Wayward Limited)
Independent Local Brewers
Merlin Way, Bowerhill, Melksham, Wiltshire

If you see a sticker in Wiltshire reading 'Mole's drinkers
do it underground' do not be too offended. The logo of a
rather dazed-looking mole with a stem of barley hanging from
its mouth and a foaming pot of ale in its 'hand' should explain
all. When Roger Catte was manager of Cascade Soft Drinks, he
was known as 'Mole' (Cattemole?). Not surprisingly, when he
decided to establish a brewery on the site he called it Mole's.
  The brewery began in 1982, producing a traditional cask
bitter from Suffolk Premium Pale Ale malt, a small amount of
crystal malt, Golding hops from Kent and an open fermenting ale
yeast. The hopped wort is collected at an original gravity of 1040
and fermented over five days to produce Mole's Cask Bitter. To
this brew have been added Mole's PA, a lighter, daytime drink,
and Brew 97, a strong ale.
  The brewing equipment has been assembled along traditional
lines, using mash tun, copper, hop back and open fermenter.
This design is ideally suited to a one-man operation to brew
10-gallon batches of all-malt beers (usually two mashes per
week).
  Mole's has the ready-made advantage of a delivery service
on its doorstep. The lorries of the adjoining soft-drinks firm
transport the beers to the free trade in Wiltshire and Avon.
Mole's own pub, the Rising Sun at Lacock, is pleasantly situated
and serves all of the company's ales.

REAL ALES
PA (OG 1035) – a gentle session bitter
Cask Bitter (OG 1040) – a full-bodied, well-hopped bitter
Brew 97 (OG 1050) – a smooth strong ale

FREE TRADE
Mole's has burrowed its way into a lot of clubs in the area.
Besides the one tied house referred to above, it is also available
in a number of free houses. The following are regular customers:

*Avon*
Bath: Hatchett's

*Gloucestershire*
Stroud: Clothier's Arms
Woodchester: Ram Inn

*Wiltshire*
Bromham: Oliver Cromwell
Castle Combe: Castle Hotel
Corsham: Two Pigs
Corsley: Cross Keys
Devizes: Bell
Malmesbury: Horse and
  Groom
Marlborough: Savernake
  Forest
Melksham: Red Lion
Pewsey: Swan
Salisbury: Malet Arms
Sherston: Rattlebone Inn
Urchfont: Nag's Head

## J. C. and R. H. Palmer Limited
Independent Regional Brewers
Old Brewery, West Bay Road, Bridport, Dorset

Palmers' is a case of the old surviving the new. When the family
purchased the company in 1896, there were 100 public houses
and two breweries. There was no real need for two separate
breweries and it was the New Brewery which was closed. The
Old Brewery was retained. It stands at the confluence of the
Rivers Asker and Brit, and is believed to date back to 1794.

For anyone interested in the architecture of the industry
the Bridport Brewery has some unusual features. It had a
working under-shot water wheel of 18 feet diameter which
drove the belts of the bottling room until well into the 1930s.
The bottling hall itself is the only thatched brewery building in
the country.

After purchasing the business and concentrating production on the river-bank site, the family closed several pubs in
Bridport and replaced them with houses towards Lyme Regis
and Axminster. New brewhouse plant was acquired, including
an open copper which is still in use today.

Water has always been available to them in abundance –

river water to turn the 6-ton wheel, spring water for the brewing liquor, two artesian wells for water for cooling and the nearby sea as a means of transport. The brewery had its own maltings until after the First World War. In those years beers in casks and bottles were shipped from West Bay (Bridport harbour) to Weymouth, Southampton and London. Many changes had taken place within the brewery, including internal structural rebuilding and the installation of much new equipment.

In 1958, when Tony Palmer became the sole proprietor, the company was experiencing a tremendous increase in trade and a new Briggs single-tier pasteuriser was installed to cope with the demand for bottled beers. Fortunately the surge in interest in cask-conditioned beers followed in the 1970s, coinciding with the arrival of Peter Seed as head brewer, and three new fermenting vessels were installed. J. C. and R. H. Palmer became a limited company in November 1975.

It is a true community brewery. Members of the family have held high local office, including that of mayor of Bridport, and there is a good sense of tradition about the place. In 1985 the oldest-surviving dray, probably 100 years old, was lovingly restored by two of the company's craftsmen. In the summer it can be seen giving rides to children at charitable events and on special occasions it is used to make deliveries to the pubs near the brewery.

There is one craftsman of Palmer's who deserves particular mention – George Biles, for so many years the master signwriter of them all. Just take a look at the works of art (and historical accuracy) which hang outside many of the company's pubs and you will realise why George became a legend in his own time. Sadly, he passed away in March 1988, well into his eighties. As is the case with artists, his works remain as a lasting testimony to his genius.

REAL ALES
Bridport Bitter (OG 1030) – a light easy session bitter
IPA (OG 1040) – a stronger bitter of fuller flavour
Tally Ho! (OG 1046) – a dark nutty ale

TIED HOUSES
*Devon*
Axminster: Axminster Inn, Millwey, New Commercial
Kilmington: New Inn
Uplyme: Black Dog, New Inn
Salcombe: Ferry Inn

*Dorset*

In addition to fourteen pubs in the brewery town of Bridport, you will find Palmer's at:

Bradpole: King's Head
Beaminster: Eight Bells, Greyhound, Royal Oak, Sun
Bothenhampton: George Inn
Broadwindsor: White Lion
Burton Bradstock: Three Horseshoes
Charmouth: Coach and Horses, Royal Oak, Star
Chideock: George Inn
Drimpton: Royal Oak
Eype: New Inn
Litton Cheney: White Horse
Loders: Loders' Arms
Lyme Regis: Angel, Cobb Arms, Pilot Boat, Royal Standard, Ship Inn, Three Cups
Maiden Newton: Castle Inn

Melplash: Half Moon
Morcombelake: Ship Inn
Nettlecombe: Marquis of Lorne
Powerstock: Three Horseshoes
Punchknowle: Crown Inn
Seatown: Anchor
Shipton: Traveller's Rest
Shipton Gorge: New Inn
Stoke Abbot: New Inn
Symondsbury: London Inn
Toller Porcorum: Old Swan
Uploders: Crown
Waytown: Hare and Hounds
West Bay: Bridport Arms, George Hotel, West Bay Hotel
Whitchurch Canonicorum: Five Bells

*Somerset*

Yeovil: Great Lyde, Phelip's Arms, Plucknett

## Poole Brewery
Single-pub and Free-trade Brewers
The Brewhouse, Sandbanks Road, Poole, Dorset

The Poole Brewery started life in an industrial building using second-hand equipment. David Rawlins, having gained experience at Watney's, began brewing there in June 1981 with a single bitter called Dolphin.

In 1983 he purchased the Brewhouse pub in Sandbanks Road and brewed there also. For a time the two breweries were in operation, but in 1987 he closed the original Poole Brewery and concentrated his business at the Brewhouse.

Behind the pub is a full-mash, thirty-five-barrels-per-week, eleven-barrel brew-length brewery. It has 316 stainless-steel mash tun, wort kettle and 'cold-wall' fermenting vessels. A bottling hall has been added and there are plans for a kegging line.

David Rawlins is managing director of Poole Brewery as well as being the licensee of the Brewhouse. He provides a large amount of Dolphin Bitter and Purbeck Lager for sale in 2-litre PET bottles for the take-home trade. These are filled under contract by Gibbs Mew of Salisbury, but he hopes to undertake the work himself very shortly.

REAL ALES
Dolphin Bitter (OG 1038) – a clean-tasting hoppy bitter
Bosun Bitter (OG 1044) – a premium bitter of full flavour

OUTLETS
Draught Poole Brewery beers are not easy to find. The main market for them is in the clubs of the South Coast. You can, of course, drop in at the Brewhouse if you are in Poole. Otherwise you will have to watch out for Dolphin or Bosun in the free trade.


**Ringwood Brewery**
Independent Regional Brewers
Christchurch Road, Ringwood, Hampshire

When the Ringwood Brewery was established in 1978, it was to resume a tradition which had lapsed fifty-four years earlier. Carter's Brewery had been situated near the River Avon on West Street. The family had brewed Ringwood Ale there since the end of the eighteenth century, but sold out to Strong and Co. of Romsey in 1923 and the brewery was closed down and the site is now home to the bus station.

At one time Ringwood had a number of small breweries and was famous for its strong ales. Using the river water and barley from the nearby chalklands, at least six brewers operated from the town in the eighteenth century. Gradually they dwindled – down to three by 1850 – until only Carter's remained.

Peter Austin has been one of the major influences of the new brewery revolution and it was he and his partner, David Welsh, who opened Ringwood in 1978. Their first base was an old bakery, but they moved to the existing premises in Christchurch Road in 1986. The stone buildings are of eighteenth-century

Ringwood Brewery

origin and may well have formed part of the premises of one
of those three Victorian brewers of Ringwood.

As you would expect of Peter Austin, the beers are brewed
strictly along traditional lines. The brewhouse is a scaled-down
version of a standard brewery, with hot liquor-back, mill, mash
tun, copper and fermenting vessels. Stainless steel is much in
evidence and in-place cleaning techniques are used, so that real
ales can be brewed in the age-old way but with the benefits of
modern technology. The result is 'Thumping Good Ales'.

REAL ALES
XB (OG 1031-5) – a light refreshing session bitter
Best Bitter (OG 1037-41) – a distinctive hoppy bitter
Fortyniner (OG 1046-50) – a rich premium bitter
XXXX Porter (OG 1046-50) – dark and fruity
Old Thumper (OG 1057-61) – a warming well-rounded strong
   ale

OUTLETS
Ringwood is now quite common throughout Hampshire and
you should have little difficulty in finding one of the thirty-eight

houses there (if you are in Ringwood do not miss the opportunity
to drop in at the Inn on the Furlong, opposite the main car
park, for a pint). The beers are also available in neighbouring
counties:

*Dorset*

Branksome: Inn in the Park
Bransgore: Lamb Inn
Christchurch: Castle Tavern
Fiddleford: Fiddleford Inn
Hinton St Michael: East Close
Horton: Horton Inn
Hurn: Avon Causeway

Parley Cross: Dudsbury
Swanage: Durlston Court
  Hotel
Wimborne: King's Head
Winkton: Fisherman's
  Haunt

*Surrey*

Boundstone: Bat and Ball
Englefield Green: Beehive
Frensham: Mariner's Hotel
Holmbury St Mary: King's
  Head

Gomshall: Compasses Inn
Guildford: Clavadel Hotel
Ockham: Black Swan
Shackleford: Cyder House
West Clandon: Onslow Arms

*Sussex*

Chichester: Victoria
Chidham: Old House at Home
Donnington: Blacksmith's
  Arms
Elsted: Three Horseshoes
Hooksway: Royal Oak
Lavant: Earl of March,
  Hunter's Inn

Midhurst: Royal Oak
Oving: Gribble Inn
Pagham: Lion Hotel
South Harting: Coach and
  Horses
West Ashling: Richmond Arms
Yapton: Maypole

*Wiltshire*

Broadchalke: Queen's Head
Salisbury: Hobnobs
Winterslow: Pheasant Hotel

## Wadworth and Company Limited
Independent Regional Brewers
Northgate Brewery, Devizes, Wiltshire

In 1875, at the age of twenty-two, Henry Alfred Wadworth purchased the old Northgate Brewery. He had already gained six years' experience of brewing, including the time he spent as manager of a small brewery in Long Street, Devizes. Harry, as he was known, was a man of tremendous energy. At that tender age he had just returned from a trip to Australia and, despite a regular 5.30am start at Northgate, he still managed to join the local hunt on two or three days a week.

In his first year as owner of the brewery he also indulged himself in some rather dangerous balloon voyaging and in long-distance cycling. He was the first man to cycle the 100 miles from Bath to London (in two and a half bone-rattling days). Unfortunately, but perhaps not surprisingly, these distractions did little for the business. In his first year at the old Northgate Brewery he made a loss. 'I know little about the business,' he wrote to his mother.

But he learned quickly. Soon he was channelling his remarkable energies in the right direction and had turned that loss into a profit. The reputation of his beers began to grow. At that time there were still several publican and common brewers in Devizes. One by one they fell – Wild's, Humby's, Blencoe's and Tylee's all closed or were absorbed by Wadworth. By 1885 a new brewery was needed. The rather austere old premises were replaced by the attractive Victorian Northgate Brewery on a nearby site. Harry and his brother-in-law were able to improve the beers to such an extent that some of their original recipes (with scarcely any alteration) are still in use today. Harry died in 1929 at the age of seventy-eight, after a fall from a horse. In his time as chairman he had established Wadworth as a major force in brewing in the South of England, with over 3,000 customers within a 30-mile radius.

Like many of its competitors, the company faced several problems during the Second World War. The brewery workers went off to battle and most of the raw materials of brewing were rationed, yet Devizes was swamped with thirsty American regiments. Petrol rationing necessitated a 'zoning' system and arrangements had to be made with other brewers to meet demand. However, the crisis was overcome and after the war expansion could be resumed. The attractive Cotswold brewery

Wadworths Brewery

The Raven Inn, Poulshot

at Burford, established in 1798, was acquired as a base for supplying the company's products to new territory.

The essence of the success of the firm has been its two prime traditional beers – 6X and Old Timer. In 1984 a third was added when Wadworth's honoured the Wiltshire journalist and broadcaster A.G. Street by naming a new beer after his first book, *Farmer's Glory*. This rich and distinctive ale is brewed with 50 per cent more hops than normal and uses crystal and roasted malts.

REAL ALES

Devizes Bitter (OG 1030) – a very light refreshing bitter
IPA (OG 1034) – a hoppy session bitter
6X (OG 1040) – a popular well-rounded bitter
Farmer's Glory (OG 1046) – the dark ale referred to above
Old Timer (OG 1055) – a malty old ale

TIED HOUSES

Wiltshire and Avon are the main homes of Wadworth public houses – there are 118 of them. However, there are also a good number in nearby counties:

*Berkshire*
Enborne: Craven Arms
Newtown: Tally Ho
Reading: Eldon Arms

*Gloucestershire*
Cheltenham: Bayshill Inn, Beaufort Arms, Colesbourne Inn, Cotswold Hotel
Cirencester: Greyhound
Dursley: King's Head

Gloucester: British Flag
Stow-on-the-Wold: Talbot
Tetbury: Trouble House Inn
Tewkesbury: Berkeley Arms

*Hampshire*
Andover: Lamb Inn
Bursledon: Linden Tree
Shirley: Park Inn

Southampton: Guide Dog Inn
Winchester: St James Tavern

*Oxfordshire*
Alvescot: Plough
Bampton: Jubliee
Burford: Royal Oak
Carterton: Beehive
Faringdon: Bell Hotel

Iffley: Prince of Wales
Oxford: Temple Bar, Victoria Arms
Stanton St John: Star Inn
Witney: Griffin

*Somerset*
Chilcompton: Sword and Castle
Frome: George Hotel
Glastonbury: Becket's Inn

Sunningdale: Yellow Wagtail
Yeovil: Armoury Inn, Great Western

**The Wiltshire Brewery Company**
Local Brewers
Stonehenge Brewery, Tisbury, Wiltshire

The Wiltshire Brewery Company is based in the quiet south Wiltshire village of Tisbury, not far from Stonehenge. The history of brewing in the buildings, which were erected in the 1730s as a workhouse, has been a chequered one.

The former home of the parish poor was purchased by one Archibald Beckett in 1868 and converted into a brewery. After a fire which necessitated a complete rebuild in 1885, it was named the Wiltshire Brewery. By the end of the century it had come into the hands of Frederick Styring.

The Styrings kept a pet monkey which was loved by the brewers. It followed them around as they performed their daily tasks and copied everything they did, including tasting the beer. On one sad day the monkey overindulged to the extent that it was virtually legless. In full swing from one piece of equipment to another it lost its grip. The horrified brewery workers could only watch as it slipped into a vat of ale and drowned. For some time afterwards Tisbury beer was known locally as monkey beer.

The Styrings, no doubt chastened by this event, sold out to Eldridge Pope and the brewery was closed just before the First World War. The buildings were used as a grist mill for fifty years and then by publishing firms. Brewing was eventually revived in the late 1970s when Tisbury Brewery was set up in part of the old workhouse. That venture collapsed in 1985. The Wiltshire Brewery Company was formed and, after several crises and changes of ownership, the new company finally settled under the direction of Jeff Scoby into a successful operation.

A full range of traditional beers was established to serve the company's tied houses in the vicinity and the free trade further afield. One interesting addition to the normal fare is a bottled ginger beer (OG 1055-64) which blends ginger with beer malts to produce a unique pale golden drink which is well worth a try. After a series of setbacks the Wiltshire Brewery has become a fine example of modern brewing. There is never a monkey in sight these days!

REAL ALES
Local Bitter (OG 1033-7) – a well-balanced session bitter
Stonehenge (OG 1039-41) – a full-bodied malty bitter
Olde Grumble (OG 1047-51) – a special premium bitter
Old Devil (OG 1057-61) – a dark warming winter ale

TIED HOUSES
*Dorset*
Shaftesbury: Crown Inn
Weymouth: Moorings Bar

*Somerset*

| | |
|---|---|
| Langport: Black Swan | Stoke-sub-Hamdon: Half Moon |
| Oakhill: Oakhill Inn | Wells: Full Moon |
| Shepton Mallet: Horseshoe Inn | Westbury-sub-Mendip: |
| Stembridge: Rusty Axe | Westbury Inn |

*Wiltshire*
Great Bedwyn: Cross Keys
Tisbury: South Western Hotel

The company also owns the famous Old Swan at Netherton in the West Midlands, which is dealt with in Chapter Nine.

CHAPTER FOUR

# The South East

## First in Last Out
Home-brew Pub
14 High Street, Hastings, Sussex

The two main attractions of the First In Last Out (FILO) are the home-brewed ales and the splendid open fire in winter. It is a homely single-bar pub behind which is a small brewery. You can see through to the brewhouse from a window at the back of the bar. The choice of refreshment includes the two house beers and a guest ale.

David Harding assembled the equipment, which includes a converted milk pasteuriser, and began the enterprise in 1985. Three years later he sold the business to Mike and Jean Bigg. Mike enjoys brewing his own ales. He mashes most weeks, averaging four barrels in summer and three in winter, and the only place where you can taste Old Crofter's or Cardinal Sussex is at the FILO in Old Hastings. The regulars make sure that there is no surplus for the free trade.

REAL ALES
Old Crofter's (OG 1040) – a dryish hoppy bitter
Cardinal Sussex Ale (OG 1044) – a dark and malty premium ale


## P. and D.J. Goacher
Independent Local Brewers
Bockingford Brewery, Hayle Mill, Maidstone, Kent

Maidstone has a long tradition of producing quality ales. Not so long ago there were four breweries in the town centre but they all fell into disuse and for ten desperate years it looked as if local brewing had died forever. Happily, in 1983 Philip and Deborah Goacher decided to revive the tradition.

The Bockingford Brewery is at Hayle Mill in the scenic Loose Valley. This is the hop county, of course, and the proud boast on Goacher's trade mark is that the beer is 'guaranteed bittered entirely with hops'. The plant is a modern, purpose-built one constructed along classical lines with a full-mash system and open fermentation in stainless-steel vessels. The potential output is twenty-one barrels of real ale per week.

The original beer was a full-bodied Dark Maidstone Ale, brewed with a liberal dash of dark and crystal malts in the mash tun. A year later a Light Maidstone Ale was added for summer drinking, with a tang of mid-Kent Golding hops. On the other hand, winter can now be warded off with the old ale which has been added to the range.

The brewery is an ambitious one, selling through wholesalers to the free trade as far away as Cumbria and Cornwall. A barrel of Goacher's is a common sight at beer festivals. There are plans in the future to open a few Goacher's alehouses and the beer lovers of Kent must surely relish that prospect.

REAL ALES

Light Maidstone Ale (OG 1036) – an easy-drinking hoppy bitter
Dark Maidstone Ale (OG 1040) – rich in colour and flavour
Old Maidstone Ale (OG 1066) – a dark hoppy strong ale

FREE TRADE

The free trade is well served by Goacher's but outlets vary from time to time. In Kent drop in to one of the following for your 'real Maidstone ales':

Biddenden: Three Chimneys
Canterbury: Canterbury Tales
Chatham: Ropemakers
Fairseat: Vigo

Maidstone: Frobisher's
  Wine Bar
Pluckley: Dering Arms
Rochester: Britannia
Smarden: Bell

**Gribble Inn**
Single-pub Brewers
Oving, Near Chichester, West Sussex

The beers brewed at Madam Green Farm have seen several changes in recent years. Originally the Bosham Brewery, the small brewhouse is situated near to the Gribble Inn. Several

brewers have dabbled there, supplying the Inn and marketing
ales in the free trade under the Bosham name.

Badger Inns of Hall and Woodhouse have now purchased
the enterprise and a local midwife has been enjoying herself in
temporary charge of the new-born brews. At present the beers
can be obtained only at the picturesque Gribble Inn but there
are plans to venture back into the free trade. Oving is between
the A27 and the A259, just outside Chichester and not far from
Bognor Regis. The thatched village pub is well worth a visit.

REAL ALES
Gribble Ale (OG 1042) – a distinctive premium bitter
Reg's Tipple (OG 1050) – stronger and well rounded


**Harvey and Son Limited**
Independent Local Brewers
Bridge Wharf Brewery, Lewes, Sussex

Bridge Wharf is a fine example of a country brewery in the
Victorian Gothic style. The tower and brewhouse dominate the
scene from Cliffe Bridge, while behind them stand the remaining
buildings, the Georgian fermenting room, cellars and former vat
house. The setting is close by the River Ouse, overlooking Cliffe
Bridge. When a new brewing tower was erected in 1985, it was
deliberately designed to match the style of the existing structure.

The brewery was established on this impressive site by
John Harvey (1784–1862). The tower and brewhouse were
constructed in 1880. Outwardly little has changed since then,
but modern plant and equipment have been installed over the
years. The addition of a second mash tun in recent times doubled
capacity to 50,000 barrels a year.

Harvey's remains a family firm, proud of its independence.
The seventh generation of John Harvey's descendants are currently involved in the brewery's affairs. They have the benefit
of their own supply of fresh spring water and a yeast which has
remained unchanged for over thirty years.

The list of prizes which have been awarded to Harvey's at
the International Brewers' Exhibition is a long one. In 1968, for
example, the brewery carried off a gold medal, one first prize,
two second prizes and two third prizes, with its Elizabethan
Ale featuring very prominently. Its owners will tell you that
it is simply a question of selecting the finest quality mild and

Harvey's Bridge Wharf Brewery

pale ale malts and combining them with the choicest Kent and Sussex hops, but the locals know that those seven generations of family experience are perhaps the most important factor in the success of the brewery.

REAL ALES
XX Mild (OG 1030) – a dark mild with a gentle sweetish
   palate
IPA (OG 1033) – a well-balanced session bitter
Sussex BB (OG 1040) – a full well-hopped bitter
XXXX (Old Ale) (OG 1043) – a dark nutty winter ale

Harvey's is sold under two names – its own and that of

Beard's of Sussex. (Beard's ceased brewing and was purchased by Harvey and Son, but the name is still retained.)

TIED HOUSES
With the exceptions of the Brecknock Arms and the Crystal Palace, both in Tunbridge Wells, all of the Harvey's pubs are in Sussex.

Berwick Village: Cricketer's
  Arms
Blackboys: Blackboys' Inn
Brighton: Lord Nelson,
  Mitre Tavern
Crawley: White Hart
Eastbourne: Arlington Arms,
  Hurst Arms, Lamb,
  Terminus Hotel,
  Victoria Hotel
East Hoathly: Forester's Arms
Glynde: Trevor Arms
Hailsham: Grenadier Hotel

Hastings: Crown Inn
Herstmonceux: Bull's Head
Isfield: Halfway House
Lewes: Dorset Arms
Magham Down: Red Lion
Midhurst: Swan
Newhaven: Jolly Boatman
Plumpton: Plough Inn
Polegate: Dinkum
Southover: Swan
Stone Cross: Red Lion
Turners Hill: Red Lion
Uckfield: Alma Arms

**Jolly Fenman, Sidcup**
See **Clifton Inns** in Chapter Six.

**King and Barnes Limited**
Independent Regional Brewers
Horsham Brewery, Bishopric, Horsham, West Sussex

The testing time for independent family breweries came in the period from 1945-70, when there was the twin-pronged attack from national keg beers and from hungry big brewers looking for takeovers. Many companies fell, but King and Barnes is a proud example of those members of the brewing industry which did not. There was sufficient resolve in Horsham to survive those hard times. Throughout the period traditional draught beers were produced for the tied estate and then, when fashions changed away from keg and conglomerates, the determination which the family had shown found its reward in new demand for those traditional beers.

King and Barnes has always been a family affair and
its origins go back to the early 1800s. At that time there
were several common and publican brewers in Horsham. The
Bishopric itself, then being the wide cattle market of the town,
housed six pubs. In 1850 James King came to trade at the
maltings there. He supplied Satchell's North Parade Brewery
and the two businesses merged in 1870. Gradually James King
acquired the whole of Satchell's interest in North Parade and it
was renamed King and Sons.

Under the King family's control a new well was dug and
new maltings built. The brewery was the first premises in
Horsham to use electric lighting and the small steam engine
which generated it can still be seen in the office building. It
is also interesting to see a price list for the company's products

around 1900 – whereas the strong Amber Ale sold for 2s (10p) per gallon and the lighter BA Bitter for 1s 4d (7p) per gallon, the brewery made available for domestic consumption 'household beer' called 'H' at the very reasonable price of 9d (just under 4p) per gallon, 'brewed exclusively from finest malt and hops'.

While the King family was forming a limited company and expanding into wines and spirits, the Barnes, also of Horsham, were brewing at the East Street Brewery in direct competition. This business had been producing beers since around 1800, being acquired by G.H. Barnes and Company around 1878. The unification of the two came in 1906, all of the brewing being transferred to the Bishopric's North Brewery. When the only other brewery in the locality closed a few years later, the directors of King and Barnes Limited were able to adopt the exclusive title of the Horsham Brewery.

The supposedly inexhaustible well which had been dug in 1898 began to dry up in 1937 and after the war a new one had to be drilled (to a depth of 288 feet in the Tunbridge Wells greensand stratum). The old maltings buildings were destroyed in a fire in 1961. Yet, despite all these problems, the company has continued to produce real ales of local character for Sussex and Surrey and to maintain an individuality in its public houses to this day. Sussex Bitter was voted CAMRA's Best Standard Bitter in 1987.

REAL ALES
Sussex Mild (OG 1034) – a smooth sweet dark mild
Sussex Bitter (OG 1034) – a clean-drinking hoppy bitter
Old Ale (OG 1046) – dark and malty but not too strong
Festive (OG 1050) – a strong pale ale of character
In 1989 a new ale, Broadwood (OG 1040), was added

TIED HOUSES
*Surrey*

| | |
|---|---|
| Blackbrook: Plough | Ockley: Old School House, |
| Cranleigh: Leather Bottle | Scarlett Arms |
| Leigh: Plough Inn | Reigate: Nutley Hall |

*Sussex*
There are thirteen King and Barnes houses in Horsham. Elsewhere in the county you will find them at:

Ardingly: Avin's Bridge Hotel
Balls Cross: Stag
Billingshurst: Blue Ship,
  Ye Old Six Bells
Bucks Green: Fox
Colgate: Dragon
Copsale: Bridge House
Copthorne: Cherry Tree
Dragon's Green: George and
  Dragon
Eridge: Huntsman
Faygate: Cherry Tree
Hailsham: King's Head
Horley: Gatwick Hotel
Ifield: Gate, Plough
Kingsfold: Dog and Duck,
  Wheatsheaf
Kirdford: Forester's Arms
Lindfield: Snowdrop Inn
Lodsworth: Halfway Bridge
Lower Beeding: Crabtree,
  Plough

Loxwood: Onslow Arms,
  Sir Roger Tichbourne
Midhurst: Rother Inn,
  Wheatsheaf
New Pound: Bat and Ball
Partridge Green: Windmill
Pease Pottage: Black Swan,
  Grapes
Plaistow: Bush
Plummer's Plain: Wheatsheaf
Rusper: Royal Oak
Selham: Three Moles
Shoreham-by-Sea: Burrell
  Arms
Tillington: Horseguards
Upper Beeding: Bridge Inn
West Chiltington: Elephant
  and Castle, Five Bells
Withyham: Dorset Arms
Worthing: Jolly Brewers,
  Swan Hotel

Try also any of the twenty-three Beard's of Sussex public
houses – there are five in Lewes.


**Larkins' Brewery Limited**
Independent Local Brewers
Rusthall, Tunbridge Wells, Kent

The Larkins family contributed to the quality of English ales for
many centuries before they actually started brewing. Since the
sixteenth century they have been nurturing the finest Kentish
hops for others to use in their beers.

In October 1986 it was decided that a new brewery should be
established. Ted and Marjorie Dockerty, with the considerable
assistance of their son Bob, purchased the former Kentish Ales
brewery in Rusthall and began brewing. The great advantage
which they have is that they can use those splendid Golding hops
which are grown and harvested at their own Chiddingstone farm
and dried in their own oast houses.

A great deal of attention is paid to traditional quality. Pure malt, with no artificial additives, is used for the sweetness and strength of Larkins' 'Real Kentish Beers'. Twenty barrels a week are produced for customers in Kent, Surrey, Sussex and south-east London. Perhaps the most famous outlet is the Dickens Inn near the Tower of London – the Dickens Bitter sold there is in fact brewed by Larkins.

REAL ALES
Traditional (OG 1035) – a well-hopped session bitter
Sovereign Bitter (OG 1040) – a pleasant bitter of mid-strength
Best Bitter (OG 1045) – a well-rounded premium bitter
Porter (OG 1055) – a rich porter of good strength

FREE-TRADE OUTLETS
Larkins' beers are found mostly around Tunbridge Wells, but do try the Dickens Inn.


**Martin Ales**
Free-trade Brewers
Martin, Dover, Kent

As a boy Merrick Johnson used to play in the old brewhouse at the family home. He would look at the abandoned coppers in the 200-year-old building and imagine them back in use. It is not certain when brewing ceased at Marston Hall, but it was probably towards the end of the nineteenth century. Although the well was sealed when the local pumping station opened, the donkey wheel is still there as a reminder of those days.

Merrick had tried his hand at home brewing before he decided to fulfil his boyhood ambition. First he had to invest £2,000 in reroofing the listed building. A seven-and-a-half-barrel-brew-length Peter Austin plant was installed ready for production in 1983. Merrick mashes on Saturdays after he has returned from a four-day lecturing stint in London. By Monday evening the fermentation is well under way and he can leave his son John to keep an eye on things while he returns to the capital.

There were some problems with the system in the early years but Martin Ales are now on a sound footing and output is gradually increasing as the free trade becomes more and more interested in the unusual beer. Merrick used to brew a high-gravity beer called College Ale, but he is concentrating these days on his Johnson's Bitter. He keeps meticulous notes to aid consistency and quality and he will tell you that a brewer must depend upon his own palate in judging his ale. The beer has a dark bitterness imparted by the use of roast barley, which Merrick sees as the way to give piquancy without the excessive sharpness which some beers develop from the use of an overdose of hops.

The unusual bitter is regularly available in a few free trade outlets and as a guest beer in several others. Merrick is confident of further progress and hopes to add more ales in future years.

REAL ALE
Johnson's Bitter (OG 1040-4) – a dark rather dry bitter

FREE TRADE
*Kent*

Dover: Louis Armstrong
Lower Hardres: Three
  Horseshoes

Sandwich: Bell Hotel
Walmer: Green Beret

*Yorkshire*
Halifax: Santa Fe

## Shepherd Neame Limited
Independent Regional Brewers
Court Street Brewery, Faversham, Kent

In the deep South East of England lies the country's oldest independent. Shepherd Neame has its brewery in Faversham, north Kent, and its business can be traced back through the town's history to 1698. The Court Street Brewery was established four years before the creation of the Bank of England, during the reign of William and Mary.

The founder of the business was Richard Marsh, twice mayor of Faversham, who was succeeded by his son Richard. Samuel Shepherd, who came from near Deal, purchased the business from Richard's widow in 1741. For over 125 years the brewery was under the sole control of the Shepherd family. During that era many public houses were acquired and the considerable benefits of the Industrial Revolution were introduced to the brewing process.

Queen Court

The first Neame to become associated with the company was Percy Beale Neame, who was invited into partnership by Henry Shepherd in 1869. As often happened in such cases, one dynasty gave way to another. When Henry Shepherd died, control passed to Percy Neame. Despite the company's name, the joint ownership lasted for only a few years. Since 1877 the Neame family has been the sole proprietor.

On his farm at Dunkirk Percy Neame bred the magnificent shire horses for which the brewery was then famous. However, even he was eventually forced to succumb to the new technology. He purchased one of the first steam traction engines as a superior means of transporting beer to the surrounding towns and villages. Shepherd Neame has always had a geographically 'tight' estate, with most of its houses in nearby areas of Kent. At that time the longest journey necessary for the draymen was to Ashford. A man carrying a red flag had to walk in front of the traction engine as it made the 26-mile round trip.

Harry Neame, Percy's son, received his education in brewing at the famous Carlsberg Brewery in Copenhagen in the 1880s. In more recent times Robert, grandson of Harry, studied the art at the same brewery. Combine this expertise with the excellence of the local hops and you have the basis for the success of Abbey Ales from Faversham. Shepherd Neame has a single hop farm, the splendid Queen Court at Ospringe, which supplies all of the company's requirements. The farm grows several varieties of the English hop – Early Bird, Eastwell Goldings, Tutsham and Cobs. In recent years some of the new hop varieties have been added to this list.

Shepherd Neame is a large independent with a proud history but it maintains a modern approach to its traditional ales and to its public houses. In the Garden of England you will find quaint country inns in a rural setting as well as houses which have been developed for the leisure requirements of the modern age. The common factor is that they all sell good real ale.

REAL ALES
Master Brew Bitter (OG 1036) – a clean-drinking hoppy bitter
Master Brew Best Bitter (OG 1039) – a full-flavoured premium
   bitter
Stock Ale (OG 1039) – a dark well-rounded drink

TIED HOUSES
Abbey Ale public houses number more than 250. Most of them are in Kent and are easily located – there are eight in Canterbury, eight in Dover, eighteen in Faversham, nine in Maidstone and eleven in Sheerness. Beyond Kent you will find Shepherd Neame at a few hostelries in London and East Sussex:

*London*
EC1 : Rutland
SE1: Simon the Tanner
SE1: Sultan
SE8: Harp of Erin
SE10: Ashburnham Arms,
   Royal George

SE11: Court Tavern
SE15: Beehive
SE18: Anglesea Arms
SE23: Railway Telegraph

*East Sussex*
Battle: Abbey Hotel
Hastings: Duke of Wellington,
   Prince Albert, Royal
   Standard

St Leonards: Marina,
   Prince of Wales

**Sussex Brewery**
Single-pub and Limited Free-trade Brewers
Main Road, Hermitage, Emsworth, West Sussex

The tavern at 36 Main Road, Hermitage, brewed its own beer in the nineteenth century. It was one of three small breweries in the immediate vicinity of Emsworth. The earliest record of brewing there dates from 1869 – hence the claim by the modern Sussex Brewery of having been founded in that year.

In fact brewing on the premises ceased over 100 years ago. The pub itself closed down in the 1960s. By the time that the real ale revival swept through the country, the building had fallen derelict and had been abandoned to its history. It took a resolute group of enthusiasts to restore it. The public house required nearly four years of dedicated work before it was reopened in late 1979. By 1981 a full-mash brewery had been constructed in the old brewhouse. Hermitage Ales had been revived.

The present owner, Malcolm Roberts, came on to the scene in 1985 and soon began to build upon the work of his predecessors. At one time five different ales were produced and quite a large proportion found its way into the free trade. The five-barrel brew-length full-mash system currently produces around ten barrels a week of a less extravagant range of beers. Malcolm has to some extent opted out of the highly competitive free-trade market to concentrate upon supplying his own pub, the Sussex Brewery, and just a few local outlets.

REAL ALES
Wyndham's Bitter (OG 1038) – a distinctive hoppy bitter
Hermitage Best Bitter (OG 1048) – a smooth premium bitter
Warrior Ale (OG 1058) – a rich strong ale

TIED HOUSE
Hermitage: Sussex Brewery

FREE TRADE
Emsworth: Brookfield Hotel

# CHAPTER FIVE

# The West Country

## Ash Vine Brewery
Local and Free-trade Brewers
White Hart, Trudoxhill, Somerset

Rob Viney has a purpose-built brewery behind the White Hart at Trudoxhill, which is off the A361 south of Frome. He brews a single bitter there for two tied houses and for an extensive free trade. Bob concentrates on brewing and leaves most of the deliveries to agencies.

Originally the brewery was set up by Ted Bishop, of Cotleigh Brewery fame, and the beer was marketed as Bishop's Best Bitter. Ted found it difficult to make the venture work to his satisfaction and he sold the business to Rob. The brewery was moved to the rear of the White Hart in 1988, housed in a new brewhouse and renamed Ash Vine.

The impressive single bitter is brewed with stainless-steel equipment of ten-barrel brew-length. There are four fermenting vessels and the average weekly output is sixteen barrels. The 'brewery tap' is an attractive country inn with a long bar where you will discover several guest beers as well as a lively trade in meals and bar snacks. Ash Vine bitter also finds its way into some distant pubs both as a guest ale and on a more permanent basis. In some places you may find it sold under a house name.

REAL ALE
Ash Vine Bitter (OG 1039) – a dry, well-hopped and tasty
  bitter

TIED HOUSES
  *Avon*
Bath: Pig and Fiddle

The White Hart, Trudoxhill

*Somerset*
Trudoxhill: White Hart

FREE TRADE
*Cornwall*
Callington: Coryton Arms

*Dorset*
Sherborne: Britannia Inn,
   Digby Tap, Skippers, Three
   Owls

*Somerset*
West Pennard: Red Lion

*Wiltshire*
Bradford-on-Avon: Ham Tree

**Barron**
Free-trade Brewers
Silverton, Exeter, Devon

Richard Barron's is a farm brewery in the true sense set in rolling countryside north of Exeter and not far from the M5. The farm spring provides the liquor for Richard's brews and there is no need for him to make any chemical adjustment to it. The system is a full mash and three different beers are produced. The business provides a good example of a farmer making a success out of an unusual diversification.

The improbable location of the small brewery is a redundant sheep pen but it is perhaps not totally surprising that Richard has turned to brewing – the licensed trade is in his blood. For many years he was the landlord of the Three Tuns in Silverton and that establishment had its own brewery at one time.

Sales are mainly local and you will find Barron's in the free houses in Silverton, which is just off the A396 between Tiverton and Exeter, and in and around Exeter itself.

REAL ALES
Barron's Draught (OG 1040) – smooth and of good strength
Exe Valley Bitter (OG 1043) – a well-balanced premium bitter
Devon Glory (OG 1050) – a rich modestly strong ale

FREE TRADE
Crediton: Crediton Inn          Sandy Park: Sandy Park
Exeter: Imperial Hotel,          Silverton: Lamb, Three Tuns
   Well House

**The Beer Engine**
Local and Free-trade Brewers
Newton St Cyres, Exeter, Devon

The Beer Engine is the complete pub. It has a bar with a darts board and a log fire if required, a food bar round the corner where an extensive snack and meal menu is available and the Boiler Room Bar below where regular live music gives a special atmosphere. From the latter you can view the in-house

The Beer Engine

brewing operation. Peter Hawksley made his first mash in March 1983 with a plant made by SPR Stainless Steel Products of Ramsbottom. The system has a three-barrel brew-length and originally was served by two fermenting vessels (a third has since been added). It is situated in the narrow basement of the split-level building, which was previously called the Olde Barne Owl Inn. The theme these days is obviously that of the steam engine – the ales are named to fit the image and as you take a drink you are quite likely to hear the rattle of a train on the nearby line. The brewery's publicity material carries an amusing sketch of a railway wagon powered by a frothing and overflowing beer copper.

Peter produces three ales, mainly for consumption at the Beer Engine and the other pub which he took over in 1989, the Sleeper at Seaton, but you can find one or more of them at outlets in the free trade. Sleeper Heavy is sometimes marketed as a limited edition in self-conditioned bottled form.

The pub is well served by the station across the road, which is just a short steam from Exeter St David's. If you are travelling by a less appropriate mode of transport, the pub is half a mile off the A377 between Exeter and Crediton. It is well worth a visit. Peter is one of the new breed of caring and enthusiastic brewers who have introduced stability and quality into the small brewery revolution.

Rail Ale (OG 1037) – light and bitter
Piston Bitter (OG 1044) – a darker maltier bitter
Sleeper Heavy (OG 1055) – a rich strong ale of character

OUTLETS
Besides the Beer Engine itself, try:

*Devon*
Exeter: Mill on the Exe,      Nomansland: Mount Pleasant
    Well House               Seaton: Sleeper

**Berrow Brewery**
Free-trade Brewers
Coast Road, Berrow, Burnham-on-Sea, Somerset

James Johnstone set up his own small brewery in 1982 after travelling the world and gaining a great deal of experience in the industry. He installed a John Hickey stainless-steel plant behind the old farmhouse in buildings which were once the home for a coach and its horses.

The plant is of ten-barrel length and output is around seven or eight barrels per week in summer and a little less in winter. 4B is brewed from pale malt with a crystal malt addition which gives it a golden hue, and both beers are hopped by a mixture of Goldings and Fuggles.

These days the lady of the house, Andrea, takes the leading role in the brewery and she does a splendid job, particularly when you consider that she also has to face the demands of five children. The ales are sold to various clubs (including the social club at Westland Helicopters) and are well received in the free trade, mainly as guest beers distributed by agencies. You will find Berrow on pump in places very far from Burnham-on-Sea.

REAL ALES
4B (OG 1038) – a distinctive golden bitter
Topsy Turvey (OG 1055) – a powerful strong ale, light in
colour

OUTLETS
*Somerset*
Burnham-on-Sea: Ritz Social Club
Mark: Pack Horse

**Blackawton Brewery**
Local and Free-trade Brewers
Washbourne, Totnes, Devon

This small brewery was founded in 1977 by Nigel Fitzhugh in a workshop which had been a smithy, opposite the Normandy Arms in the village of Blackawton. The first brew was of Blackawton Bitter and it was almost two years later when Headstrong, a warming winter strong ale, was added.

By 1981 larger premises were needed and Nigel moved the brewery to a barn next to his house in Washbourne. He introduced 44 Special in 1985 as a mid-strength bitter to complete the range of draught beers.

The available market in Devon for a free trade brewer is a difficult one. Most of the pubs have ties and it requires great industry and salesmanship to find customers in the limited number of free houses. Blackawton is fortunate enough to have a hard core of customers who have remained faithful to the brewery for a decade or more.

In August 1988 enthusiast Barry Quiggin purchased Rowden House and the brewery from Nigel Fitzhugh. He set about improving the quality of the beers and encouraging his landlords to nurture them in their cellars. The brewery has a capacity of about forty-five barrels a week and reaches around forty in the summer months. Inevitably output is rather less during the quiet season. Barry matures his beers for two or three weeks before he delivers them direct in the south Devon area, from Plymouth to Exeter. He has wholesale agents serving east Devon and Cornwall and an agency supplier in Kent.

Blackawton is 'on the up'. Under Barry Quiggin's careful direction it is gradually making its mark on the conservative drinking habits of the locals and attracting more and more interest from visitors to Devon and from free houses elsewhere.

REAL ALES

Blackawton Bitter (OG 1036-9) – a refreshingly hoppy bitter

44 Special (OG 1043-6) – a well-balanced premium bitter

Headstrong (OG 1050-3) – a dark strong ale now brewed all year round

FREE TRADE
*Devon*

Blackawton: Normandy Arms
Bolberry Downs: Portlight
Brixham: Smuggler's Haunt
California Cross: California
    Inn
Coffinswell: Linny
Cornworthy: Hunter's Lodge
Dartmouth: Cherub
Exeter: Bystock
Holbeton: Mildmay Colours
Holne: Church House Inn
Meavy: Royal Oak

Milton Combe: Who'd Have
    Thought It
Newton Ferrers: River Yealm
    Hotel
Peter Tavy: Peter Tavy Hotel
Plymouth: Drake Hotel,
    Pym Arms
Slapton: Queen's Arms,
    Tower Inn
Torcross: Torcross Hotel Pub
Totness: White Hart
Woodland: Rising Sun


**Blue Anchor**
Renowned Home-brew Pub
Coinagehall Street, Helston, Cornwall

By the early 1970s there were only four home-brew establishments left in Britain – the publican brewer was almost extinct.
The Blue Anchor is perhaps the best-known of the quartet of
survivors, despite its location deep in the South West.

Three generations of the Richards family had brewed there
for a century and the changing fashions in beer drinking had not
bothered them. The thatched building in which they sold their
beers was built somewhere around the end of the fourteenth
century.

Simply because almost 600 years have passed, do not expect
much to have changed. There is no fancy modern parlour here.
The atmosphere is just right for drinking in the style that
your grandfather might have enjoyed. You can choose from
two high-gravity 'Spingo' bitters which themselves seem to
have come from a different age and, at particular times like
Christmas and Easter, two 'Special' strong ales which are not
for the faint-hearted. The brewery which produces these amazing brews is situated behind the pub and has its own well for
the liquor.

The historic Blue Anchor is just there, a part of our heritage
– it does not advertise or even particularly welcome publicity.
Drop in for a rare experience in beer drinking if you are in

Cornwall. One word of warning however: be careful of the deceptive strength of the ales – there is a hill to climb and men have been known to stagger on their way out!

REAL ALES
Medium (OG 1050) – a pale premium bitter
Best Bitter (OG 1053) – a full-flavoured ale
Special (OG 1066) – a rich strong ale
Extra Special (OG 1070) – as strong an ale as you would
  wish to drink

## Butcombe Brewery Limited
Independent Local and Major Free-trade Brewers
Butcombe, Bristol, Avon

When Simon Whitmore decided to go it alone, he had the perfect pedigree. His experience had been gained at Guinness and eventually as managing director of Courage Western. The result has been the most successful of the new breweries and it has all been achieved with a single bitter.

With the assistance of his wife, Simon began brewing in September 1978. Gradually Butcombe Bitter has spread through the free trade from its base on the Avon-Somerset border. The company owns three public houses and no doubt will in due course expand its estate. Sales from the brewery are currently around 8,000 barrels a year – an incredible performance for a small business of its type. Real-ale agents ferry Butcombe to eager free traders in many distant parts of the country.

The brewery is situated in redundant farm buildings adjoining the Whitmore's house in Butcombe, near Blagdon Lake. No chemicals or substitutes are used in production and you will find the beer dispensed in one of two ways – straight from the cask or from a traditional handpump.

About 250 free-trade outlets are supplied at any one time and the number is increasing. Perhaps some of the new breweries which produce five or six different beers might benefit from considering that Simon has worked in two companies which have concentrated on a single product in order to achieve remarkable success – Guinness and Butcombe.

REAL ALE
Butcombe Bitter (OG 1039) – a refreshing rather bitter ale

TIED HOUSES
*Avon*
Compton Martin: Ring O'Bells
Rowberrow: Swan

*Somerset*
Axbridge: Lamb

FREE TRADE
The outlets vary and are well-spread around the country.
A few of the local regular customers are listed below:

*Avon*

Bath: Bladud Arms,
   Rose and Crown
Churchill: Crown
Marshfield: Lord Nelson

Oldbury-on-Severn: Anchor
   Inn
Weston-super-Mare: Regency

*Somerset*

Broadway: Bell Inn
Cannington: Malt Shovel
Coleford: Rose and Crown
East Harptree: Castle of
   Comfort
Fivehead: Crown Inn

Holcombe: Ring O'Roses
Nunney: George
Rudge: Full Moon
Upton Noble: Lamb Inn
Yeovil: Armoury

**Cornish Brewery Company**
Subsidiary Major Regional Brewers
The Brewery, Redruth, Cornwall

The Cornish Brewery is now the sole brewing arm of J.A.
Devenish PLC, serving almost 400 public houses with real ales.
The old Devonish Brewery in Weymouth was closed in 1985 to
concentrate all production at Redruth.

Beers have been brewed in Weymouth from at least 1252
and the Devenish establishment there dated back to 1742. The
Flew family sold the business in 1824 to a William Devenish.
It is said that in 1872 the Prince of Wales was in the locality
and requested a glass of beer to aid his recovery from illness.

He was sufficiently impressed that a year later, when on the royal yacht off Weymouth, he called again for Devenish's pale ale and promptly granted the company a royal warrant.

By 1900 Devenish beers were well known throughout the West Country. When the company purchased pubs in Falmouth and Penryn after the First World War, deliveries to them were made by train from Weymouth. It was during this period that smaller breweries were acquired at a rapid rate – Carnes of Falmouth, Malletts of Truro, the Redruth Brewery and the Treluswell Brewery.

The Weymouth brewery suffered badly from its proximity to the naval base at Portland during the Second World War: it was bombed twice. In 1940 the brewery offices, hop store and laboratory were destroyed and other buildings were severely damaged. Within a year the roof of the bottling store was ablaze from another wayward raid. Bottles had to be filled in the open air during the following few days and the brewery was actually closed for over a year as a result of the damage. During that dry period the Devenish houses in Dorset were supplied by Eldridge Pope and John Groves (who occupied a site next to Devenish in Weymouth). Full production was not restored until after the war.

Vallance's Brewery of Sidmouth was a major force in the area which had won many awards at brewing exhibitions. It fell to Devenish in 1957, together with its thirty-two pubs. Part of the old company's name is retained in Wessex Royal – Wessex was the name of its famous India pale ale. In 1960, after a merger with John Groves, the expanding company took stock of its requirements and rationalised its brewing interests in just the Weymouth and Redruth establishments. Devenish and Groves traded until 1965 when the combined company was changed to Devenish Weymouth Brewery Limited.

The year 1985 saw great changes. The Weymouth Brewery was closed after a history of almost 250 years and all brewing was moved to Redruth. Around that time a merger was agreed with Inn Leisure, and ambitions have run high at Devenish ever since. In 1989 plans to spend £8.7 million were announced, the funds being made available for new pubs and pub/entertainment complexes, particularly in the North East. The bottled Newquay Steam Beers are marketed throughout the land. While the intention is obviously to transform Devenish from a regional to a major national brewer, the expanding range of real ales will remain an important aspect of the business.

REAL ALES

JD Dry Hop Bitter (OG 1032) – a tangy bitter of modest
  strength
Cornish Original (OG 1038) – a rounded session bitter
Wessex Royal (OG 1042) – a distinctive premium ale
Great British Heavy (OG 1050) – a full-flavoured strong ale

In 1989 two new beers were introduced – Vallance's Best Bitter
( a dark premium bitter) and Draught Steam (a dryish session
bitter).

TIED HOUSES

There are 121 houses in Cornwall and the former Devenish pubs
in Dorset number sixty-two. Elsewhere the following examples
may be of interest:

*Avon*
Bath: Coeur de Lion
Bristol: King's Arms

*Devon*
The beers are found in the nine former Vallance's houses
in and around Sidmouth, as well as in the following:

Aylesbeare: Halfway House
Axmouth: Ship Inn
Budleigh Salterton: King
  William
Church Knowle: New Inn
Crediton: White Hart
Exminster: Royal Oak
Haven Banks: Welcome Inn

Honiton: White Lion
Ottery St Mary: Plume of
  Feathers, Volunteer Inn
Plymouth: Mowbray's Railway
  Inn
Seaton: King's Arms
Whimple: New Fountain
Withycombe: County House

*Somerset*
North Newton: Harvest Moon

*Wiltshire*
Salisbury: Horse and Groom
Swindon: Glue Pot, Queen's
  Hotel

**Cotleigh Brewery**
Free-trade Brewers
Ford Road, Wiveliscombe, Somerset

At first glance Wiveliscombe seems a tranquil place. A tourist in the docile and charming Somerset countryside would take it for another quaint, sleepy, rural haunt. In fact, there are two vibrant members of the brewing industry in 'Wivey', despatching beers to many parts of the country. Closer inspection shows the visitor that the town is dominated by old brewery buildings which date back to 1807. In that year William Hancock bought land at Golden Hill and began the buildings for the family's new brewing business. By 1845, when William died, the firm had acquired six pubs in the town and twice as many in the surrounding districts. His son of the same name took control of the business and expansion was even more rapid under his management. Hancock's was said to be the West's largest brewery towards the end of the century.

One of the advertisements used around that time by the company showed a photograph of a matron aged 101 with the legend: 'A great comfort to me has been Wiveliscombe Old Ale. I have had half a pint every night for 70 years; it gives me strength and sleep.' And they used to claim that 'Guinness is good for you'!

The firm owned sixty houses in 1896, a number which had increased to eighty-five by 1906. A brewery in Tiverton was purchased to aid this growth and the company amalgamated with S.W. Arnold and Sons in 1927, so gaining an interest in breweries in Taunton. The new company purchased another brewery, in Crewkerne, in 1938.

This rapid expansion made Arnold and Hancock Limited vulnerable to the hovering big brewers after the Second World War. It fell to Ushers in 1955 and all brewing ceased in Wiveliscombe four years later. The Monday whiff of malt and hops was missing from the town for twenty years. Fortunately, 1979 saw Golden Hill Brewery commence business in part of Hancock's old buildings and a year later John and Jennifer Aries arrived to establish Cotleigh in a part of Hancock's brewhouse.

They had started in the stable block of Cotleigh Farmhouse, Washfield, with Tawny Bitter. The move to Wiveliscombe enabled them to double production and add new beers – Old Buzzard in 1982 and Kingfisher Ale in 1985. Perhaps 1984

was the best year for them – Tawny Bitter won an award at
the Great Western Beer Festival and John and Jennifer were
married at Holcombe Rogus (the latter event being celebrated
by the issue of 250 bottles of Wedding Ale).

With trade continuing to increase, they moved out of Hancock's to a new sixty-barrel purpose-built brewery in Ford Road.
Again they achieved a doubling of capacity. The brewery which
they designed is a super-modern one and is under the charge of
brewer Peter Elvin. The barley used (mainly Triumph) is grown
in the Dart Valley and malted by Edwin Tucker and Sons of
Newton Abbot, and the main source of hops is a single farm
in Kent.

When Cotleigh began back in 1979, the aim was merely
to supply six local pubs. Today you will find the 'bird beers' in
more than seventy outlets at any one time and you need not
necessarily travel to Somerset or Devon to find them. It is all
down to a three-person operation – John, Jenny and Pete, the
Cotleigh Brewery.

REAL ALES
Kingfisher Ale (OG 1035-7) – a light and hoppy bitter
Tawny Bitter (OG 1039-41) – a smooth well-balanced bitter
Old Buzzard (OG 1047-9) – a dark and warming strong brew

FREE TRADE
It is not possible to list all of the outlets, as the market is an
ever-changing one, but the following free houses usually carry
one or more of the beers:

*Devon*
Broadhembury: Drewe Arms
Butterleigh: Butterleigh
  Arms

Holcombe Rogus: Prince
  of Wales
Molland: Black Cock,
  London Inn

*Somerset*
Bridgwater: Fountain Inn
Dulverton: Rock House
Exford: White Horse
Middlezoy: George
Pitminster: Queen's Arms

Porlock: Ship Inn
Stogumber: White Horse
Wellington: Globe Inn
Williton: Forester's Arms
Winsham: Bell Inn

**Exmoor Ales Limited**
Free-trade Brewers
Golden Hill Brewery, Wiveliscombe, Somerset

Golden Hill was the first of the two new Wiveliscombe breweries to open (in 1979) after a twenty-year lapse. The history
of the town's brewing heritage has been outlined in the entry
on Cotleigh Brewery.

The old Hancock's loading bay was chosen for the first
brew of Exmoor Ale. Tim Gilmour-White gathered second-hand
brewing equipment from all over the country – he knew that
it had been the massive investment in modern plant that had
caused many new ventures to fail. Just eight weeks after the
first mash a cask from the thirteenth brew of the ale was sent
to the Great British Beer Festival at Alexandra Palace and
achieved the ultimate award – Best Bitter of the Year, 1980.
You cannot have a much better start than that! The number
of customers rose rapidly from eight to 120.

Exmoor Ale has been Somerset's best-selling traditional beer
for some years and can be obtained in eleven southern counties
from Cornwall to Kent. Golden Hill quickly reached the top ten
of the nation's small breweries in output terms. This success
allowed for capital investment at the right time and the original
self-assembled brewing equipment was systematically replaced
by modern and larger plant, increasing potential capacity from
500 gallons a day to 800. One of the biggest items of expenditure
has been on casks of various sizes. A free-trade brewer needs at
least three times his weekly gallonage in barrels.

On 2 October 1986 Exmoor Brew 1000 was mashed and
this signalled the moment for new beers. Exmoor Dark, a
dry-hopped dusky ale, was introduced. The celebration ale which
was brewed to commemorate the 1000th brew formed the basis
of Exmoor Gold, which was introduced in early 1988. As in the
case of Cotleigh, malt for these beers comes from Edwin Tucker
and Sons of Newton Abbot, who use traditional floor-malting
processes and are the only remaining maltsters in the West
Country.

The brewery was the subject of a management buyout in
1988 and is now owned and managed by Jim Laker and Colin
Green – hence the change of name from Golden Hill to Exmoor
Ales Limited. In the same year production topped a million pints
for the first time.

Keep your eye open for Exmoor Ales in the free trade. The

long tradition of fine ales from Wiveliscombe is ably maintained on that historic site by the Golden Hill Brewery.

REAL ALES
Exmoor Ale (OG 1039) – a tasty well-malted bitter
Exmoor Dark (OG 1039) – darker and dry-hopped
Exmoor Gold (OG 1045) – a strong smooth premium bitter

FREE TRADE
Exmoor Ales are prolific in the free trade but they are obviously most easily found in Somerset and Devon:

*Devon*

Exeter: Double Locks, Old Firehouse
Plymtree: Blacksmith's Arms
Slapton: Tower Inn
Lutton: Mountain Inn
Topsham: Bridge
Plymouth: Royal Adelaide
Trusham: Cridford Inn

*Somerset*

Bishops Lydeard: Bell Inn
Stogumber: White Horse
Crewkerne: King's Arms
Taunton: Mason's Arms
Exford: White Horse
Watchet: Bell Inn
Hillcommon: Royal Oak

**Fleece and Firkin**
Subsidiary Home-brew pub
St Thomas Road, Bristol, Avon

Allied's subsidiary Hall's owns a few interesting home-brew establishments. When David Bruce (one of the pioneers of the new brewery movement – see the Firkin chain in Chapter 6) decided that he had made a geographical error and sold off his first venture outside London, the company was quick to step in with an offer. Bruce had been brewing Bootlace there and his famous Dogbolter. Like many of the Firkin pubs, the Fleece is situated in a converted large building with plenty of room for customers. The usual fun and puns are also present.

The brew-pub first opened in 1982 and it was in the following year that the sale to Hall's of Oxford took place. Situated south of the river in Bristol, the emporium is housed in a Georgian former wool-merchant's stone-built warehouse. A wide range of beers are brewed from the full-mash system. They are dispensed under blanket pressure. You are guaranteed plenty of entertainment at the Fleece and on busy nights there is a good atmosphere from the hubbub which emanates from a mainly youthful clientele.

REAL ALES
Brunel Bitter (OG 1038) – a refreshing light bitter
Bristol Best (OG 1043) – a well-balanced premium bitter
Coal Porter (OG 1050) – stronger and darker
Rambo (OG 1058) – a rich strong ale
Old Woolly (OG 1088) – a mind-blowing winter ale

## Marisco Tavern
Home-brew Pub
Lundy Island, Bristol Channel

If you fancy trying something different, why not set up a brewery on a 3-mile-long island 12 miles from the mainland and with a population of around twenty? That is exactly what John Ogilvie did in 1984, in between his other jobs such as restoring the grounds of the Old Hotel into a productive kitchen garden. The malt-extract plant was supplied by Inn Brewing, and Robin Richards assisted in the first season.

Initially a beer of 1040.5 OG was brewed but this proved a little too heady for the visitors and John O's bitter was reduced to OG 1037. In the summer the beer is brewed in a 36-gallon batch each Monday and fermented out for five days so that a weekly cycle can be maintained. Production is limited by the available water supply and temperature control can be a problem in hot summers. The brewery is situated in farm buildings and the beer is sold only in the nearby tavern shop.

The name Lundy is derived from two Norse words meaning puffin island. If you want to see the puffins for which the island is famous or the numerous seals, or if you wish to investigate Brazen Ward, Gannets' Bay, Jenny's Cove or Devil's Slide, you will need to take a trip on Lundy's ship, MS *Oldenburg*, which sails from Bideford Quay and Ilfracombe Pier throughout the summer. The journey takes about two hours but at the end of it you will have four hours to enjoy the tranquil island and its unique beer.

John Ogilvie has now retired and brewing was taken over by David McBride in early 1989. Later that year Peter Hawksley of the Beer Engine near Exeter was called in to review the operation. It is likely that changes will be made to the brewing process – perhaps even conversion to a full mash. Given the fact that Peter has been involved, the results are likely to be well appreciated by future visitors to Lundy.

REAL ALE
Lundy Pale Ale (OG 1037) – a fruity malt-extract bitter

## Mill Brewery
Local Free-trade Brewers
Bradley Lane, Newton Abbot, Devon

Mill Brewery was designed and built from mainly second-hand brewery and dairy equipment by Dave Hedge, Paul Bigrig and Simon Swindells. Brewing commenced in mid-summer of 1983, one of those rare sweltering summers when thirsts are high. Although Simon has departed for a career in advertising, Dave and Paul remain the proprietors of the business.

The installation was made with the help of technical advice from Phil England of Wakefield and originally had a brew length of just three and a half barrels. This has since been extended to seven barrels and the next plan is to increase to ten barrels by converting an existing hot liquor vessel into a new mash tun.

The company's symbol is an elderly Devonian ('Old Janner'). Around December he appears on pump clips in full Father Christmas costume with pint in hand, signifying that Janner's Christmas Ale is available. In summer it is the Old Dark which sells particularly well, probably because of the high numbers of mild-drinking Midlanders holidaying in the area. You will find the beers locally in the free trade but you might sometimes not recognise them as being from Mill Brewery, because they are sold under house names: 'Queen's Ale' at the Queen's Hotel, Newton Abbot; 'Old Rydon Ale' at the Old Rydon, Kingsteignton, Newton Abbot; 'Castle Ale' and 'Dungeon Bitter' at the Castle Inn, Stoke Gabriel.

REAL ALES
Janner's Old Dark (OG 1038) – a dark mild, Midlands style
Janner's Ale (OG 1038) – light, hoppy yet with a fruity flavour
Janner's Old Original (OG 1045-9) – strong, light and full-flavoured
Janner's Christmas Ale (OG 1050) – a stronger version of Old Original

FREE TRADE
*Devon*

Broadhempston: Monk's
  Retreat
Coombinteignhead: Wild
  Goose
Kingskerswell: Barn Owl

Kingsteignton: Old Rydon
Newton Abbot: Queen's Hotel
Stoke Gabriel: Castle Inn
Woodland (Ashburton): Rising
  Sun

## Miner's Arms Brewery
Single-pub and Free-trade Brewers
The Well House, Westbury-Sub-Mendip, Somerset

Paul Leyton rather anticipated the new micro-brewery revolution when he started brewing a bottled beer in 1974 for his restaurant, the Miner's Arms in Priddy. Own Ale, with an original gravity of 1048, was sold in $1/3$ and $1/2$ pint bottles to the diners there. At that time it was one of only seven beers naturally conditioned in the bottle.

Miner's Arms Brewery

Such was the interest that it soon became apparent that a cask beer was a necessity and a rather less powerful draught Own Ale was produced. A. Barry Haslam purchased the business in 1977 and four years later he closed the restaurant to concentrate on brewing for the free trade. The brewery was moved to its present site at Westbury-sub-Mendip, a small village on the southern slopes of the Mendips between Wells and Cheddar. New equipment was installed to increase the capacity and Guv'nors Special Brew was introduced in 1985.

Miner's Arms sells to the free trade within a radius of 35 miles from Wells and now owns its own public house in Bath. Own Ale carried off prizes at the Great Western Beer Festival in 1983 and 1984 and Guv'nors Special Brew also received an accolade in 1986. Both beers are becoming more widely available through agents in many parts of the country.

REAL ALES
Own Ale (OG 1040) – a well-balanced bitter of good strength
Guv'nors Special Brew (OG 1048) – a distinctive premium bitter

TIED HOUSE
Bath: Hatchett's


**North Cornwall Brewers**
Home-brew Pub
Min Pin Inn, Tintagel, Cornwall

If the Beer Engine combines the themes of railways and beers and Paradise Park brings together beer and birds (the feathered variety), the Min Pin creates a link between dogs and ale. Marie Hall breeds pinschers of the name Min Pin. The sign outside the family inn depicts one of the dogs on top of a beer barrel.

With her daughter Stephanie, Mrs Hall brews two beers for the public house in legendary Tintagel. Since the untimely death of Doris 'Ma' Pardoe, Mrs Hall and Stephanie could claim to be the most prominent lady brewers in the land. They brew with second-hand equipment which has an 8-gallon capacity in a converted coalhouse. The ladies use malt extract rather than a full-mash brewing process. The heating for their boil is provided by Calor Gas because there is no mains supply.

You will have to call at the popular Min Pin Inn in north Cornwall if you want to sample the two unusual beers – Legend and Brown Willy (which is named after Cornwall's highest 'mountain', you might be relieved to learn).

REAL ALES
Legend Bitter (OG 1036) – a hoppy malt-extract bitter
Brown Willy (OG 1055) – a rich strong ale

## Oakhill Brewery
Free-trade Brewers
The Old Brewery, High Street, Oakhill, Somerset

Brewing has been connected with Oakhill since the eighteenth century. The building in use today is the last remaining part of a substantial brewery which was burned down in the 1920s. Since the fire it has been used for several purposes related to brewing, particularly as a grain store, but it was not until 1981 that the tradition of Oakhill ales was revived.

First the Beacon Brewery was established, only to founder within two years. Reg Keevil stepped in and injected fresh cash into the enterprise, ensuring that Oakhill stayed on the brewery map. The only sadness is that the town's most famous product, Oakhill Invalid Stout, (which at one time sold better than Guinness), will never again be brewed on the premises. The recipe was lost in that fire over sixty years ago.

Nevertheless, the two new draught beers have found considerable success in the local free trade. There is a maximum capacity of fifteen barrels per week, using three fermenters of various sizes. Now that the original brewer, Gerry Watts, has retired, Nigel Freestone has been assisting Reg Keevil in the brewing operations. Look out for Farmer's Ale and Yeovil Ale in the free trade.

REAL ALES
Farmer's Ale (OG 1038) – a full-flavoured bitter
Yeovil Ale (OG 1050) – a premium bitter of good strength

FREE TRADE
*Avon*
Priston: Ring O'Bells

*Somerset*

Camerton: Camerton Inn
Chelynch: Poacher's Pocket
Priddy: Hunter's Lodge

Shepton Mallet: Cannard's
Well


**Paradise Park**
Home-brew Pub
Trelissick Road, Hayle, Cornwall

Mike Reynolds has a burning ambition – to see the 'native bird' of Cornwall, the chough, re-introduced and saved from extinction there. The attractive black bird with its long, downward-curving, red bill used to nest on the cliffs and in the old tin mines of Cornwall. Now the only pairs breeding in the county are in captivity.

Paradise Park at Hayle in Cornwall is the base for 'Operation Chough' and a great deal of Mike's time is spent in working towards re-establishing his favourite bird. However, he does find the odd moment to brew a surprising array of real ales.

The brewery was opened in 1981 in outbuildings behind the licensed premises there and produces at least three different beers at any one time. They are sold only in the Bird in Hand, the pub created out of the old coaching house on Paradise Park.

If you are holidaying in deepest Cornwall, find an afternoon to visit the bird paradise at Hayle. It is situated in the grounds of a large Victorian manor house. There are many endangered species of birds to be seen and the 'real Cornish ale' brewed there, which is obviously Mike's second love in life, is interesting and different.


REAL ALES

Paradise Bitter (OG 1040) – a distinctive bitter
Artist's Ale (OG 1055) – a smooth heavy bitter
Chough's Bitter (OG 1062) – a strong ale brewed in celebration
   of the most important resident of the park

## Royal Clarence
Single-hotel and Free-trade Brewers
The Esplanade, Burnham-on-Sea, Somerset

Dennis Davey and his family have a splendid business on the sea front at Burnham. The Royal Clarence is a seventeen-bedroom hotel with plans for further extensions. In addition to the hotel accommodation there are two public bars and a function room. Each member of the Davey family has a role in running this successful enterprise.

Local beer experts will tell you that the bars are a haven for real-ale lovers. Butcombe Bitter and Wadworth 6X are always available and there are three handpumps for guest beers. In a single year the family can offer a choice of up to 140 different beers. To make things even more interesting there is a house ale, Clarence Pride.

Alan Jones is the brewer of the single bitter, which he produces from a full-mash Peter Austin stainless-steel plant. It is a five-barrel brew-length system and these days up to fifteen barrels per week are brewed. Happily for beer drinkers outside Somerset, the agents who deliver the staggering range of guest beers to the hotel are now taking away with them casks of Clarence Pride. The unusual bitter is beginning to find its way into the free trade and it is bound to be well received.

REAL ALE
Clarence Pride (OG 1036) – a full-flavoured malty bitter

## Royal Inn
Home-brew Pub
Horsebridge Brewery, Horsebridge, Tavistock, Devon

The Royal Inn, situated close by a fourteenth-century bridge over the River Tamar, is a delightful free house which was originally built as a convent by local monks. It first became a tavern during the reign of Charles I, prior to the Civil War.

Peter Waymouth began the brewery in 1981 but as a result of injury was forced to close down two years later. The current landlord, Terry Wood, and his family took over the business in 1984 and his son Simon reopened the brewery.

Royal Inn, Horsebridge

The stainless-steel, full-mash equipment has a capacity of just a single barrel. It is situated at the rear of the Royal Inn near an aviary, fitting snugly into a room measuring only 6©12 feet. The malt used in the mash is crushed on the premises. Brewing takes place twice a week with a constant production of three real ales and sometimes four. The beers are made in the natural way, using no added sugars, colourings, preservatives or head retainers.

The fifteenth-century inn would be worth a visit without a bonus of home-brewed ales. It can be found a mile south of Sydendam Domeral by travelling along narrow lanes. The range of Royal Inn 'small beers' is a welcome surprise for the casual traveller and there is the added attraction of an extensive range of succulent bar meals.

REAL ALES
Tamar Ale (OG 1039) – a light malty bitter
Horsebridge Best (OG 1045) – a hoppy premium bitter of
  light hue
Right Royal (OG 1050) – an occasional celebratory brew,
  dark and full-flavoured
Heller (OG 1060) – a strong ale, rich in colour and flavour

# St Austell
Independent Regional Brewers
Trevarthian Road, St Austell, Cornwall

St Austell ales were first brewed to satisfy the thirsts of the weather-beaten fishermen and farmers of Cornwall. The brewery operation dates back to 1851, the original buildings being sited near the Market House in St Austell. It was in 1893 that the brewhouse was moved to its present imposing position high on the hill overlooking the town and its bay.

Walter Hicks, whose family had owned and farmed Menadhu, Luxulyan, since the sixteenth century, founded the brewery. His name is still retained by the wines-and-spirits part of the company. When the brewing division was renamed St Austell in 1934, this did not signify a change of ownership – the company remains a fiercely independent family firm, all the directors being direct descendants of Walter Hicks.

St Austell prides itself on using the best malted barley of the season and takes its hops from Kent, Sussex and Hereford and Worcester. Thousands of visitors to Cornwall enjoy the beers after a day on the beach. There are around 130 tied houses (virtually all of them selling traditional ales) for them to choose from, many in harbour locations with breathtaking views – the Fire Engine at Marazion, the Lugger at Polruan and the King of Prussia at Fowey are just a few examples of favourite watering-holes for holiday-makers.

The two stronger beers in the range of real ales have been added fairly recently. It is worth searching out Hicks Special Draught, which is not available everywhere because of the special care and stillaging required to keep it at its best.

REAL ALES
Bosun's Bitter (OG 1034-8) – a light well-balanced bitter
XXXX Mild (OG 1037-41) – a dark sweet mild with strength
Tinner's Ale (OG 1037-41) – a balanced bitter, dry-hopped
Hicks' Special Draught (OG 1049-53) – a strong ale of character

TIED HOUSES
You do not have to look far for St Austell pubs in central Cornwall (there are five in Bodmin, six around Redruth and seven in and around Truro) or in south Cornwall (five in Falmouth and twelve in and around St Austell). Elsewhere in the county look out for:

*North Cornwall*

Bude: Globe Hotel
Camelford: Bettle and Chisel,
  Darlington Hotel, Mason's
  Arms
Newquay: Central Inn
Padstow: Harbour Inn,
  London Inn, Shipwright's
Polzeath: Oyster Catcher
Port Isaac: Golden Lion

St Agnes: St Agnes Hotel
St Merryn: Cornish Arms,
  Farmer's Arms,
  Great Western Hotel,
  Traveller's Rest, Victoria
  Bars
Wadebridge: Earl of
  St Vincent, St Kew Inn,
  Swan Hotel

*West Cornwall*

Hayle: Angarrack Inn,
  Bucket of Blood, Cornish
  Arms, Cornubia Hotel, Royal
  Standard, Turnpike Inn
Helston: Rodney
Isles of Scilly: Bishop and Wolf
Land's End: Logan Rock Inn
Marazion: Crown Hotel,
  Falmouth Packet, Fire
  Engine, King's Arms,
  Old Inn
Mousehole: King's Arms,
  Ship Inn

Newbridge: Fountain Inn
Newlyn: Fisherman's Arms
Pendeen: North Inn, Radjel
Penzance: Dolphin Tavern,
  Fountain Tavern, Rock Inn,
  Sir Humphry Davy, Yacht
Porthleven: Harbour Inn
St Ives: Badger Inn, Queen's
  Tavern, Sheaf of Wheat,
  Western Hotel
St Just: King's Arms, Star Inn,
  Wellington Hotel

Fox and Hounds, Comford

## Smiles Brewing Company
Independent Local Brewers
Colston Yard, Bristol, Avon

Smiles is a cheerful place. In a relatively few years the company
has grown from humble beginnings to become one of the most
successful of the new wave. Having started brewing on a very
small scale for his restaurant, Bell's Diner, John Payne decided
that he preferred brewing to serving vegetarian food. He moved
to Colston Yard and established Smiles Brewery in 1978.

By the end of his first year he was supplying Smiles Best
Bitter and Smiles Exhibition to a number of free houses in
Avon. The brewery was enlarged in 1981 and can now turn
out 100 barrels per week. These are delivered to the company's
three tied houses and to an ever-increasing free trade in the
West Country and South Midlands.

Smiles brews only bitter beers. Traditional methods are
used and there are no additives, preservatives or colourings
present. The malt is chosen carefully and the hops are Goldings.
Unusually for a small brewery, the company has its own laboratory, which is used to monitor the brews and to culture Smiles'
own yeast. It is this yeast and the local hard water in Bristol
which contributes to the special qualities and flavours of the
bitters.

As well as being sold in traditional barrels the beers are also
supplied in collapsible beer boxes. These are disposable and come
in various sizes up to 5 gallons. They enable the lucky people of
Avon to do their 'Smiling' at private parties or just on their own
at home.

REAL ALES
Brewery Bitter (OG 1036-7) – a hoppy bitter
Best Bitter (OG 1040-1) – a well-rounded premium bitter
Exhibition (OG 1051-2) – a darker stronger and smooth ale

TIED HOUSES
*Avon*
Bristol: Arnolfini, Highbury Vaults
Littleton-on-Severn: White Hart

**Thompson's**
Independent Local Brewers
London Inn, West Street, Ashburton, Devon

The Thompson family made its first brew for public sale in May 1981 at its own pub, the London Inn, in Ashburton. Originally the beer was brewed on the first floor of the premises in what had been a bar next to the ballroom. The brewing plant was largely made by Danny Thompson and his son Melvyn.

In 1987 they began building a new brewery, a project which took them two years to complete. The effort was certainly worthwhile, as the improved facility enabled them to increase production by eight times while still using the original equipment. They operate a full-mash system.

The family now has two tied houses – the London Inn and the Mutton Cove Tavern in Devonport, which was opened in 1987. In addition to these and several free houses, the recipients of Thompsons' beers include clubs, wine stores and several companies (including the Dart Valley Railway). Most of the brewery's customers are in the Dartmoor area.

Unusually for a 1980s 'new wave' brewery, Thompsons' has extended its range beyond real ales and now includes a keg Dartmoor Bitter and a Dartmoor Lager in its steadily growing production.

REAL ALES
Bitter (OG 1040) – a full-bodied bitter of good strength
IPA (OG 1045) – a hoppy premium bitter

TIED AND FREE TRADE
Ashburton: Ford's,
  Holne Chase
Bigbury: Royal Oak
Buckfastleigh: Waterman's
  Arms, White Hart
Dartmeet: Badgers Holt
Frogmore: Globe Inn
Holbeton: Mild May Colours
Hope Cove: Lobster Pot
Kingsbridge: Ship and Plough
Mary Tavy: Mary Tavy Inn
Modburty: Pickles
Morleigh: New Inn
Mortonhampsted: Plymouth
  Inn
North Bovey: Black Aller
Plymouth: Mutton Cove,
  Tavern, Pym Arms,
  Thistle Park Tavern
Princetown: Two Bridges
Ringmore: Journey's End
St Anne's Chapel: Pickwick
Slapton: Tower Inn

CHAPTER SIX

# London and the Home Counties

### The Alford Arms Brewhouse
Subsidiary Home-brew Pub
Frithsden, Hemel Hempstead, Hertfordshire

The Alford Arms was Whitbread's first venture into home-brew in 1981 and it is perhaps the most surprising survivor. Most of its sister pubs are in town centres, often drawing upon the enthusiasm of students and other young drinkers who enjoy a novelty. The pub is a far less conspicuous country inn.

Malt extract is used rather than a full mash and the equipment employed is particularly modest – only one and a half barrels can be brewed at a time. This means that you can never be sure which of the house ales will be available at any one time. They are brewed in rotation.

The brewer for eight years was Martin Winship but he handed over control to a former butcher, Ted Atkins, in 1989. One of the first challenges for Ted was to produce a commemorative beer based upon an historical event which related to William the Conqueror. Not surprisingly his target original gravity was 1066. This was a difficult task for a novice brewer but he made his plans in the converted barn next to the pub. Ted gained considerable credit when the hydrometer revealed an OG of 1065 for the limited edition bottling. It seems likely that Ted has a flair for the job.

REAL ALES
Cherrypicker's Bitter (OG 1036) – a light malt-extract bitter
Pickled Squirrel (OG 1044) – a sweetish premium bitter
Ruldolf's Revenge (OG 1053) – a rich strong ale

## Banks and Taylor
Independent Local Brewers
The Brewery, Shefford, Bedfordshire

From modest beginnings in 1981 Mike Desquesness and Martin Ayres have built their business into a major local brewery. Their success has been based upon an early penetration of a receptive free trade followed by the assembly of a dozen tied houses. The usual problem of capital outlay has largely been avoided by the policy of taking pubs on lease from regional brewers. As a result, Banks and Taylor has gone from strength to strength.

The brewery is situated on an industrial estate which was built on a former railway embankment near the centre of Shefford. The full-mash plant is an impressive one for a small brewery. An eighteen-barrel brew-length plus seven fermenters produce an output of sixty barrels per week and there is scope for more. As well as the four cask-conditioned ales the partners sell bottled beers and PETs. They are introducing a Shefford Pils Lager of OG 1047. The original industrial unit of 1,300 square feet became insufficient for their needs and an adjoining unit of similar size was added in early 1989.

As well as supplying the tied estate of twelve widely distributed houses, some of them in London, Martin and Mike have outlets in around forty free houses, including the Stone Jug at Clophill (the first pub to take their beers) and the Eastcote Arms at Eastcote (where SPA is sold as Eastcote Ale).

The combination of modern equipment and a modern approach to business has made certain that the partnership is firmly established as a permanent and real force in the industry. Banks and Taylor beers are deservedly popular. They are likely to become more available as Mike and Martin seek further outlets in the free trade.

REAL ALES
Shefford Bitter (OG 1038) – a refreshing, well hopped bitter
SPA (OG 1041) – a well-balanced premium bitter
Shefford Old Dark (OG 1050) – a dark brooding ale
Shefford Old Strong (OG 1050) – golden and full of flavour

TIED HOUSES
*Bedfordshire*

| | |
|---|---|
| Carlton: Royal Oak | Luton: Bricklayer's Arms, |
| Deadman's Cross: White Horse | Two Brewers |

Brewer's Arms, Northampton

*Cambridgeshire*
Cambridge: Cambridge Blue

*London*
E1: Lord Rodney's Head
E8: Pembury Tavern
EC1: Eagle, King's Arms

SE1: Trinity Arms
SE10: William IV

*Northamptonshire*
Northampton: Brewer's Arms

FREE TRADE
*Bedfordshire*
Clophill: Stone Jug

*Hertfordshire*
Old Knebworth: Lytton Arms

*Northamptonshire*
Eastcote: Eastcote Arms

**Battersea Brewery**
Subsidiary Home-brew Pub
The Prince of Wales, Battersea Park Road, London SW11

The Prince of Wales is home to Watney's representative in-house brewery in SW11. It is situated not far from Battersea Park and the Thames. Conway Taverns run the enterprise for Watney's and the pub is a popular venue for beer drinkers seeking a variety in their diet.

There is a full-mash plant producing six barrels a week for the bars. The normal range of beers is the standard one – a session bitter, a premium bitter and a strong ale – but occasionally there are others to try.

REAL ALES
Battersea Bitter (OG 1036) – a hoppy session bitter
Best Bitter (OG 1040) – a full-flavoured premium bitter
Power House (OG 1050) – a dark rich strong ale

**Brixton Brewery**
Home-brew Pub
The Warrior, Coldharbour Lane, London SW9

The Warrior is home to a similar operation to that of the Battersea Brewery at the Prince of Wales. However, this particular public house is wholly owned by Conway Taverns. The two enterprises are not much more than a couple of miles apart.

Michael Conway began brewing at the Warrior in 1984. He installed a larger plant with a view to supplying the beers brewed there to his other pubs in the area. If you are in a Conway Tavern and see a house beer where there is no evidence of a brewhouse, the ale was probably brewed in Coldharbour Lane. The beers follow the normal pattern with the addition of a strong winter warmer for days when there is a frost in the air. A deceptively strong lager, Front Line, is also brewed there.

REAL ALES
Brixton Bitter (OG 1036) – a refreshing session bitter
Brixton Best (OG 1041) – a well rounded premium bitter

Warrior Strong Ale (OG 1050) – a dark rich strong ale
Winter Warmer (OG 1058) – a strong old ale


## Chiltern Brewery
Free-trade brewers
Nash Lee Road, Terrick, Aylesbury, Buckinghamshire

Since the closure of Wethered at Marlow, Chiltern is the sole
representative of the brewing industry in Buckinghamshire. It
is a tribute to the enterprise of Richard Jenkinson, who left his
job in the City to concentrate on brewing ales. When he first
purchased the farm which is home to the Chiltern Brewery, he
was faced with an agricultural restriction which resulted in his
setting up a rabbit breeding operation there.
     However, his ambition was to brew traditional beers and
he opened the Chiltern Brewery in 1980. These days the
rabbits have gone and the former calf-rearing sheds house
a fifteen-barrel brew-length brewery. There is a shop on the
premises where you can purchase a pint or a polypin of the
ale as well as beer-flavoured mustards, beer-flavoured cheeses
and Old Ale Chutney. As well as the draught beers there is a
bottled Three Hundreds Ale (OG 1050), which is also available
in the farm shop.
     Chiltern beers are sold to order in the free trade – 'Bucking-
hamshire's bespoke brewers', to borrow Richard's expression.
Beechwood bitter is sold in Allied's Aylesbury pubs and British
Rail Staff Associations take some of the output. There are several
other free-trade outlets.


REAL ALES
Chiltern Ale (OG 1036) – a refreshingly hoppy session bitter
Beechwood Bitter (OG 1041) – distinctive and full-flavoured


FREE TRADE
  *Buckinghamshire*
Aylesbury: White Swan
Butler's Cross: Russell's Arms

  *Oxfordshire*
Long Crendon: Churchill Arms
Towersley: Three Horseshoes

## Clifton Inns
Subsidiary Home-brew Pub Chain
Grand Metropolitan Brewing Limited, Brick Lane, London E1

Grand Metropolitan has a very successful chain of in-house breweries under the Clifton Inns banner. They are popular venues for drinkers in South and West London and there is a further example in Sidcup. Although you might find several similarities with the Firkin chain, at least you will be excused the David Bruce style of humour.

Clifton Inns made its foray into the home-brew business in 1983 and 1984, beginning with the Orange Brewery in Pimlico Road. Each of the pubs has its own stainless-steel brewing plant, which in some cases can be glimpsed by the visitor as he strolls about with his pint. The beers are dispensed under blanket pressure and there are two of them worth special mention. Greyhound XXXX Mild is one of London's few traditional milds and Pimlico Porter from the Orange Brewery was voted best in class at the Wimbledon Beer Festival.

The Flamingo Brewery (a former Firkin pub) is dealt with separately, as is the Northamptonshire representative of the chain, Abington Park (see Chapter Eight). The four original home-brew pubs in and around London are listed below.

*The Greyhound, Greyhound Lane, Streatham, London SW16*
XXX Pedigree Mild (OG 1036) – a rare dark mild
Greyhound Special (OG 1038) – the standard session bitter
Streatham Strong (OG 1048) – a full-bodied premium ale
Streatham Dynamite (OG 1056) – a rich strong ale

*The Jolly Fenman, Blackfen Road, Sidcup*
Blackfen Bitter (OG 1037) – a light session bitter
Fenman Fortune (OG 1047) – a well-rounded premium bitter
Fenman Dynamite (OG 1056) – a rich strong ale

*Orange Brewery, Pimlico Road, London SW1*
Pimlico Light (OG 1036) – a light session bitter
SW1 (OG 1040) – a hoppy bitter of good strength
Pimlico Porter (OG 1046) – the prize-winning dark porter
SW2 (OG 1050) – a well-rounded premium bitter

*Yorkshire Grey, Theobalds Road, London WC1*
City Bitter (OG 1035) – a light session bitter

Headline Bitter (OG 1037) – a tasty standard bitter
Holborn Best (OG 1047) – a well-balanced premium bitter
Regiment Bitter (OG 1054) – a rich strong ale


**The Firkin Chain**
Subsidiary Home-brew Pubs
Greater London

The Firkin pubs offer a different sort of drinking experience
in various parts of London and beyond. A whole new concept
in large alehouses, the modern version of London's lost publican
breweries, was started by David Bruce when he opened the Goose
and Firkin at Southwark in 1979. Other similar establishments
quickly followed, mostly by conversion of a redundant building
into an open-plan pub with its own brewhouse. Alliteration
and risqué puns are the hallmark of the chain. Everything is
designed to amuse and the main attraction is for youngsters.

The beers, which are dispensed under top pressure, follow
a regular pattern of a session bitter, a premium bitter and
Dogbolter, a strong ale. The lower-gravity beers are named to
accord with the individual title of the pub – after the Goose and
Firkin David concentrated on the letter 'f'.

The origin of Dogbolter is one of the legends of modern
brewing. David was mashing for a beer called Earthstopper
in the cellar of the Goose and Firkin when the telephone rang.
He rushed upstairs for a protracted conversation which rather
spoiled his intended gravity of 1075. Instead he had to settle
for an OG of 1060. A new ale was launched and he called it
Dogbolter from an incident in his family's history. It seems that
his uncle had once inflicted a brew of similar gravity upon some
friends. When they had tried to make their own way home on a
stormy night, they had staggered off the path and fallen into a
stream. The commotion had been so great that their two dogs
had bolted off into the night and had not been seen again until
morning.

In 1988 David Bruce sold out to Midsummer Leisure PLC
of Loughborough and Watford. Midsummer has retained the
unique character of the pubs and has even expanded the chain.
The company opened the Flamingo and Firkin in Derby in 1988
(see Chapter Nine) and the Frigate and Firkin (formerly the

Beaconsfield) in Olympia and the Frigate and Firkin (formerly the Lamb) in Dalston in 1989. Jeremy Walsingham oversees the chain for Midsummer.

Firkin pubs are normally sparse, basic and fun. They are especially popular with the younger element. Live music is often in evidence and several guest beers are frequently offered to supplement the house ales. The following is a list of the pubs within the London area. The slogans under which they entice their customers are added as an indication of the humour which you must expect if you visit them.

*Falcon and Firkin, 360 Victoria Park Road, London E9*
'Falcon Well Buy Me a Firkin Pint'
Falcon Ale (OG 1036) – the session bitter
Hackney Bitter (OG 1045) – a rounded premium bitter
Dogbolter (OG 1060) – a rich strong ale
As all of the house beers follow a similar pattern, further
 description of the ales themselves is not necessary.

*Ferret and Firkin (in the Balloon up the Creek),*
*114 Lots Road, Chelsea Green, London SW10*
'Bruce's Beer – You'll PreFerret to Any Other'
Stoat Bitter (OG 1036)
Ferret Ale (OG 1045)
Dogbolter (OG 1060)

*Flock and Firkin, Dalston, North London*
'For Flock's Sake Wool Ewe Baa Me Another Firkin Pint'
Shear Beer (OG 1036)
Shepherd's Delight (OG 1045)
Dogbolter (OG 1060)

*Flounder and Firkin, 54 Holloway Road, London N7*
'I've Flounder Great Plaice for a Firkin Pint'
Fish T'Ale (OG 1036)
Whale Ale (OG 1045)
Dogbolter (OG 1060)

*Fox and Firkin, 316 Lewisham High Street, London SE13*
'For Fox Sake Buy Me a Firkin Pint'
Vixen Ale (OG 1036)
Fox Bitter (OG 1045)
Dogbolter (OG 1060)

*Frigate and Firkin, Olympia, West London*
'Don't Frigate to Buy Me a Firkin Pint'
Wingspan (OG 1036)
Frigate Ale (OG 1045)
Dogbolter (OG 1060)

*Frog and Firkin, 41 Tavistock Crescent, London W11*
'Frog Od's Sake Buy Me a Firkin Pint'
Tavistock Ale (OG 1036)
Bullfrog Bitter (OG 1045)
Dogbolter (OG 1060)

*Fuzzock and Firkin, 77 Castle Road, Kentish Town, London N1*
'Donkey me waiting for a Firkin Pint Eeyore I might get
   Fuzzock Ale'
Ass Ale (OG 1036)
Fuzzock Ale (OG 1045)
Dogbolter (OG 1060)

*Goose and Firkin, 47 Borough Road, London SE1*
'Bruce's Firkin Beer Always Goose Down Well'
Goose Bitter (OG 1036)
Borough Bitter (OG 1045)
Dogbolter (OG 1060)

*Phantom and Firkin, 140 Balaam Street, Plaistow, London E13*
'I Spectre Firkin Ghoul Pint when I Ghost to the Phantom
   and Firkin'
Phantom Ale (OG 1036)
Spook Ale (OG 1045)
Dogbolter (OG 1060)

*Pheasant and Firkin, 166 Goswell Road, London EC1*
'I'm a Firkin Pheasant Plucker'
Pheasant Bitter (OG 1036)
Barbarian Bitter (OG 1045)
Dogbolter (OG 1060)

*Phoenix and Firkin, Windsor Walk, London SE5*
'Phoenix My Pint I'll Firkin Thump Him'
Rail Ale (OG 1036)
Phoenix Bitter (OG 1045)
Dogbolter (OG 1060)

**The Flamingo Brewery Company**
Subsidiary Home-brew Pub
88 London Road, Kingston-Upon-Thames

The Flamingo was opened by David Bruce in 1987 as the
Flamingo and Firkin, brewing Flamin' Ale as its session bitter.
The property had been a Watney outlet and when David sold
out to Midsummer Leisure during the following year it was the
only pub which did not pass to the Leicestershire-based company.
Grand Metropolitan reclaimed it for its own use.

There are still many reminders of the Firkin chain, including
the brewing equipment and style of operation, but the names of
the beers have been changed. Simon Bussell is the brewer and he
has extended the range to four regular beers and a special. Every
month he brews a strong fifth beer (with an original gravity of
around 1070) and names it to celebrate a suitable event.

Like all of the former David Bruce establishments, it is
a lively and interesting place to visit.

REAL ALES
Fairfield (OG 1036) – a standard session bitter
Royal Charter (OG 1044) – a well-rounded premium bitter
Surrey Stout (OG 1044) – a dark tasty stout
Coronation (OG 1060) – a rich strong ale

**Fuller, Smith and Turner Plc**
Independent Regional Brewers
Griffin Brewery, Chiswick, London

There is a tradition of well over 300 years of brewing in
Chiswick. The first brewery recorded there, in the days of
Oliver Cromwell, was situated in the gardens of Bedford House.
That area of Chiswick Mall is now part of the Griffin Brewery.
It is known that the Mawson family purchased the brewhouse
in 1685 and this connection is still recalled by the Mawson's
Arms not far away.

In 1740 the Mawsons leased the brewery to William Harvest
for the sum of £180 per annum. The freehold rights passed
to John Thompson, a maltster, and his friend David Roberts,
a distiller. By the beginning of the nineteenth century the
Thompson family had taken full control. However, financial
problems caused by deception and distrust between two brothers

brought the business to crisis point. John Fuller of Wiltshire was called in to join the ailing enterprise in 1829 and he injected funds and a degree of the required stability. The last of the Thompsons fled to France with his creditors on his heels.

Since then Fuller's has prospered and become one of the most respected members of the brewing industry. Henry Smith and head brewer John Turner arrived from the Romford Brewery of Ind and Smith and the partnership, which is still proudly used as the name of the present PLC, was established. The acquisition of Brentford's Beehive Brewery and its pubs in 1910 helped to consolidate the partnership's status as a major regional brewer.

Fuller, Smith and Turner has won many awards for its fine beers but there is more to the company's reputation than just excellence in brewing. It also prides itself on being a family concern. Many of the firm's tenants have been loyal for years and their parents were tenants before them. The same sort of relationship exists with the 200 or more employees of the Griffin Brewery, plenty of whom have family connections with the firm going back several generations.

REAL ALES
Chiswick Bitter (OG 1035-6) – a light easy-drinking bitter
London Pride (OG 1041-2) – a distinctive and popular premium
   bitter
ESB (OG 1055-6) – a powerful and full-flavoured ale

TIED HOUSES
There are 149 tied houses and fifty-seven off-licences in the estate. Most of the pubs are within a 20-mile radius of the brewery and are easily found. The following are in outlying areas of the company's territory:

*Bedfordshire*
Luton: Midland Tavern

*Berkshire*
Binfield: Victoria Arms          Slough: Wheatsheaf
Maidenhead: Royal Oak          Wokingham: Ship
Reading: Butler, Fisherman's
   Cottage, Flowing Spring

*Buckinghamshire*
Aylesbury: Aristocrat
High Wycombe: Bell, General
   Havelock, Queen

*Hertfordshire*
Berkhamsted: Boat
Harpenden: Harpenden Arms
Hemel Hempstead: Post Office Arms
St Albans: Garibaldi

*Kent*
Ashford: Master Spearpoint

*Oxfordshire*
Wallingford: Coach and Horses

*Surrey*
Dorking: Cricketer's Arms,
   Wooton Hatch Hotel
Farnham: Castle, Hop Blossom

FREE TRADE
The beers are also well represented in the free trade. A few
examples below will give you a good chance of finding London
Pride many miles from Chiswick:

*North Cornwall*
Altarnum: Rising Sun
Blisland: Royal Oak
Lostwithiel: Royal Oak

*Wales*
Hirwayn: Glancynon Arms,
   Lamb Hotel
Ystrad: King's Head

**Guinness Brewing GB**
Renowned National and International Brewers
Park Royal Brewery, London NW10

Guinness Brewing GB is a division of Guinness Brewing Worldwide Limited. From modest origins in Dublin the progress of Arthur Guinness and Son has been relentless as it has set up breweries and distribution depots in many parts of the world. Even in Britain, Guinness could not possibly cope with demand and much of the famous Extra Stout is bottled under licence.

At the age of thirty-four in the year 1759, a certain Arthur Guinness leased a run-down brewery and 1 acre of land in Dublin for £45 per annum. He founded the St James's Gate Brewery in the Liberties area of the city. For 175 years that brewery was the sole source of Guinness, with bottles being shipped all over the world. Increasing sales in the South East of England brought about the construction of the Park Royal Brewery in North West London in February 1936.

This was only the first step in what was to become an international movement. The twin thrust of Guinness and Harp Lager necessitated brewing plants much further afield. Four breweries were built in Nigeria between 1963 and 1982, one in Malaysia in 1966, one in Cameroon in 1970 and another in Ghana in 1972. The Guinness brewery in Jamaica was sold in 1985 but still is one of at least twenty locations around the world where Guinness is brewed under licence for twenty-six different markets.

It has all been based upon that Extra Stout – a self-conditioned bottled beer which is unique. The creamy lacework of the head on a dark glass of Guinness together with that distinctive bitter taste has been the foundation of the company's spectacular success. There is no tied estate of public houses to bother Guinness. Why buy pubs when your products will be sold there anyway? Seven million glasses of the famous stout are sold every day in 140 countries.

Today Guinness is a vast business empire with interests far beyond that original brew. In 1960 the company engaged a German master-brewer to produce Harp Lager. Around the same time Irish Ale Breweries was set up to produce another best-seller, Smithwick's. Draught Guinness, which is a pressurised and sweeter version of the original brew, has become very popular. The company also has many other interests, including several brand-leading whiskies and other spirits and the

Guinness Superlatives publishing division. Guinness Worldwide is one of Britain's top ten companies and one of the top five drinks companies in the world. It all grew from a single real ale sold in bottles.

In 1988 an expensive reconstruction of the Dublin Brewery was undertaken. Throughout the world the company continues to march on. In 1988 sales of £2,776 million were recorded, but brewing these days accounts for only about 16 per cent of total sales.

Guinness Extra Stout (OG 1042) – a splendid black and
  bitter creamy stout in bottle

## McDonnell's Freehouse
Single-pub and Free-trade Brewers
428 Woolwich Road, Charlton, London SE7

McDonnell's is a lively place with a special atmosphere. It provides overnight accommodation as well as a welcome watering-hole for those who want to try some different ales. John McDonnell and his wife run the successful operation on Woolwich Road, Charlton. John began brewing in nearby Woolwich in 1983, but he moved to his present pub in 1987 and settled down there to supply his own bar and a limited free trade.

The beers, which (much like those from Pitfield) provide unusually good value for money by London standards, are Country Bitter and the stronger Sidekick. They can be found as guest beers in several outlets in South London and sometimes beyond. John's former public house, the Queen Victoria, where the brewing operation began, still dispenses them. McDonnell ales are one of the few welcome reliefs from the usual fare of the area.

REAL ALES
Country (OG 1036) – a light hoppy session bitter
Sidekick (OG 1047) – a well-balanced distinctive premium
  bitter

FREE TRADE
Woolwich (Wellington Street): Queen Victoria

## McMullen and Sons Limited
Independent Regional Brewers
The Hertford Brewery, Hertford, Hertfordshire

Peter McMullen brewed his first pint eleven years before Queen Victoria came to the throne. Ever since 1827 the family has remained an independent concern and the great-great-grandsons of Peter are continuing that tradition today. The original brewery was situated in a small building in what is now Railway Street and the first McMullen pub, the Bengeo near Hertford, was opened in 1836.

The family was forced to move twice to keep pace with its increasing market. The first move was to Mill Bridge (where the Woolpack now stands) and the second to new purpose-built premises in Hartham Lane in 1891. That site, which houses the present, much enlarged brewery, has three wells. They are sufficient to provide the daily requirement of thousands of gallons of pure water. It is the character of that well-water which gives McMullen's ales their individual flavour.

The company was the sole survivor of Hertfordshire's independent breweries. At the turn of the century there were thirty-nine of them and by the end of the Second World War only eight. The reason for McMullen's resilience can largely be explained by the family's great attention to quality over the years. The two all-year draught ales are honest and full-flavoured. AK Mild has changed little since its first brew in 1829. The company is proud of its beers and of the skill and knowledge which has been handed down from one generation to the next in order 'to preserve this distinctive McMullen flavour – as popular today as it was over 150 years ago'.


REAL ALES
AK Mild (OG 1033) – a light refreshing mild
Country Bitter (OG 1041) – distinctive and full-flavoured
Christmas Ale (OG 1070) – a strong heavy seasonal ale


TIED HOUSES
Hertfordshire is McMullen's back yard – there are over 130 houses to choose from, including fourteen in Hertford and twelve in Ware. Elsewhere you will find McMullen's beers in the following hostelries:

*Essex*

Burnt Mill: Dusty Miller
Harlow: Hare, Herald, Shark
High Beach: Owl
Loughton: Hollybush
Roydon: Crusader
Tawney Common: Moletrap
Theydon Bois: Queen Victoria,
16 String Jack

Thornwood Common:
Carpenter's Arms
Waltham Abbey: Coach and
Horses, Crown, Old English
Gentleman, Plough, Queen's
Head, Spotted Cow,
Volunteer, Welsh Harp
Wheatsheaf, White Lion

*Greater London*

Barnet: Green Man, King's
Head, Lord Kitchener, Old
Red Lion, Queen's Arms,
Sebright Arms, White Hart
Botany Bay: Robin Hood
Chingford: Royal Oak
Enfield: Cricketers, Jolly
Farmers, Wonder

Woodford Green: Cricketers
N7 (Hargreave Place): Admiral
Mann
NW3 (Hampstead): Nag's Head
WC2 (Covent Garden): Nag's
Head

**Market Brewery**
Home-brew Pub
Market Porter, Stoney Cross, Borough Market, London SE1

The Market is London's smallest brewery. It is situated in a tiny room beneath some flats, next to the Market Porter. Nick Jurczak is the brewer who supervises output from the eight-barrel-brew-length malt-extract plant. He learned his skills from Andrew Bishop, the proprietor of the pub, and took over the brewing role in the summer of 1989.

The Market Porter is a vibrant place which sells guest beers as well as its house ales. It is a large establishment with various bars and a restaurant. Brewing began there in 1981 and new plant was installed in the present 'brewhouse' in 1985. Market Brewery beers have appeared in other London pubs but are currently restricted to the home base. However, Nick is optimistic that opportunities in the local free trade may encourage him towards his maximum potential output of twenty-four barrels per week.

REAL ALES
Market Bitter (OG 1038) – a well-hopped malt-extract bitter
Market Special (OG 1048) – an occasional winter premium ale

**Nix-Wincott Brewery**
Home-brew pub with Free-trade Outlets
Three Fyshes, Bridge Street, Turvey, Bedfordshire

The Three Fyshes is a splendid riverside public house about half-way between Bedford and Northampton. Built in the seventeenth century, it stands on the banks of the Great Ouse and offers a welcome to travellers in its single bar, at tables in the garden or in the games/children's room.

Partners Charles Wincott and Martin Nix began brewing at the free house towards the end of 1987. They operate from a full-mash plant which is in an outbuilding just across the garden at the rear of the pub. There is a four-and-a-half-barrel brew-length capacity with two fermenting vessels and their output averages twelve barrels per week. This enables them to sell some of the ale to the free trade.

You may find Nix-Wincott beers at quite a distance from Bedfordshire. John Hallam, the cider wholesaler, distributes the products of the Three Fyshes brewery as far afield as Norfolk, Wales and North Yorkshire.

REAL ALES
Two Henry's Bitter (OG 1038) – a hoppy yet fruity bitter
Old Nix (OG 1056) – a rich strong ale

FREE TRADE
*Northamptonshire*
Cosgrove: Navigation

**The Pilgrim Brewery**
Free-trade Brewers
West Street, Reigate, Surrey

Surrey's only mini brewery was founded in 1982 near the village of Woldingham. It was named after the Pilgrims' Way, an ancient pathway which runs across the downs nearby. The first beer was named, perhaps not surprisingly, Pilgrim and that theme has been continued with Talisman, a strong ale, which recalls the good luck tokens which the pilgrims used to carry.

It became necessary to move from the original building in

Pilgrim Brewery

1985 and larger premises were taken in the centre of Reigate. David Roberts has steadily built up to a full range of traditional English ales. He began with a premium bitter, added a lighter pale ale (Surrey) in 1983, to be followed by Talisman and then Dark XXXX in early 1987.

The emphasis is on quality at Pilgrim. David concentrates on producing a small range of beers to a very high standard and prides himself on a reliable local delivery. He uses East Anglian malt and choice hops from east Kent. His prices are very competitive and the beers are of above-average gravity. The traditionally designed brewing equipment is of stainless steel. It is a ten-barrel plant which can turn out up to 15,000 pints a week for an appreciative free trade.

REAL ALES
Dark XXXX (OG 1037-9) – a dark mild of good strength
Surrey Bitter (OG 1037-9) – a light hoppy bitter
Progress BB (OG 1041-3) – a malty best bitter
Talisman (OG 1048-50) – full-flavoured and strong

FREE TRADE
Pilgrim has progressed well in recent years and can be found

in many free houses in London and in Surrey. The following are regular outlets:

*London*
Waterloo: Hole in the Wall

*Surrey*

| | |
|---|---|
| Mickleham: William IV | Outwood: Bell |
| Nutfield: Inn on the Pond | Oxted: Crown |
| Ockley: Cricketers | Westcott: Cricketers |

## Pitfield Brewery
Local and Free-trade Brewers
The Beer Shop, Pitfield Street, London N1

The Beer Shop in Pitfield Street is a fascinating attraction for beer lovers. Over 140 examples of ales and lagers from all over the world can be found there as well as paraphernalia and books relating to the subject. Pitfield's own products are also sold on draught.

Not only are the Pitfield ales the cheapest in London but they are also some of the finest. Dark Star, in particular, has received many prizes since the business was opened in 1981. It began as an unpretentious brewery in the basement of the off-licence (then called the Two Brewers), but when partners Martin Kemp and Rob Jones took over in 1982 things began to happen. From their base at the Beer Shop they established themselves and expanded the operation until, in 1986, it became necessary to move the brewery. Although the alternative premises in nearby Hoxton Square provided greater potential, they were far from ideal. A flight of stairs meant that every barrel had to be humped in and out.

Rob was the brewer in the early days. One of the staff whom he employed was a young Canadian, Andrew Skene, who wanted to learn about brewing. Andrew started as a labourer but showed such flair that he is now Pitfield's head brewer. He brews about twenty-five barrels a week from a twelve-barrel-brew-length plant. At one time a form of Burton Union system was used, but these days open fermenters, which are much easier to clean, are employed.

Pitfield is run by a team of four. Rob oversees the brewing, Martin is often out on the road, the Beer Shop is managed by Terry Jennings and Andrew Skene does the brewing. You will find the beers at the one tied pub, the Ship and Blue Ball in Boundary Lane, on pump at the Beer Shop and in several free-trade outlets. The latter are no longer confined to London. Premier Ales of Stourbridge distribute them further afield and a pint of Pitfield is becoming more and more common in the West Midlands.

Needing greater potential for expansion and a release from the physical limitations of Hoxton Square, the partners began negotiating for larger premises outside London with a view to moving the brewing operation in late 1989. With the space for more fermenting vessels and perhaps even a second mash tun, Pitfield's future should be set fair.

The enterprise is a rare example of quality at a reasonable price – new-wave brewing at its best.

REAL ALES
Pitfield Bitter (OG 1038) – a well-hopped session bitter
Hoxton Best Bitter (OG 1048) – a well-rounded premium bitter
Dark Star (OG 1050) – a dark strong ale with a growing
    reputation
Original London Porter (OG 1058) – dark and dryish porter,
    occasionally on draught
Christmas Special (OG 1066) – a rich winter wobbler

TIED OUTLETS
E2: Ship and Blue Ball
N1: Beer Shop

FREE TRADE
E1: Pride of Spitalfields
E2: Approach Tavern
E2: Marksman


**Charles Wells Limited**
Independent Regional Brewers
The Eagle Brewery, Havelock Street, Bedford, Bedfordshire

The very modern Charles Wells Brewery in Havelock Street, Bedford, which was opened by the Duke of Gloucester in 1976, has a five-vessel brewhouse with a mash capacity of almost 5 tons and a brew-length of about 140 gallons. It can produce seven brews a day if required. These impressive facts about the stainless-steel ultra-modern plant are not likely to excite the real-ale enthusiast – he or she would prefer a Victorian tower system. However, the present brewery was opened in the company's centenary year. Charles Wells has a long and distinguished history of brewing in Bedford.

The founder was born there in 1842. He went to sea for many years but returned to be married at the age of thirty. Needing stability for himself and his bride, he purchased the old brewery in Horne Lane together with its thirty-five public houses. From the sales particulars we know that 'a five quarter mash tun, Iron Liquor back to hold fifty barrels, thirteen barrel open copper, with iron wort back, hop and under backs, coolers, refrigerator, working tuns, pumps, pipes and cocks, horse wheel machinery and gear' were included in the auction. Charles Wells had bought himself an instant business and he soon showed that he could adapt to his new vocation. In 1902 he sank a well to improve his liquor supply (that well is still used today, the water being pumped 3 miles to Havelock Street). He was regarded as one of the most honest of businessmen in the area and he had tremendous energy and enthusiasm. By the time of his death in 1914 his brewery had become a flourishing enterprise with an expanding estate.

The growth of the company was achieved through several acquisitions. Charles had purchased the Cardigan Brewery in 1910. After his death his family continued the expansion. In 1917 the Phoenix Brewery in Bedford was bought from the Jarvis family and two years later the Newport Pagnell Brewery was acquired. In 1920 the Estate of Days Brewery at St Neots was purchased. In 1963 the Abington Brewery of Northampton was added to the list. All of these small businesses had their own public houses (on average twenty to twenty-five in number each) and this enabled the family to increase production and spread its territory.

The purchase of the Abington Brewery made it obvious that the Horne Lane premises had become inadequate for the company's needs. Being fairly central, that site had considerable value to developers and the family was able to use the sale proceeds to fund the purchase of the 11-acre site and build a new brewery at Havelock Street. The independent firm produces around 200,000 barrels a year (half of this is lager) and now has approaching 300 public houses. The Ancient Druids in Cambridge, which sells Wells beers in addition to home-brew products, is dealt with separately in this book.

REAL ALES
Eagle Bitter (OG 1035) – a well-hopped standard bitter
Bombardier (OG 1042) – rounded premium bitter

TIED HOUSES
Charles Wells outlets are common in Bedfordshire (the company has thirty-six pubs in Bedford itself) and in the south of Northamptonshire. Other neighbouring counties have plenty of representatives:

*Buckinghamshire*
Aylesbury: Saracen's Head
Bletchley: Dolphin
Bradwell: Prince Albert
Cheddington: Rosebery Arms
Fenny Stratford: Foundry
   Arms
Great Brickhill: Duncombe
   Arms
Hanslope: Watts Arms
Lavendon: Horseshoe
Mentmore: Stag Inn
New Bradwell: Cuba,
   Forester's Arms, New Inn
Newport Pagnell: Dolphin,
   King's Arms, Newport Arms,
   Plough, Rose and Crown

Oakley: Bedford Arms
Olney: Bull
Padbury: Robin Hood
Poundon: Sow and Pigs
Sherington: Swan Inn
Stoke Goldington: White Hart
Stony Stratford: Plough
Wendover: Halfway House
Whaddon: Antelope
Winslow: Windmill
Wolverton: North Western,
   Royal Engineer

*Cambridgeshire*
Brampton: Dragoon
Buckden: Falcon Inn, Spread
   Eagle
Eaton Socon: Bell Inn,
   Wheatsheaf
Fenstanton: Chequers, Crown
   and Pipers
Gamlinghay: Fountain
Great Eversden: Hoops
Great Gransden: Crown and
   Cushion
Great Staughton: New Tavern
Hail Weston: Royal Oak,
   Crown Inn

Hartford: Barley Mow
Haslingfield: Jolly Brewers
Huntingdon: Territorial
Kimbolton: Half Moon
Offord Cluny: Swan Inn
St Neots: Angel Inn, Cannon
   Inn, Globe Inn, Golden Ball
Southoe: Bell Inn, Three
   Horseshoes
Thriplow: Green Man
Tilbrook: Three Shuttles
Wyboston: Wait-for-the-
   Wagon

*Hertfordshire*

Ashwell: Bushel and Strike
Bushey: Royal Oak
Harpenden: Silver Cup
Hemel Hempstead: Olde
   King's Arms

Hitchin: Bricklayer's Arms,
   Fountain
Pirton: Cat and Fiddle
St Albans: Jolly Sailor

*Greater London*

N1 (Downham Road): Mitre
NW1 (Ashmill Street): Marquis of Anglesey
NW1 (Werrington Street): Neptune
NW8 (Queen's Terrace): Knights of St John
SE1 (Southwark): Anchor and Hope

## Young and Company's Brewery Plc
Independent Regional Brewers
The Ram Brewery, Wandsworth, London SW18

Young and Company is one of the famous established regional
breweries. The company's fine shire horses can still be seen
making deliveries around Wandsworth. It is London's most
highly respected member of the industry and there is a great
deal of character and tradition about the place.

From small beginnings on a corner of the present site near to
the River Wandle, the Ram Brewery has spread to occupy about
6 acres. Records show that there was a brewery run by a Draper
family on the banks of the river as far back as 1675. The Surrey
Iron Railway, one of the first public railways authorised by Act
of Parliament, opened in 1803 and ran from near the original
brewery to Croydon. Some of the original stone sleepers are built
into the wall of the exercise yard for the twenty shire horses.

The Young family arrived on the scene in 1831, when Charles
Young and his partner Anthony Bainbridge purchased the
business. Four years later a beam engine was installed in
the brewery and this was in regular use until the early
1980s. A second similar engine, added in 1867, is still in use.
In the early days barges on the nearby canal (known as 'the
Cut') delivered coal and malt. Despite two fires the company
has always prospered and steadily increased its trade. In 1884
Young and Company was formed on dissolution of the original
partnership. The company moved forward under the control of
Charles Young, son of the founder.

An eighteenth century brewer's house still stands on the site and it is the oldest surviving part of the original brewery. Although the roof was removed by a bomb in the Second World war, there are still delightful plaster panels to be seen on the ground floor with portrait busts of Inigo Jones and Hogarth. The ceiling which was lost was decorated with scrolls of hops and barley. Bombs also destroyed the brewery cask shed and damaged the Ram Inn (now the Brewery Tap). The span of different ages of architecture on the site was increased in 1984 when a new brewhouse was built at a cost of £5 million.

Royalty has long been associated with Young and Company. In 1981 Her Majesty the Queen was present for the celebrations to mark the company's 150th anniversary and the Queen Mother has been known on a special occasion to pull a pint at the Queen's Head, Stepney. Both the pubs and the beers have won many awards. Special Bitter was voted best premium bitter at the Great British Beer Festival of 1985, for example. Although Young's houses comprise only 3 per cent of the pubs in Greater London, six of them have been adjudged first in the Standard Pub of the Year competition.

Young and Company and its pubs are an integral part of life in South West London. The brewery is held in high esteem, not least for its steadfast resistance of the keg onslaught of the 1960s and 1970s. Every one of Young's pubs sells real ale. Although the tied-house estate is a fairly compact one, increased capacity in recent years has meant that the beers will become more readily available in the free trade and more prominent at beer festivals.

REAL ALES
Bitter (OG 1036) – light, hoppy and refreshing
Special (OG 1046) – a premium bitter full of character
Winter Warmer (OG 1055) – a full-flavoured old ale

TIED HOUSES
Young's has an estate of 149 public houses and is looking to increase its holding. Most of them are within a 5-mile radius of Wandsworth and are easily discovered. The following are a little further from the brewery:

*Berkshire*
Eton Wick: Pickwick

*Kent*
Dartford: Malt Shovel

*Greater London*
Barking: Britannia
Beddington: Plough
Chislehurst: Bull's Head
Croydon: Dog and Bull,
    Gloucester, Tamworth Arms
Greenford: Bridge
Kingston: Albert Arms,
    Bishop out of Residence,
    Grey Horse, Spring Grove

Surbiton: Black Lion, Victoria,
    Waggon and Horses
Sutton: Lord Nelson, New
    Town, Robin Hood
Wallington: Dukes Head

*Surrey*
Betchworth: Dolphin
Chertsey: Crown
Claygate: Foley Arms
Epsom: King's Arms
Esher: Bear
Gomshall: Black Horse

Redhill: Home Cottage
Shere: Prince of Wales
Walton-on-Thames: Royal
    George, Swan
Walton-on-the-Hill: Chequers

*East Sussex*
Plumpton Green: Fountain

CHAPTER SEVEN

# *Eastern Counties*

**Adnams and Company Plc**
Independent Regional Brewers
Sole Bay Brewery, Southwold, Suffolk

The Sole Bay Brewery has an imposing Victorian facade which conceals the much renovated and extended accommodation within. Adnams is an independent seaside brewery with a proud tradition. It is known that beers have been brewed on the site for over 350 years.

The brewery which we see today largely dates from an 1890 rebuild, but it stands on the site of the Swan Inn where a brewhouse existed from 1641. In fact company archives reveal photographs of the actual purchase of the old brewery in 1872 by George and Ernest Adnams. It was eighteen years later that Adnams became a public company in order to finance the rebuilding.

Much in the style of the industry, the successful firm expanded by absorbing and closing down other breweries (C.J. Fisher of Eye in 1904, G. Rope and Co. of Orford in 1907 and Flintham and Hall of Aldeburgh in 1924). The company has shown its enterprise in other ways too over the years. Brewers often diversify and the establishment of a fine wine and spirits business is by no means unique to Adnams. However, establishing pig units (the company set up two in the early 1980s) is perhaps less traditional. It is said that the pigs fed on surplus yeast and ullage beer are plump indeed – 'Adnams Pigs are Happy Pigs' the advertisements pronounce.

Today Adnams is the largest employer in Southwold. It is a major factor in the life of its community and in its economy. Fortunately Adnams goes from strength to strength. A five-year building plan which culminated in 1985 enabled the company to double its capacity of production without destroying any of the traditional brewing methods.

Locals will tell you that it is a blend of barleys grown on the light soils of East Suffolk and best hops from Kent which produces the fine Southwold ales. The yeast currently in use at the brewery has not been changed since 1943. As a testimony to these raw materials and to the skill of the brewers, Adnams has been awarded the Championship Cup for the Best Beer in Britain.

REAL ALES

Mild (OG 1034) – a soft slightly sweet mild
Bitter (OG 1036) – a hoppy favourite bitter
Extra (OG 1044) – a premium bitter with a distinctive Fuggles
  hop flavour, introduced in 1985
Old (OG 1042) – a malty winter warmer without undue 'kick'

TIED HOUSES

*Essex*

Colchester: British Grenadier,
  Castle Inn
Wivenhoe: Horse and Groom

*Norfolk*

Great Yarmouth: Allen's Bar,
  Clipper Schooner
Harleston: Cherry Tree,
  Duke William

Norwich: Horse and Dray
  Tavern, Rose Inn

*Suffolk*

Aldeburgh: Bury Cottage,
  Cross Keys, Mill Inn,
  Railway Hotel, White Hart
Badingham: White Horse
Blyford: Queen's Head
Blythburgh: White Hart
Bramfield: Queen's Head
Brampton: Dog Inn
Brandeston: Queen's Head
Bungay: Fleece Hotel
Butley: Oyster Inn
Clare: Cock Inn

Darsham: Stradbroke Arms
Eastbridge: Eels' Foot Inn
Framlingham: Railway Inn
Geldeston: Wherry Inn
Gislingham: Six Bells
Halesworth: Angel Hotel, Star
  Inn
Haverhill: Red Lion
Ipswich: County, Duke of
  York, Greyhound,
  Lord Nelson
Kelsale: Poacher's Pocket

Leiston: Engineer's Arms
Lowestoft: Marquis of Lorne,
    Prince Albert
Orford: Jolly Sailor, King's
    Head
Oulton Broad: King Alfred
Reydon: Randolph Hotel
Sizewell: Vulcan Arms
Snape: Crown Inn, Golden Key
Southwold: Crown Hotel,
    Harbour Inn, King's
    Head, Lord Nelson,
Pier Avenue Hotel, Red
    Lion, Sole Bay Inn,
    Southwold Arms, Swan
    Hotel
Sudbury: Bull Inn
Walberswick: Anchor Hotel,
    Bell Hotel
Wangford: Plough Inn
Wrentham: Five Bells, Horse
    and Groom, Spread Eagle
Yoxford: Blois Arms

## Ancient Druids
Subsidiary Home-brew Pub
Napier Street, Cambridge, Cambridgeshire

The Ancient Druids is a tiny enterprise with a brewhouse constructed for its own needs. The brewery was built in 1984, giving the former Wells tied house the status of a home-brew pub. You will find the Ancient Druids on the edge of the Grafton Shopping Centre in Cambridge.

Several of the major national combines have dabbled with the idea of home-brew establishments, with varying degrees of success. The Ancient Druids is the only example of a regional brewer – Wells of Bedford – entering the field and the venture has proved to be popular.

One of the attractions is that the interior of the brewery can be glimpsed from the street. Malt extract, rather than a full mash, is used in the brewing process. This method is cheap and less exacting than mashing from malt and produces distinctive, rather fruity beers. Various ales have been brewed from the ten-barrel plant since 1984.

REAL ALES
Kite (OG 1040) – a malty bitter
Druids' Special (OG 1047) – a premium bitter
Merlin Ale (OG 1055) – a distinctive strong ale, formerly
    known as Frost Bite

## George Bateman and Son Limited
Independent Regional Brewers
Salem Bridge Brewery, Wainfleet, Lincolnshire

The story of Bateman's over the last ten years, a famous tale
with a notable hero, is guaranteed to warm the heart of every
real-ale drinker.

It all started in 1985. At that time the family business was
held in three shareholdings. George had a minority holding of
40 per cent, but he certainly did not want to dispose of his
interest. His brother and sister, however, were prepared to
release their combined 60 per cent to the highest bidder.
They were hoping to invite interest from one of the Big Six
brewers or even from a multi-national giant: there is always
a queue of companies waiting to gobble up a regional brewer.
George knew that, if a big company bought out his relatives,
closure of many of the 100 or so pubs would be a certainty
and that the loss of the brewery itself would become a distinct
possibility.

The battle began. George went to the public and the public, who loved the unique flavour of their Bateman's beers,
responded with petitions and even with financial contributions.
But the cash from the man at the bar was not sufficient to buy
off the majority shareholders. They were determined to sell, yet
George persisted in trying to stop them. He suffered moments of
acute depression as he struggled against the odds. Even when a
takeover seemed inevitable, he still fought on to try to guarantee
the future of the brewery.

The fight continued, looking a hopeless one, until suddenly
the beer itself came to the rescue. XXXB Bitter was awarded
the title Beer of the Year. The free-house trade took notice of this
and orders came pouring in. At around the same time George was
lucky enough to find an ally in a London solicitor who specialised
in takeovers. This legal eagle studied the papers and realised
that the family assets could not that easily be dispersed. There
were problems at law for the brother and sister. So convincing
was his case that they had to agree to sell to George at a much
lower price than the outside world of big business would have
paid. George went to see his bank manager and a loan package
was arranged.

The banners went up in Batemans' brewery: 'Victory at
Bateman's. Two years' battle to preserve independence won!

Bateman's is still Bateman's.' It was the sweetest of victories, which to a small extent offset the many failures of regional breweries to resist the vultures in recent years. 'Lincolnshire's only Brewers' had been saved.

The story becomes even more unlikely when the history of the family firm and its methods is delved into further. It was not just the beer that George had been fighting to preserve.

His grandfather, of the same name, had come into the brewing business almost by accident nearly 150 years earlier. He had been invited to join a William Crow (who owned the original brewery from at least 1824) and he had done so only because a farm purchase which he had been negotiating had fallen through. Within a few years Crow had sold the brewery to him for about £500 and Bateman's beers began their steady rise in popularity. The main competition, from a brewery in Wrangle, failed to match the quality of the Bateman ales and closed down.

An estate of pubs had been built up in the villages, towns and hamlets of Lincolnshire by George's son Harry during the 1920s. Many of them were not enormously profitable, but they did provide a focus for each local community. The brewery style of operation was a benign one, if rather uneconomical, and at the time of the battle for independence it was suggested that Bateman's had arrived in the 1980s still with that 1920s style of management.

George Bateman the Younger believed in the brewery as part of the social fabric and not just as a ruthless pursuer of profits. He knew that during those 1920s his father had been forced to lay off all his employees because of a slump in demand – only to invite them all back into the brewery when he saw them standing around Wainfleet with their hands in their pockets. It was this sort of attitude which George fought to maintain and not just to save 'the beer that made Lincolnshire famous'.


REAL ALES

Dark Mild (OG 1032) – dark, smooth and creamy
Bitter (OG 1036) – well-hopped and malty, a distinctive bitter
XXXB Ale (OG 1048) – the full-bodied smooth premium
    bitter which was named the country's Beer of the Year
    in 1986.

TIED HOUSES IN LINCOLNSHIRE

Aby: Railway Tavern
Alford: White Hart
Baumber: Red Lion
Benington: Admiral Nelson
Billinghay: Golden Cross
Bilsby: Three Tuns
Boston: Ball House, Britannia, Carpenter's Arms, Coach and Horses, Duke of York, Indian Queen, King's Arms, King William IV, Mill Inn, New Castle, Roper's Arms, Ship Tavern
Burgh-le-Marsh: Red Lion, White Swan
Burwell: Stag's Head
Butterwick: Five Bells
Chapel St Leonards: Ship
Coningsby: Castle, White Swan
Croft: Old Chequers
Dogdyke: Packet Inn
East Kirkby: Red Lion
Fishtoft: Golden Lion, Red Cow
Fosdyke: Ship Inn
Freiston: Bull and Dog, Castle, Nag's Head
Friskney: Anchor Hotel, Barley Mow
Gosberton Risegate: Duke of York
Halton Holegate: Bell
Heighington: Butcher and Beast
Hemingby: Coach and Horses
Hogsthorpe: Victoria Tavern
Horncastle: Black Swan, Crown, King's Head
Huttoft: Axe and Cleaver
Ingoldmells: Three Tuns
Keal Cotes: The Vanguard
Kirkstead: Railway Hotel

Kirton Holme: Waggon and Horses
Legbourne: Queen's Head
Lincoln: Golden Eagle
Louth: Boar's Head, Malt Shovel, Woolpack
Maltby-le-Marsh: Crown
Mareham-le-Fern: Forester's Arms
Marshchapel: Greyhound
Metheringham: Londesborough Arms
Minting: Sebastopol Inn
Mumby: Red Lion
Nettleham: Plough, White Hart
New Bolingbroke: Royal Oak
New Leake: Wheatsheaf
Old Leake: Bricklayer's Arms
Revesby: Red Lion
Ruskington: Black Bull
Scamblesby: Green Man
Sibsey: White Hart
Skegness: County Hotel, Parade Hotel, Vine Hotel
Skendleby: Blacksmith's Arms
Sleaford: Nag's Head
Spilsby: Bull Hotel, Nelson Butt, Queen's Head, Red Lion
Stickney: Rising Sun
Surfleet: Crown, Great Northern
Thimbleby: Durham Ox
Thorpe St Peter: Three Tuns
Ulceby: Gate
Wainfleet: New Inn, Red Lion, Royal Oak
Wigtoft: Golden Fleece
Willoughby: Willoughby Arms
Winthorpe: Royal Oak
Woodhall Spa: Gamecock
Wrangle: Angel Inn

Bateman's beers are also available in numerous free houses, extending well beyond the boundaries of Lincolnshire.

**Crouch Vale Brewery**
Single-pub and Free-trade Brewers
South Woodham Ferrers, Chelmsford, Essex

This thirty-five-barrels-a-week brewery was set up in 1981 by a former engineer and a former civil servant. The two real-ale enthusiasts undertook some painstaking research before going into production and they have reaped the rewards of their thorough groundwork.

Operating from a brewery on an industrial estate, they began with just a Best Bitter, which they sold to the free trade. A year later they added SAS (Strong Anglian Special), a powerful bitter that enhanced their growing renown, for Crouch Vale had already established itself as a success.

In those early days when they went looking for outlets, the first free house to take Best Bitter was the fifteenth century Cap and Feathers at Tillingham. In 1986 the two partners derived great pleasure from being able to purchase that public house and so provide a retail base for their operation. The pub is a comfortable one – you will find a family room there, plenty of pub games, folk nights and vegetarian food if you want it. The beers are equally interesting and cover a wide range of types through the seasons.

REAL ALES
Woodham Bitter (OG 1035.5) – a light, refreshing bitter
Best Bitter (OG 1039) – the original distinctive brew
SAS (OG 1048) – a full-flavoured premium bitter with a
    drop kick of its own
Essex Porter (OG 1050) – a strong dark porter
Willie Warmer (OG 1060) – a powerful dark ale which may
    or may not have the desired effect

FREE TRADE
Crouch Vale beers are found in a number of houses in Essex and Greater London. The following are examples of regular outlets:

*Essex*
Leigh-on-Sea: Smack Inn          Rochford: Golden Lion
Pleshey: White House

**Earl Soham Brewery**
Twin-pub Brewers
The Victoria, Earl Soham, Woodbridge, Suffolk

John Bjornsson began brewing at the Victoria in 1985. He built his own stainless-steel plant behind the pub in a building which he believes was once, perhaps around the turn of the century, the brewhouse for the publican who then occupied the place. The Victoria is a tiny unpretentious public house – there are no juke-boxes, one-armed bandits or fancy carpets there.

The small plant has a five-barrel capacity and John brews in 750-litre batches, usually three times a week, for the two tied houses which he and his brother Sandy own. There are no sales to the free trade. The basis of the beers is malt extract, for John is a long-time employee of Edme, the home-brew specialists.

He has a refreshingly honest approach to his brewing. 'It's up to the brewer how he produces the flavour of his beers,' he will tell you and explain that malt extract itself is made from a full mash. If you ask him about the variable gravity of his winter warmer Jolabrugg (which means 'Christmas Ale' in his native Iceland), he will tell you that it depends how the beer comes out of the mash – it's as simple as that.

John's beers are as honestly distinctive and individualistic as his own approach to brewing. Certainly they have plenty of devotees and should be sought out if you are in the vicinity of Woodbridge or Cambridge.

REAL ALES
Gannet Mild (OG 1033) – a dark fruity mild
Victoria Bitter (OG 1037) – a light well-hopped house ale
Albert Ale (OG 1045) – a malty premium bitter
Jolabrugg (OG around 1055-60) – a strong ale for Christmas

TIED HOUSES
*Cambridgeshire*
Cambridge: Tram Depot

*Suffolk*
Earl Soham: Victoria

# Elgood and Sons Limited
Independent Regional Brewers
North Brink Brewery, Wisbech, Cambridgeshire

Elgood's is a typical, rather stern-looking Georgian brewery situated on the River Nene close by the Wash. In 1978 the firm celebrated a century of brewing on the premises but the existing facade dates back to an earlier age. John Cooch, a local brewer, converted the North Brink brewery around 1790. By the time it was sold to John Elgood and his partners, there had been a number of different owners who between them had put together an estate of forty pubs.

The first mash of Elgood's ales was in fact on 10 October 1878. Within a year John Elgood was the sole proprietor. Elgood and Sons Limited was formed in 1905 and since then the firm has displayed all the characteristics of a traditional family business, with control being handed down from one generation to the next.

In the 1950s an extensive modernisation of the interior of the brewery was undertaken. The brewhouse was updated with new coppers and other modern equipment was married with the best of the old. The original facade was not affected by these improvements and it still provides a fine example of a Georgian brewery.

REAL ALES
Bitter (OG 1036) – a distinctive brew of character
Greyhound Strong Bitter (OG 1045) – a more recently introduced premium bitter with a full flavour

RECOMMENDED TIED HOUSES
*Cambridgeshire*

Christchurch: Dun Cow
Elm: Bell
Guyhirn: Chequers
Leverington: Rising Sun
March: Cock, Great Northern, Red Lion
Peterborough: Blue Bell (Dogsthorpe), Blue Bell (Werrington), Royal Arms
Rings End: Black Hart
Thorney Toll: Black Horse
Whittlesy: Boat
Wisbech: Angel, Black Horse, Bowling Green, Hare and Hounds, King's Head, Red Lion, Spread Eagle, Three Tuns
Wisbech St Mary: Wheel

*Lincolnshire*

Fleet Hargate: Rose and
  Crown
Gedney Drove End: New Inn
Gedney Hill: Red Lion

Holbeach: Bell
Throckenholt: Four
  Horseshoes

*Norfolk*

Clenchwarton: Victory
Outwell: Red Lion
Stanhoe: The Crown
Tilney St Lawrence: Coach and
  Horses
Upwell: Globe

Walton Highway: Clipper's
  Arms
Welney: Lamb and Flag, Three
  Tuns
West Walton: King of Hearts

**Forbes Ales**
Free-trade Brewers
The Brewery, Harbour Road Industrial Estate, Oulton Broad,
Suffolk

Derek Longman took over the former Oulton Broad Brewery
premises near Lowestoft in March 1988 with a completely fresh
enterprise, Forbes Ales. The equipment in the small industrial
unit is modest – a three-and-a-half-barrel brew-length system
which was once used for a model brewery in a public house.
Having taught in prisons and steam-cleaned aircraft in his time,
Derek thought that brewing would be a comparatively quiet
occupation. How wrong he was! His life has been hectic ever
since he came into the business. He travels the area tirelessly
seeking new outlets in one of the most tightly tied regions of
the country.

The beers are brewed to be sold either self-conditioned in
bottles or in the cask and Derek has a purist's approach to his
art. No sugars are added and the expensive full mash is heavy
on malts to give a prolonged fermentation. This produces ales
with an exceptionally high percentage alcohol content – even
the strong ale is not oversweet. Up to five different hops are
used in the boil, in particular Target, and Derek is experimenting
further as he seeks the perfect dry bitterness.

Not many stouts are brewed by new-wave enterprises but
Forbes has the interesting Black Shuck, which is usually bottled
but can be found on draught. The strange name comes from a
local legend of a devil in the form of a black beast with red

eyes which attacks churches and is occasionally seen on stormy nights.

Derek has to fight for his outlets and the beers are not yet too easy to find. Several clubs and free houses take one or more of the ales from time to time and it is hoped that more regular outlets will be established in the near future. Recently he has been providing the refreshment at Green Party barbecues and there are plans to produce a Green Beer. This is likely to be a self-conditioned premium bitter in bottle.

REAL ALES

Forbes Best Bitter (OG 1048) – a well-hopped premium bitter
Black Shuck (OG 1060) – a strong stout, dark and bitter
Merrie Monarch (OG 1068) – not oversweet, a stronger version
    of Best Bitter

## Greene King and Sons Plc
Large Independent Regional Brewers
(1) Westgate Brewery, Bury St Edmunds, Suffolk
(2) The Brewery, Biggleswade, Bedfordshire

Many real-ale drinkers have been indoctrinated with the idea that small is beautiful and that large is suspect. The image they have understandably gained is one of massive organisations, particularly prior to the Monopolies Report of 1989, setting out to buy up and close down smaller rivals and generally to exploit the drinker (if only by reducing choice).

Despite some sizeable non-brewing shareholders, Greene King is an example of big and beautiful. In 1987 the company had a gross turnover of almost £94 million. It owns 750 pubs in eight counties and has two large breweries (three until relatively recently) and five depots to serve the estate. The company owns a 25 per cent share in Harp Lager. And yet it produces excellent real ales and genuinely cares how its public houses are run.

'Fine ales since 1799' is the proud boast. This was the date when nineteen-year-old Benjamin Greene began brewing in Westgate Street, Bury St Edmunds. It was not until 1887 that the Greene business was merged with that of former rival brewers King to create the beginnings of the present company.

The bedrock of growth has been the two prime beers which have stood the firm in such good stead over the years. Much like Bass of Burton-on-Trent, Greene King was in the forefront

of the early exporting of beer. Its basic bitter, IPA, harks back
to colonial days – India Pale Ale was originally brewed for the
East India Company. The stronger (and renowned) Abbot Ale is
named after the last abbot of Bury St Edmunds, whose house in
Crown Street was on the present brewery site.

Both of the breweries are examples of modern efficient
beer production. They both sustain a consistently high output.
Whereas the company has diversified over the years, notably
into Harp Lager, wines and spirits, sports, leisure and hotels, the
cornerstone of its success has always been its real ales. When you
consider that, even though Greene King owns 750 pubs, sales to
the free trade are around 50 per cent of its beer output, you begin
to appreciate the extent of the popularity of the company's beers.

REAL ALES
KK (OG 1030-4) – a light mild brewed at Biggleswade
XX (OG 1030-4) – a dark mild of fuller flavour produced
    at both breweries.
IPA (OG 1034-8) – a hoppy dry bitter from both breweries
Rayments (OG 1034-8) – Rayments was absorbed into Greene
    King; this bitter, brewed at Bury St Edmunds is refreshingly
    hoppy
Abbot Ale (OG 1046-52) – the pride of both breweries, a
    full-flavoured robust premium bitter

TIED HOUSES
There is no problem in finding Greene King in Bedfordshire
(153 tied houses), Cambridgeshire (167), Essex (92), Hertfordshire
(101) or Suffolk (201). Outlets are less common elsewhere and are
listed below:

*Buckinghamshire*
Chicheley: Chester Arms          Milton Keynes: Cricketers
Clifton Reynes: Robin Hood       Newport Pagnell: Kingfisher
Haversham: Greyhound

*London*
City: Scottish Pound             King's Cross: Skinner's Arms
Fleet Street: Tipperary          St John's Wood: Blenheim
Islington: Compton Arms,
    North Pole

John Barleycorn, Duxford

*Norfolk*

Barnham: Grafton Arms
Burnham Thorpe: Lord Nelson
Castle Acre: Ostrich Inn
Colkirk: Crown
Dereham: Bull
Gayton: Crown Inn
King's Lynn: Crossways,
  London Porter House, Prince
  of Wales, Wenns
Norwich: Benedicts Wine Bar,
  Brown Derby, Coach and
  Horses, Ferryboat Inn,
  Golden Star, King's Arms,
  Lillie Langtry, Ten Bells,
  White Cottage, Windmill

Oxborough: Bedingfeld Arms
Stow Bardolph: Hare Arms
Thetford: Albion Chase
Wells-Next-The-Sea: Globe
Wiggenhall St Germans:
  Crown and Anchor
Wimbotsham: Chequers Inn

*Northamptonshire*

Newton Bromswold: Swan
Northampton: Barn Owl
Wellingborough: Swallow

## Mauldon's
Free-trade Local Brewers
Chilton Industrial Estate, Sudbury, Suffolk

Mauldon's is advertised as 'a family tradition since 1795', but this does not tell the whole story. The vastness of the Greene King estate was not achieved without side effects, of course: one of the casualties was the original Mauldon's brewery.

Anna Maria Mauldon had started brewing at the Bull Hotel in Ballingdon on the outskirts of Sudbury in 1795. As the business prospered, new premises were needed within a few years. A larger brewhouse was established in Ballingdon Street. There was steady growth over the next 150 years, so that by 1960 the brewery boasted an estate of thirty tied houses, a farm and a wine and spirits merchant. At this point the jolly Green King giant stepped in with its takeover bid. Suddenly Mauldon's became but a memory etched in old glass windows here and there.

However, in 1981 Peter Mauldon, great-grandson of Anna Maria, decided to revive the family tradition. He had learned his skills as head brewer at Watney's Mortlake Brewery. By 1982 he had re-established a brewery in Sudbury, on the Chilton Industrial Estate, and a pint of Mauldon's could be supped again. The extent of his current penetration into the free trade is a tribute to his brewing talents. Peter is proud that he uses only the finest natural ingredients (including East Anglian barley, of course). At the Ipswich Beer Festival, Mauldon's was voted Best Beer in each of the four years from 1983 to 1986.

REAL ALES
Bitter (OG 1037) – a sound session bitter
Porter (OG 1042) – a dark rich porter
Special (OG 1044) – a full-flavoured bitter
Suffolk Punch (OG 1050) – a popular premium bitter
Christmas Cracker (OG 1065) – seasonal strong ale to warm
  the cockles

FREE TRADE
Mauldon's is prolific in East Anglia and beyond. Try some of the following free houses as examples:

*Cambridgeshire*
Cambridge: Jug and Firkin
Stow-cum-Quy: Prince Albert
Weston Colville: Fox and
  Hounds

*Essex*
Ashdon: Bonnet
Beazley End: Cock
Braintree: Flack's Hotel
Chelmsford: B.J.'s
Colchester: Odd One Out,
  Waffles
Easthorpe: House Without A
  Name
Ford End: Spread Eagle
Great Bromley: Cross
Great Dunmow: Queen
  Victoria
Halstead: Dog
Kelvedon: Sun
Little Walden: Crown
Roydon: White Hart
Thaxted: Cuckoo
Widdington: Fleur de Lys
Wix: Wagon
Wrabness: Wheatsheaf

*Hertfordshire*
Bishop's Stortford: Brahms
Buntingford: Crown
Hoddesdon: Huntsmen

*Norfolk*
Diss: White Elephant
Great Yarmouth: Red Herring
Norwich: Pottergate Tavern,
  Reindeer

*Suffolk*
Bildeston: Crown, King's Head
Bungay: Chequers
Bury St Edmunds: Suffolk
  Hotel
Chignal Smealy: Pig and
  Whistle
Crowfield: Rose
Dickleburgh: Crown
Haughley: Railway Tavern
Hundon: Plough
Ipswich: Malt Kiln, Toad and
  Raspberry, Trafalgar
Lindsey: Red Rose
Long Melford: Crown
Monks Eleigh: Swan
Rumburgh: Buck
Sproughton: Beagle
Stradbroke: Queen's Head
Sudbury: Boat House, Mill,
  Ship and Star
Thelnetham: White Horse
Thurston: Black Fox
Wallisfield: Turpuns, Suffolk
  Barn
West Row: Jude's Ferry
Wetheringsett: Cat and
  Mouse

## Nethergate Brewery Company Limited
Free-trade Brewers
Clare, Suffolk

Nethergate is a modern brewery built in a converted commercial vehicle workshop in the centre of Clare. It is run by the well-qualified brewer I.S. Hornsey and R. Burge. Brewing commenced on 1 April 1986 and in the following year Nethergate was chosen to feature in a documentary made for Finnish television – appropriately called 'The Quest for a Perfect Ale'. Obviously reputations spread quickly and over great distances.

The bitter brewed at Clare was voted the Best Bitter at the Cambridge Beer Festival in 1986. In the following year it reached the finals of the Great British Beer Festival at Brighton – the only East Anglian beer to reach that stage of the competition. Nethergate attracts some of the longest queues at beer festivals – perhaps the discerning in their quest for the perfect ale?

An all-malt old ale was produced for Christmas 1987 but the brewery has turned its attention to a porter of the same gravity to supplement its popular bitter. After concentrating on the free trade in East Anglia, Nethergate is now becoming more available in the East Midlands.

REAL ALES
Bitter (OG 1939) – a particularly well-balanced bitter, malty and yet with good hop content
Old Growler (OG 1055) – a rich strong porter

FREE TRADE
*Cambridgeshire*

Cambridge: Dobbler's Arms, Cambridge Blue, St Rhadigund
Comberton: Grapevine
Linton: Crown
Milton: Wagon and Horses
Soham: Carpenter's Arms
Toft: Red Lion
Waterbeach: White Horse
Withersfield: White Horse

*Essex*

Belchamp St Pauls: Half Moon
Braintree: Flack's Hotel
Chelmsford: B.J.'s
Debden: White Hart
Gestingthorpe: Pheasant
Great Dunmow: Kicking Dickey
Great Yeldham: White Hart
Halstead: Dog Inn
Magdalen Laver: Green Man
Pebmarsh: King's Head
Widdington: Fleur de Lys

*Suffolk*

Bury St Edmunds: Glad Abbot
Clare: Bell, Seafarer
Glemsford: Cherry Tree
Great Bradley: Royal Oak
Haverhill: Queen's Head

Hundon: Plough
Ipswich: Trafalgar
Lavenham: Swan
Long Melford: Black Lion
Market Weston: Mill


**Reepham Brewery**
Local Free-trade Brewers
Collier's Way, Reepham, Norfolk

Reepham has much in common with Nethergate. It is also a purpose-built ten-barrel plant of stainless steel construction. The location is a small industrial unit in Reepham on the B1145. The brewer is Ted Williams, who was also a former employee of Watney's.

The brewery was established in 1983, originally marketing Granary Bitter. Among the good range of real ales produced by Ted is a stout, which is unusual for a small brewery and is very tasty. A self-conditioning bottled version of Rapier Pale Ale is also available.


REAL ALES

Best Bitter (OG 1043) – malty and full-bodied
Rapier Pale Ale (OG 1045) – a full-flavoured premium bitter
    which replaced Granary Bitter
Reepham Stout (OG 1048) – a black stout, brewed infrequently
Brewhouse Ale (OG 1055) – a dark strong old ale


FREE TRADE
    *Norfolk*
Great Yarmouth: Talbot
Norwich: Ribs of Beef, Rosary Tavern
Reepham: Old Brewery House
Wymondham: Feathers

**Reindeer Freehouse and Brewery**
Home-brew Pub
Dereham Road, Norwich, Norfolk

It is a sad commentary on the industry that a one-time great brewing centre, Norwich, now has only one tiny brewery. In the bad old Red Barrel days the city became dominated by Watney's outlets which sold fizzy beers. The Reindeer serves up the only Norwich-brewed real ales and it is a very popular brew-pub.

When Wolfe Witham and Bill Thomas hatched the idea of becoming brewers, they were considering supplying the free trade. Sensibly, after further thought, they decided that they needed a retail base. In 1986 they found and purchased the Reindeer. A brewery was installed in the cellar and the place was extensively refurbished. It is now a comfortable free house offering a range of guest ales as well as the house beers.

Bill brews with a five-barrel-brew-length plant and has sufficient fermentation capacity to conduct his full mash three times a week. You can glimpse his equipment from a window in the bar. Besides the three regular brews there is a Winter Ale of around 1067 OG to lift the chill should cold winds blow through Norwich. Storage of the beers is in tanks and top pressure is used to dispense them.

It may well be that the pair will open a second outlet in the near future. In the meantime you will have to head for Dereham Road if you want to sample the fine beers from Wolfe and Bill.

REAL ALES
Bill's Bevy (OG 1037) – a fresh easy-drinking bitter
Reindeer Bitter (OG 1047) – a premium bitter of fuller flavour
Red Nose (OG 1057) – a strong ale, rich and dark

**T. D. Ridley and Sons Limited**
Independent Regional Brewers
Harford End, Chelmsford, Essex

Ridley's Brewery, built in 1842, is one of the most attractive 'tower' breweries still in use in Britain. It stands prominently beside the River Chelmer in rolling countryside. The only thing that has altered outwardly since 1842 is the disappearance of a couple of the original cottages and the addition of a car park.

Ridley's Brewery

Inside the building, though, there have been several changes. The steep, narrow, wooden staircases are still there but much of the actual brewing equipment has been renewed in recent years. There are a few surviving reminders of the past. If you are fortunate enough to be invited into the Chippendale Room, you will find that the oldest fermenting vessel there has a pre-1901 inscription verifying that it was made by the great man himself. Now lined with copper, the vessel was originally constructed entirely of wood.

Ridley's is a proud family firm. The founder, Thomas Dixon Ridley, ventured into brewing as a logical extension of the family milling and malting business. Two separate firms existed until 1906 when Charles Ernest Ridley formed a limited company of each enterprise. By that time the brewery had assembled forty-seven public houses.

'The Essex Brewer' continued to provide beers for the cities, towns and villages of the county in a quiet way until given fresh impetus by the upsurge in interest in real ales during the early 1970s. The emphasis at the brewery was shifted towards traditional draught beers. As a result of that sensitive and timely response to changing market forces, the company now has an estate of over sixty public houses.

REAL ALES
XXX (OG 1034) – a dark nourishing mild
PA (OG 1034) – a light well-balanced session bitter

TIED HOUSES
There are plenty of places to find the beers in Essex:

Bannister Green: Three Horseshoes
Blackmore End: Red Cow
Blake End: Oak
Boreham: Cock
Braintree: Boar's Head, King's Head, King William IV
Broad's Green: Walnut Tree
Chatham Green: Windmill
Chelmsford: Beehive, Bird in Hand, Globe, New Barn, Red Lion, Ship, Woolpack
Cock Clarks: Fox and Hounds
Dunmow: Cricketers

Dutton Hill: Rising Sun
Earls Colne: Bird in Hand
Fairstead: Square and Compasses
Felsted: Chequers, Swan, Yew Tree
Finchingfield: Red Lion
Ford End: Swan
Good Easter: Fountain
Great Bardfield: Vine
Great Easton: Stag
Great Leighs: Dog and Partridge
Great Saling: White Hart

Great Sampford: Red Lion
Great Waltham: Beehive,
  Green Man
Hatfield Peverel: Duke of
  Wellington, Wheatsheaf
High Roding: Black Lion
Little Braxted: Green Man
Little Canfield: Lion and Lamb
Little Waltham: White Hart
Littley Green: Compasses
Margaretting: Black Bull, Red
  Lion
Mashbury: Fox
Messing: Old Crown
Mountnessing: Prince of Wales
North End: Butcher's Arms

Pleshy: Leather Bottle
Power's Hall End: Victoria
Radley Green: Thatcher's
  Arms
Rank's Green: Pretty Lady
Rayne: Cock
Rettendon: Wheatsheaf
Saffron Walden: Sun
Shalford: Fox
Stisted: Dolphin, Onley Arms
Takeley: Green Man
White Notley: Cross Keys,
  Plough
White Roding: Black Horse
Wickham Bishops: Mitre
Witham: George, Swan

## Scottie's Brewery
Independent Local Brewers
Crown Hotel, Lowestoft, Suffolk

The Crown Hotel does not take residents but it is a well-appointed establishment with two bars, a bistro and a function room. Rodney Scott and his family run it as well as three other outlets in the far East of England. He had always wanted to brew his own ales and his ambition was fulfilled in the late summer of 1989.

In former stables at the rear of the Crown he installed a stainless-steel full-mash brewery with a four-barrel brew-length. David Rose is the head brewer. Within a few weeks production was up to ten to fifteen barrels a week and there is potential to double that. The new beers were an instant success, selling well not only in the family's four outlets but also in the free trade.

The Crown was, like many old pubs, the home of a small-scale brewer in bygone days. William French Bitter is named after the publican brewer who is known to have operated there as far back as 1590. Its full title is William French Strong Celebration Bitter. The initial range of three beers is likely to expand.

REAL ALES
Hopleaf Best Bitter (OG 1038) – a hoppy session bitter
William French (OG 1048) – a full-bodied premium bitter
Dark Oast (OG 1048) – a dark strong ale

TIED HOUSES
  *Norfolk*
Gorleston: Cliff Hotel, Short
  Blue
Great Yarmouth: Talbot

  *Suffolk*
Lowestoft: Crown Hotel

**Tolly Cobbold (Tollemache and Cobbold Breweries) –**
see **CAMERON** Chapter Ten.

**Woodforde's Norfolk Ales**
Single-pub and Free-trade Brewers
Spread Eagle Brewery, Erpingham, Norwich

Tales of inter-company generosity are not commonplace in
the brewing industry. The normal image is one of fierce
rivalry. However, within the brief history of the Spread Eagle
there is a splendid example of the better side of the commercial
world.

Ray Ashworth began brewing in an industrial unit at Drayton
in April 1981 after looking at several alternative sites. Soon he
encountered difficulties and ends were not meeting. In his search
for a way of reducing overheads he chanced upon the Spread
Eagle and its licensee John Marjoram. By July 1983 a converted
stable block next to the pub was producing its first brew. Three
weeks later the roof crashed in on Ray (to be more precise, an
electrical fire totally destroyed the main roof).

In this potentially disastrous situation Mauldon's Brewery of
Sudbury stepped into save the day. They brewed for him to his
own recipe until the brewhouse had been repaired. Since then
the Spread Eagle and its ales (named after Parson Woodforde,
a famous local clergyman) have grown in popularity and output
has increased in each successive year. From such precarious
beginnings the Spread Eagle has become the major brewer of

Norfolk. No wonder that one of the first brews after the fire was named Phoenix.

Up to 2,000 gallons a week are produced for the pub and an increasing number of free houses. A peak of 3,000 gallons can be reached around Christmas. The range of the ales is bewildering and changes quite often. Besides the beers listed below, there are occasional special brews. From the standpoint of variation of real ales produced, Woodforde's is probably the most adventurous brewery in the land.

REAL ALES

Norfolk Pride (OG 1036) – a light rounded bitter
Wherry Best Bitter (OG 1039) – a malty session beer
Norfolk Porter (OG 1041) – dark and full of flavour
Phoenix XXX (OG 1047) – a premium bitter which rose
   from the ashes
Norfolk Nog (OG 1049) – a strong tawny noggin
Head Cracker (OG 1069) – a winter ale which demands
   respect

PUBLIC HOUSES

Obviously, if you can, try the Spread Eagle at Erpingham. Other regular outlets in Norfolk include:

Brundall: Yare
Burston: Crown
Cantley: Cock Tavern
Dickleburgh: Crown
East Ruston: Butcher's Arms
Fye Bridge: Ribs of Beef
Great Yarmouth: Talbot

Norwich: White Lion
Salhouse: Lodge
Swanton Morley: Darbys
West Rudham: Duke's Head
Wroxham: Hotel Wroxham
Wymondham: Feathers

CHAPTER EIGHT

# The South Midlands

**Abington Park Brewery Company**
Subsidiary Home-brew Pub
Wellingborough Road, Northampton, Northamptonshire

Abington Park is the one representative of the Clifton Inns chain of home-brew establishments outside London; the others are dealt with in Chapter Six. Clifton Inns is a part of the giant Grand Metropolitan's empire.

The beers cover the usual range of a session beer, a premium bitter and a strong ale and are brewed on the premises using a full-mash plant which has a capacity of ten barrels per week. They are dispensed under blanket pressure.

If you are in Northampton and fancy a different pint, look out for the Abington Park. It is the only real ale brewing establishment in Northamptonshire.

REAL ALES
Cobbler's Ale (OG 1038) – a light session bitter
Abington Extra (OG 1048) – a full-flavoured premium bitter
Celebration Ale (OG 1050) – darker and a little stronger

**Bodicote Brewery**
Home-brew Pub
Plough Inn, High Street, Bodicote, Oxfordshire

If you are in Bodicote, ask for the 'middle pub'. The Plough is a fine early Tudor establishment with a good-sized saloon bar and an equally spacious lounge, which is below street level.

Jim Blencoe is the landlord and his son, of the same name, is the brewer. Jim Junior learned his craft during a spell at the Ringwood Brewery.

The Plough became a home-brew pub in 1982 when a full-mash Peter Austin plant was installed in an outbuilding across the rear yard. There is a maximum seven-barrel brew-length and the three fermenting vessels provide plenty of scope for a considerable output from Bodicote. The tendency, however, is to concentrate upon supplying the pub itself. Small is beautiful as far as the Blencoe family is concerned.

Bodicote beers are sometimes found as guests in the free trade, particularly through the Northampton Beer Agency. Jim does a good trade in off-sales, selling his ales in polypins for barbecues in the summer and for indoor parties around Christmas.

REAL ALES
Bodicote Bitter (OG 1035) – a light refreshing session bitter
No. 9 (OG 1044) – a hoppy premium bitter
Old English Porter (OG 1044) – a dark winter porter
Triple X (OG 1050) – a winter strong ale of full flavour

## W.H. Brakspear and Sons Plc
Independent Regional Brewers
The Brewery, New Street, Henley-on-Thames, Oxfordshire

The famous Henley Brewery is situated near the Thames on New Street. It is one of the bastions of quality traditional ales. Without any particular fuss Brakspear's has been producing excellent beers since 1779.

It was in that year that the remarkable Robert Brakspear founded the brewery. He had been born in humble circumstances in Faringdon, but by the age of nineteen his determination to succeed in life had brought him to the position of landlord of the Cross Keys at Whitney. Ten years later he embarked upon a quite amazing career as a brewer.

Robert was a self-taught exponent of the art. The brewing process was well established but he was not content to accept that the happenings in the mash tun and fermentation vessels were insoluble mysteries. He probed and experimented, keeping notes of his findings and recording his recipes in a secret shorthand. His aim was to produce the best beers possible within the limited scientific knowledge of the time. Henley's famous corn and malt market was nearby and he made the best of it. By the end of the eighteenth century he was turning out two full brews a week and was not afraid to criticise the beers of his competitors.

The founder retired in 1812 and it was his young son, William Henry, who continued the tradition and built upon his father's success. It is perhaps surprising that the business was named after William rather than Robert.

The country brewery has remained extremely popular ever since, despite competition from London. An estate of 128 public houses has been built up within a quite compact area. Brakspear's image is perhaps epitomised by the quaint thatched pub tucked away in the Thames Valley. Both the eye and the tastebuds can be accommodated in Brakspear Country.

REAL ALES

Mild (OG 1031) – a very light delicate mild
Bitter (OG 1035) – a distinctive traditional bitter
Special (OG 1043) – well-rounded premium bitter
XXXX (OG 1043) – a premium bitter with the taste of an
   old ale

TIED HOUSES

The majority of Brakspear pubs are in south Oxfordshire and are easy to find. If you are attending the Regatta, you can choose from fourteen alternatives in Henley. The houses in nearby counties are listed below:

*Berkshire*

Cockpole Green: Old Hatch Gate
Crazie's Hill: Horns
Finchampstead: Queen's Oak
Hare Hatch: Horse and Groom, Queen Victoria
Holypont: Belgian Arms
Hurley: Black Boy
Knowl Hill: Seven Stars
Maidenhead: Hand and Flowers, Vine

Reading: Dove, Rising Sun
Sandhurst: Wellington Arms
Tilehurst: Victory
Twyford: King's Arms, Land's End
Wargrave: Bull
Wokingham: Crooked Billet, Dog and Duck, Duke's Head, Hope and Anchor, Red Lion

*Buckinghamshire*

Cadmore End: Ship
Fawley: Walnut Tree
Fingest: Chequers
Frieth: Prince Albert
High Wycombe: Wendover
   Arms

Marlow: Chequers, Clayton
   Arms
Northend: White Hart
Skirmett: Old Crown
Southend: Drover
Turville: Bull and Butcher

*Hampshire*

Mortimer: Turner's Arms

## The Brewery Tap and Brewery Limited
**Home-brew Pub**
Jolly Roger Brewery Tap, 50 Lowesmoor, Worcester

Paul Soden has been a prominent figure in the small-brewery revolution, particularly in articulating the response to the Report of the MMC in 1989. His statements to the press in his capacity as chairman of the Small Brewers' Society have kept his members' interests to the fore.

Paul began brewing in 1983 when he built the Jolly Roger

The Jolly Roger Brewery Tap, Worcester

Brewery at Upton upon Severn at the Olde Anchor Inn. Two years later he moved to his present abode at 50 Lowesmoor in Worcester. The new brewery, which again he built himself, was opened in October 1985.

The plant has a five-barrel length and, with two fermenting vessels of 200 gallons capacity each, has a potential output of ten to fifteen barrels per week. A third fermenter is being installed to cope with growing demand for the Jolly Roger ales. They are brewed from a 100 per cent malt mash and Paul and his co-director J.M. Perkins rely upon Challenger and Fuggles hops. They have their own strain of yeast.

The three regular ales are supplemented by a strong Winter Wobbler around Christmas and there have been various special brews for different events 'because it seemed like a good idea at the time!'. Although little of the output can yet be spared for the free trade (just the odd guest beer or festival appearance) the new fermenter should open up new possibilities in this respect. There is certainly no shortage of demand for the beers.

REAL ALES
Quaff Ale (OG 1038) – a light and slightly sweet bitter
Seven Bore Special (OG 1048) – a dark malty premium
    bitter
Old Lowesmoor (OG 1058) – a rich old ale with a kick
Winter Wobbler (OG 1090) – a dramatically strong Christmas
    fillip


**Donnington Brewery**
Independent Regional Brewers
Donnington, Stow-on-the-Wold, Gloucestershire

Donnington is Britain's most picturesque brewery. Situated in the south Cotswolds, it is built of local stone in an idyllic rural setting. A large mill pond is home to a collection of wild fowl and Mr and Mrs Arkell, the owners, feed the black swans and other exotic species there in total privacy. The brewery is not one which encourages casual visitors.

The old water wheel is still there, on the side of the brewery buildings, a remnant of the old days when the lord of the manor of Donnington rebuilt and converted two corn

Donnington Brewery

mills – probably around 1580. Thomas Arkell bought the mills in 1827 and his descendant, Richard Arkell, began the brewery in 1865. Not much has changed since then. The family have remained in control and the current proprietor is the grandson of the founder.

Until the mid-1960s the family grew its own barley on adjoining land but supplies of malt are obtained from Norfolk maltings now. Hops come from nearby Worcestershire and the liquor which is drawn from a strong spring beside the mill pond needs no adjustment for the brewing process. The bitters brewed at Donnington are full-bodied and, at their best, of excellent flavour to complement the splendid surroundings in which they are found. The mild is less common.

The sixteen Donnington pubs are an integral part of village and town life, built of Cotswold stone and in many cases in picture-book locations. Sit on the terrace of the Mount at Stanton and survey the rooftops of the splendid village below as you sup your pint, or enjoy the hustle and bustle of the Black Bear in Moreton-in-Marsh on market day. The inns are as traditional as the beers they serve.

REAL ALES
XX (OG 1935) – a dark mild which is hard to find
BB (OG 1036) – a balanced golden bitter
SBA (OG 1042) – a distinctive and full-flavoured premium
    bitter

TIED HOUSES
*Gloucestershire*

| | |
|---|---|
| Broadwell: Fox | Lower Swell: Golden Ball |
| Ford: Plough | Moreton-in-Marsh: Black Bear |
| Ganborough: Coach and Horses | Naunton: Black Horse |
| | Snowshill: Snowshill Arms |
| Great Barrington: Fox | Stanton: Mount |
| Guiting Power: Farmer's Arms | Stow-on-the-Wold: Queen's Head |
| Kineton: Half Way House | |
| Longborough: Coach and Horses | Willersey: New Inn |

*Oxfordshire*
Fifield: Merrymouth Inn

*Warwickshire*
Little Compton: Red Lion

## The Glenny Brewery Company
Free-trade Brewers
Two Rivers Brewery, Station Lane, Witney, Oxfordshire

The Windrush is that delightful sparkling river which bubbles through Cotswold settlements like Burford and Bourton-on-the-Water. When Patrick Glenny moved his brewery across Witney in November 1987 he named it Two Rivers in celebration of the Windrush and its tributary, which meet nearby.

Patrick tried a couple of dozen jobs after leaving school, one of which was in a brewery in West Berlin. When he decided to settle down at the age of twenty-three, it was brewing he chose. He purchased part of Clinch and Co.'s Eagle Brewery, which Courage had closed down after acquiring it in 1963. The first beer produced in 1983 was called Eagle Bitter (subsequently renamed Witney Bitter). In October 1984 Wychwood Best Bitter was added and the work-load grew to such an extent that Patrick took on a partner, Chris Moss.

After adopting the usual practice of introducing a strong ale to complete the range, the partners were forced to search out a larger building. The freehold of premises on Station Lane was purchased and David, drawing upon the experience of one of his many former jobs – engineering – designed and installed the equipment for the Two Rivers Brewery. The twenty-barrel-brew-length system produces an average weekly output of thirty-five barrels.

There is no doubt that Patrick Glenny has a flair for brewing. His fine ales can be found in about forty-five free-trade outlets at any one time. Five of the Oxford colleges take Glenny. Twice an ale from the brewery has been named Beer of the Festival at Midlands Beer Festivals.

REAL ALES
Witney Bitter (OG 1037) – a refreshing full-flavoured bitter
Wychwood Best (OG 1044) – a distinctive premium bitter
Hobgoblin (OG 1058) – a dark warming old ale

FREE TRADE
Try any of the following regular outlets:

*Gloucestershire*
Meysey Hampton: Mason's Arms

*Oxfordshire*

Chadlington: Tite Inn
Charlbury: Rose and Crown
Church Hanborough: Hand
  and Shears
Dorchester-on-Thames: Fleur
  de Lys
East End: Leather Bottle
Faringdon: Crown Hotel

Kingham: Plough
Murcott: Nut Tree
New Yatt: Saddler's Arms
North Leigh: Woodman
South Leigh: Mason Arms
Witney: Butcher's Arms, Elm
  Tree, Marlborough Hotel

## The Hook Norton Brewery Company Limited
Independent Regional Brewers
Hook Norton, Banbury, Oxfordshire

Hook Norton is a splendid example of a late Victorian tower brewery and the beers which come from it are as good as the architecture. Situated on the edge of a stone village which is on the fringe of the Cotswolds, it stands proudly as a monument to the history of the industry and yet it functions just as well as its modern counterparts.

Within the building is a magnificent 25hp steam engine. It was built around the turn of the century by Buxton and Thornley of Burton-on-Trent and has a fly wheel which measures 8 feet in diameter. This engine is still in full use and it is a treat to see steam belching as it powers to lift liquor from the brewery's well below or to pump hot wort up to the cooler on the fourth floor.

It was in 1849 that John Harris set up in the village as a maltster to supply local alehouses. Soon he turned his attentions to brewing. His small brewhouse gave him a start, but it was not long before he had to replace it with a larger, three-storey building. Hook Norton was a busy place at the end of the nineteenth century, with a lot of quarrying in the area, and the local thirst proved too great even for the new brewery. Eventually the six-storey continuous-process brewery was commissioned and it has stood there since its completion in 1900.

The ironstone industry suffered like most others during the Depression of the 1920s and Hook Norton Brewery faced a difficult time. Takeover attempts were resisted and the company fought through to the more optimistic early 1930s and gradually built up its tied estate.

Hook Norton Brewery

Bill Clarke became head brewer during that period and he made sure that a pint of Hookey was as good as ever. His son David succeeded him as head brewer and was appointed managing director in the early 1980s. Hook Norton was quite justifiably in the forefront of the real-ale revival and even today it is still gaining in popularity as it spreads further and further into the free trade.

REAL ALES
Mild (OG 1032) – light in colour but tasty
Best Bitter (OG 1036) – a hoppy full-flavoured bitter
Old Hookey (OG 1049) – a rich dark old ale

TIED HOUSES
*Gloucestershire*
Moreton-in-Marsh: Wellington
Paxford: Churchill

*Northamptonshire*
Abthorpe: New Inn
Aynho: Great Western Arms
Chipping Warden: Rose and Crown
Greatworth: Inn
King's Sutton: Butcher's Arms
Lower Boddington: Carpenter's Arms
Marston St Lawrence: Marston Inn
Sulgrave: Star Inn
Thorpe Mandeville: Three Cronies

*Oxfordshire*
Balscote: Butcher's Arms
Banbury: Coach and Horses, Reindeer Inn
Bloxham: Elephant and Castle
Brailes: Gate, George Hotel
Chipping Norton: Albion Tavern, Fox Hotel
Deddington: Crown and Tuns
Epwell: Chandler's Arms
Great Bourton: Bell Inn
Hook Norton: Gate Hangs High, Pear Tree, Sun Inn
Stoke Lyme: Peyton Arms
Wardington: Hare and Hounds
Warkworth: Bowling Green
Whichford: Norman Knight
Wigginton: White Swan
Woodstock: Queen's Own

*Warwickshire*
Edgehill: Castle Inn
Leamington Spa: Black Horse

## Morland and Company Plc
Independent Regional Brewers
The Brewery, Ock Street, Abingdon, Oxfordshire

Morland's Brewery was founded in 1711 and the company has prided itself on its independence throughout its long history. An estate of 200 public houses has been assembled (mostly in the Thames Valley) in some of southern England's most beautiful countryside.

John Morland, a local farmer, purchased West Isley House, just south of Abingdon, almost 280 years ago. There was a malthouse already there. When his son Benjamin added a brewhouse, the story of one of England's oldest brewery families began. The West Isley Brewery prospered as it was passed from one generation to the next and the Morlands displayed talents beyond that of brewing. George Morland (1763–1804) was a famous painter of traditional rustic scenes and the company's trade mark shows a painter with palette in one hand and glass of beer in the other as a celebration of his memory.

The move from West Isley to Ock Street occurred in 1816 when Edward Morland purchased the Eagle Brewery in Abingdon. The existing brewery on the site was in fact built in 1912 after the company had purchased several small local businesses and built up its list of tied houses. Between the wars five more breweries were acquired, but very little alteration to accommodate increasing output has been necessary and the brewhouse is much as it was in 1912.

Morland's has always had strong local ties. In 1974 the company opened a new public house, the Mighty Midget, to mark its association with Abingdon's MG factory and the success of that factory in producing the first 750cc car to break the 120mph speed barrier. On the fiftieth anniversary of MG, Morlands began brewing a jubilee bottled beer, Old Speckled Hen, which takes its name from a vintage MG model.

Certainly Morland's is one of those undemonstrative regional enterprises which form the backbone of the British brewing industry. The beers are distinctive and refreshing, but only about half of the tied houses dispense them traditionally.

REAL ALES

Mild (OG 1032) – a clean-tasting dark Midland mild
Bitter (OG 1035) – a well-hopped bitter
Old Masters (OG 1040) – a rich full-bodied premium bitter

TIED ESTATE

The majority of Morland houses are in Oxfordshire (nineteen of them in Abingdon) and Berkshire (twenty-one are in Reading). In surrounding counties the Morlands sign is less common – try any of the following:

*Buckinghamshire*
Princes Risborough: Whiteleaf Cross

*Hampshire*

Eversley Centre: Golden Pot
Farnborough: Fox
Hawley: New Inn
Hook: Old White Hart

Monk Sherbourne: Mole
Turgis Green: Cricketers
Yateley: Cricketers, Ely,
   Lanes, Royal Oak

*Surrey*
Camberley: Lamb
Frimley Green: Old Wheatsheaf

*Wiltshire*
Salisbury: Bishop's Mill

## Morrell's Brewery Limited
Independent Regional Brewers
The Lion Brewery, St Thomas Street, Oxford, Oxfordshire

Morrell's Brewery claims to be the only independent family brewery with a history of over 200 years of continuous production on the same site. It was founded in 1782 by Mark and James Morrell and since that time has always been in the sole control of the family. The site was once the brewhouse for Osney Abbey.

The present chairman is Colonel H.W.J. Morrell, the fifth member of his family to head the company. No other brewer has a financial stake in Morrell's and it is proud of its total independence. That pride, together with considerable skills in brewing, enabled it to remain the sole survivor among five breweries operating in Oxford at the turn of the century. After over 1,000 years of brewing in the city, there is only Morrell's left.

The colleges of the university brewed their own ale until 1956 but it was the then head brewer from the Lion Brewery, Louis Gunter, who presided over the process. He retired from Morrell's in 1983 and was succeeded in the post by Michael Sullivan. The equipment of the brewery has been much modernised and the company has even added a lager plant. However, the success of Morrell's has always been based upon its splendid range of real ales which are brewed strictly to traditional methods. In 1968 Morrell's Castle Ale won a medal at the International Brewing Convention.

REAL ALES
Light Ale (OG 1032) – a delicate lunchtime ale
Dark Mild (OG 1033) – a dark Midland mild
Bitter (OG 1036) – a smooth tasty bitter
Varsity (OG 1041) – a distinctive premium bitter
Celebration (OG 1066) – a light but strong ale for special
    occasions
College (OG 1072) – a rich and very strong ale

TIED HOUSES
Morrell's has 134 pubs within a 40-mile radius of Oxford, mostly in mid and south Oxfordshire. There are no less than thirty-three in the city itself. The following may serve as a guide to the tied houses away from the main concentrations:

*Berkshire*
Goring-on-Thames: Queen's
    Arms

*Buckinghamshire*
Ickford: Royal Oak

*North Oxfordshire*
Banbury: Constitution Tavern,     Enstone: Harrow
    Elephant and Castle             Launton: Bull
Bicester: Plough, White Horse   Marsh Gibbon: Plough
Chadlington: Malt Shovel        Nether Westcote: New Inn
Chipping Norton: Wagon and      Tackley: King's Arms
    Horses

*Wiltshire*
Swindon: Beehive, Oxford

## The Oxford Bakery and Brewhouse
Subsidiary Home-brew Pub
Gloucester Street, Oxford, Oxfordshire

The Bakery and Brewhouse was opened by Hall's, a subsidiary of Allied Breweries, in 1984. The name was changed from the Red Lion and £$^1/_2$ million spent on refurbishment to produce an interesting large pub which is very popular with students. A wide range of beers is produced on the premises and served at the bars under blanket pressure.

As the name states, the establishment provides both home-made food and beer. There is a lovely smell in the air from the different yeast actions which produce the unique food and drink. It is a lively pub with plenty of nooks and crannies. The ales are well worth a try, especially the dark porter, if you are visiting Oxford.

REAL ALES
Tapper (OG 1038) – a refreshing light bitter
Brewhouse Best (OG 1044) – a well-rounded premium bitter
Porter (OG 1045) – dark and tasty
Oxbow (OG 1059) – a rich strong ale
Old Wrot (OG 1072) – a powerful winter warmer

## Uley
Local Free-trade Brewers
The Old Brewery, Uley, Dursley, Gloucestershire

If you see a brewer driving to the Great Western Beer Festival with a pig beside him, do not be too disturbed. It will be Charles Wright from the village of Uley. Beers from his brewhouse bear close association with the pig fraternity. Charles keeps a few Old Spots about 10 miles from the brewery and they are very fond of the spent grain from the mash.

The old Prices Brewery in Uley was founded about 1780 and was rebuilt in its present form in 1833. Brewing on the premises lapsed around the turn of the century. The place was used as an agricultural store and to house the hounds of the local hunt. When Charles found the building, it was in a very poor state of repair. He purchased it in 1984 and spent six months repairing the fabric and installing his self-assembled stainless-steel brewing equipment. Uley Bitter was first marketed in March 1985: the old brewery was back in business. At first there was a resident brewer, Bill Doggett, but these days Charles brews himself on his ten-barrel-brew-length full-mash plant. He has three fermenting vessels which enables him to produce up to thirty barrels per week in summer. The beers are very popular in the free trade, especially Old Spot, and the newly introduced Pigormortis is, in the words of Charles, 'dark and deadly'.

REAL ALES
Uley Bitter (OG 1040) – well-rounded and hoppy
Pig's Ear (OG 1050) – an unusual light bitter
Old Spot (OG 1050) – the popular strong bitter
Pigormortis (OG 1058) – a rich heady strong ale

FREE TRADE
*Gloucestershire*
Dursley: Happy Pig
Woodchester: Ram Inn

Fleece Inn, Bretforton

*Oxfordshire*
Great Milton: Bell

*Worcestershire*
Bretforton: Fleece

## Wye Valley Brewery
Single-pub and Free-trade Brewers
The Barrels Inn, St Owen's Street, Hereford

Wye Valley Brewery is the culmination of a story which began back in 1981 when David Mullins opened the Abbey Brewery at Stainton in Yorkshire. That business moved south to near Retford and Peter Amor and his partner Peter Shepherd bought it from David. Soon Peter Amor took full control but he was restless and the whole enterprise was moved to Herefordshire where, in 1985, he found a struggling brewery at the Nag's Head, Canon Pyon.

Within a year he decided that his potential output was too restricted at the Nag's Head and he looked again for more suitable premises. He took a lease from Whitbread of the attractive timbered Lamb Hotel at 69 St Owen's Street. The name of the former coaching inn was changed to the Barrels and the brewery was installed in stables at the rear. It was a bold step to take – 74 per cent of Hereford's pubs carry a Whitbread tie and there is only one free house in the city. However, Peter knew exactly what he was doing and his business has prospered ever since.

The four beers are brewed from a full mash without any added sugars on his five-to-six-barrel-brew-length equipment. Currently there are two fermenters but he is hoping to add a third. Each year a mini beer festival is held in the yard at the rear of the inn and local beer lovers gather there in numbers. Special ales are produced occasionally, such as the limited edition bottled Charter Ale (to mark Hereford's 800th anniversary celebrations) in 1989. The draught beers find their way into around fifteen free-trade outlets in the West and make an appearance as guest beers further afield through wholesalers.

There are only two breweries in Hereford and Worcester – Peter Soden's Jolly Roger Tap in Worcester and Peter Amor's Wye Valley in Hereford. The pair of them demonstrate how it is possible to take on the big boys in their own territory and succeed. The quality products from Wye Valley help to add some flavour to the character of the fine city of Hereford.

REAL ALES
Hereford Bitter (OG 1038) – a refreshing well-hopped bitter
HPA (OG 1040) – a pale lightly hopped bitter
Hereford Supreme (OG 1043) – a smooth premium bitter
Brew 69 (OG 1055) – a light-coloured but full-flavoured strong ale

FREE TRADE
  *Hereford and Worcester*
Canon Pyon: Nag's Head
Colwell: Chase Inn
Fawley: British Lion
Fownhope: Forge and Ferry
Hereford: Saracen's Head

Kerne Bridge: Kerne Bridge Inn
Sellack: Loughpool
Symonds Yat: Wye Not Inn

CHAPTER NINE

# The North Midlands

## All Nations
Renowned Home-Brew Pub
Coalport Road, Madley, Shropshire

The All Nations is a splendid anachronism. Tucked away in an unimposing locality, the plain cottage pub is set back from the road and outwardly has little to recommend it. When you walk in, you will find a simple establishment. But you will have found probably the best example of an old publican brewery in the country. No one knows how long beer has been brewed at the back of the All Nations, but it has always been sold only over the bar there.

In the early 1970s the push of the big brewers with their gassy beers had reduced Britain's heritage of home-brew pubs to just four. The All Nations was one of those survivors. It had remained impassive to change, thanks to Bill and Eliza Lewis. When Bill died in 1975, Eliza did much as Doris Pardoe did at the Old Swan, Netherton – she rolled up her sleeves and took on the brewing duties herself.

These days her son-in-law Keith is the brewer. He uses the old wooden mash tun and coal-fired copper to good effect and can brew nine or ten barrels of the single beer as and when he needs them. Is it a bitter or is it a light mild? The locals do not care. If you hold up your glass to the window and study the colour and clarity of the refreshing ale, they will shake their heads in despair. They cannot understand what all the bother is about. The All Nations has never courted publicity – it is an ordinary drinking house as far as they are concerned. The ale was supped there quietly for decades before strange blokes began appearing and making a fuss about the place.

REAL ALE
Pale Ale (OG 1032) – a refreshing light ale

**Daniel Batham and Son Limited**
Independent Local Brewers
The Delph Brewery, Brierley Hill, West Midlands

The first (alphabetically) of the great Black Country brewing institutions is a small family firm with no great pretentions but the ability to brew really excellent ales. Tucked away in Brierley Hill, the Delph Brewery office and entrance are situated next to the Vine Inn and the brewhouse is at the rear.

Daniel Batham and his descendants have been brewing there since 1877. The family has a mere eight tied houses in the Midlands, but Batham's beers are much sought after by the free trade and by locals who know their ale. The mild won first prize in its class at Brewex 1972 and it is as good today as it was then.

The brewery tap is officially called the Vine Inn, yet it is known locally as the Bull and Bladder (there was a slaughterhouse nearby at one time). It is a friendly pub with a cosy bar which was refurbished in 1989. Outside the bold quote from Shakespeare adds a splash of colour to a rather drab locality.

The family brews just a mild and a bitter as it has always done, together with the time-honoured strong ale for winter nights. For many years the beers were available only in draught form but bottling has recommenced at the Delph Brewery. Batham beers are quite common in the free trade of the area. 'Blessing of your heart: you brew good ale' is entirely appropriate. The toast of the Black Country is 'Good Delph' to one and all!

REAL ALES
Mild (OG 1036) – a splendid well-flavoured dark mild
Bitter (OG 1043) – rounded, distinctive and tasty
Strong Ale (OG 1054) – a full-bodied winter brew

TIED HOUSES
*Hereford and Worcester*
Chaddesley Corbett: Swan Inn    Shenstone: Plough Inn
Kidderminster: Hare and
  Hounds

*Staffordshire*
Kinver: Plough and Harrow

*West Midlands*
Brierley Hill: Vine Inn         Pensnett: Holly Bush
Dudley: Lamp Tavern            Stourbridge: Royal Exchange

## The Brunswick Inn
Home-Brew Pub
Railway Terrace, Derby, Derbyshire

The Brunswick is an historic and impressive free house. It is situated opposite British Rail workshops, not far from Derby's station, and has the distinction of being the oldest purpose-built railway pub in the world. After 136 years of trading, from 1842, it was condemned to demolition in the late 1970s. The place was deserted and seemed doomed. However, when the Derbyshire Historic Buildings Trust set about restoring the adjoining railway cottages, the old pub was also given a new lease of life. It was refurbished and restored by Trevor Harris and John Evans.

This is no ordinary free house. Concentrating first on providing a unique experience in drinking, Trevor and John set out to serve up a choice of at least ten or twelve different ales at any one time. Bass, Pedigree and Bateman's Mild are regulars, but the remaining pumps (and sometimes jugs from the cellar) pour forth an outstanding variety of ales from around the country. The choice changes weekly and there is a blackboard behind the bar advertising forthcoming beers.

Very soon the 100 ales barrier had been broken in the Victorian-style pub and it was time to improve the other facilities. Good food was made available in the upper room (which is also used for functions); a non-smoking room was added; an annual in-house beer festival was inaugurated in October 1988.

What else could be done to complete the perfect free house? The answer came in late 1989 when work began on a brewery next to the Brunswick. By mid-1990 two home-brewed bitters and a mild should be available to supplement the numerous guest beers.

## British Oak Brewery
Single-pub and Free-trade Brewers
Salop Street, Eve Hill, Dudley, West Midlands

Ian Skitt, who learned his skills at the famous Heriot-Watt in Edinburgh, began brewing in a room on the side of the family pub in 1988. The British Oak is a free house of character. It has a single public room with barrel seats and attractive old Gornal stone masonry. As well as the beers, Ian makes cider for the bar. You will find the pub just outside Dudley on the Wolverhampton side.

Ian uses a full-mash, stainless-steel plant of ten-barrel maximum capacity to produce no less than five beers for the brewery tap and for outlets in the free trade. Although there is one regular free-trade outlet (see below) the majority of the sales out of Salop Street are found as guest beers in the West Midlands. His normal output is around five barrels per week, but this is likely to increase as interest spreads in his expanding range of beers.

The British Oak provides yet another source of ale in a locality which is already established as a stronghold of British brewing. It is certainly worth adding to the itinerary of any Black Country beer trip.

REAL ALES
Castle Ruin (OG 1038) – a sweetish pale bitter
Eve'ill (OG 1042) – hoppy, well-balanced and with a pronounced 'nose'
Colonel Pickering's Porter (OG 1046) – rich, smooth and dark
Dungeon Draught (OG 1050) – strong, fairly dark and very hoppy
Old Jones (OG 1060) – a powerful old ale

FREE TRADE
*Staffordshire*
Bradley: White Hart


## Burton Bridge Brewery
Single-pub Free-Trade Brewers
Bridge Street, Burton upon Trent, Staffordshire

Geoff Mumford and Bruce Wilkinson are the 'brewers on the bridge'. In 1982 they decided to take on the might of Bass, Allied and Marstons in their own back yard. To choose Burton upon Trent as the home for a new brewery might have seemed foolhardy to some, particularly in view of the strong tie imposed by the big brewers in the area. However, Geoff and Bruce have established a successful and refreshingly different style of brewing in the capital of the industry.

Just off the end of the 'old bridge' over the Trent, their premises are part of the one-time Joseph Nunneley Brewery (former stables and outbuildings) and there is evidence of even earlier connections with the trade from a maltings at the bottom of the yard, which dates to around 1823. Behind the small brewery bar they have a fifteen-barrel-brew-length system with eight fermenting vessels. An average of forty barrels per week is produced for the 'brewery tap' and a scattered but considerable free trade. Using a 10-ton lorry and a small pick-up (the comparison between their 'fleet' and that of Allied or Bass is an amusing one), they make their own deliveries. Customers include the Officers' Club at Sudbury Prison and Lichfield Arts Centre.

The Burton Bridge Bar is the best place to sample the beers. It is basic but warm, humid and welcoming. Certificates of awards made to the beers and to the pub itself hang on the walls, but there is no pretence about the place. There is a skittle alley to add an occasional rumble to the sound effects. Both the brewery and its pub have become important features of modern Burton upon Trent. The beers have a character which no giant brewer could possibly attempt to imitate.

REAL ALES
XL Bitter (OG 1040) – a hoppy session bitter
Bridge Bitter (OG 1042) – fruity and full-bodied
Burton Porter (OG 1045) – a dark distinctive porter
Burton Festival (OG 1055) – a rich and strong special bitter

Old Expensive (OG 1065) – a seasonal strong ale of character

FREE TRADE
*Derbyshire*
Derby: Brunswick Tavern

*Staffordshire*
Alton: Bull's Head                     Stoke: Cask and Mallet
Blythe Bridge: Blythe                  Uttoxeter: Roebuck
Cauldonlow: Yew Tree

*West Midlands*
Sedgley: Beacon


**Everard's Brewery Limited**
Independent Regional Brewers
Castle Acres, Narborough, Leicester

Everard's, based in Leicester, has had a long love affair
with Burton upon Trent. In 1849 two members of the family,
together with malster Thomas Hull, bought the Wilmot Brewery
at Narborough and leased other premises in Southgate Street,
Leicester. However, they soon realised that they were not pros-
pering to the same degree as their competitors in Burton, who
had the advantage of the special qualities of the waters there.

The company purchased the Bridge Brewery in the brewing
capital and operated from there for some time as a second base.
Eventually larger premises were needed and the family took over
the Tiger Brewery in Anglesey Road, across town. The Leicester
brewery in Southgate Street stopped production in 1931 and all
brewing was switched to Burton, the Leicester buildings being
adapted for warehousing, distribution and administration.

However, in 1979 it was decided to return home to Leicester.
Four acres of farmland were purchased at Castle Acres,
Narborough, and a modern brewing plant was built, so that
all of the company's activities could be consolidated on a single
site. The new specialist brewhouse was designed for maximum
flexibility and can brew both lager and ales in quantities from
15,000 to 75,000 barrels per year (the maximum could be doubled
if required). The move was not without its minor problems, as
it proved difficult to reproduce the distinctive flavour of the
company's Tiger Bitter and (perhaps more surprisingly) the
Mild at Narborough. As a temporary measure those two beers

are brewed under licence for Everard's at the Tiger Brewery, which is now a splendid working museum operated by Heritage Brewery.

Everard's has built up an estate of around 150 public houses, centred on Leicester. They vary from busy, utilitarian town houses to attractive thatched country inns such as the Cherry Tree at Little Bowden, the Free Trade Inn at Sileby or the Red Cow at Leicester Forest East. The company is justifiably proud of its 'friendly inns' and of its staunch independence as a family firm. 'No effort shall be wanting in the production and supply of genuine ale of first rate quality' was the wish of the three founders, and the present management strives for the same ideal.

REAL ALES

Burton Mild (OG 1033) – a dark dryish Midlands mild
Beacon Bitter (OG 1036) – a light session bitter
Tiger (OG 1041) – a distinctive premium bitter
Old Original (OG 1050) – a sweet tasty strong ale

TIED HOUSES

There is no problem in locating Everard's in Leicestershire (in Leicester itself there are forty-eight public houses selling the beers). Further afield, look out for:

*Cambridgeshire*
Market Deeping: Bull

*Derbyshire*
Derby: William Caxton
Mickleover: Honeycomb
Repton: Shakespeare
Sinfin: Ferrer's Arms

*Lincolnshire*
Stamford: Golden Fleece, Hurdler

*Northamptonshire*
Corby: Everard Arms,
  Knights Lodge, Talbot Inn
Kettering: Beeswing,
  Beeswing, Wayfarers

*Nottinghamshire*
Gotham: Sun Inn

*Staffordshire*
Moira: Ashby Woulds

*Warwickshire*
Stoke Golding: White Swan

**Fellows, Morton and Clayton**
Subsidiary Home-Brew Pub
Canal Street, Nottingham

You might think from the name that three beer enthusiasts have established a small business but, in fact, the title has been borrowed from a transport company which once occupied the premises. Fellows, Morton and Clayton is Nottinghams's representative in the Whitbread home-brew chain. The pub, which has a restaurant at the rear, has won an award for the excellence of its conversion from former offices. It is situated next to the Canal Museum, just a short walk from the Broad Marsh Centre.

The two beers are brewed from malt extract rather than from a full mash. You can glimpse the equipment used from the back of the pub. Like most of Whitbread home-brew establishments it is a lively place, much patronised by the younger generation. It offers one more choice to the drinkers of Nottingham, who are lucky enough to have three other local breweries and some excellent free houses.

REAL ALES
Fellow's Bitter (OG 1041) – a rich malt-extract bitter
Claytons Original (OG 1048) – a full-flavoured premium strong
  beer

**Flamingo and Firkin**
Subsidiary Home-Brew Pub
Becket Street, Derby, Derbyshire

Derby, that near neighbour of Burton upon Trent, was once an important brewing centre. After Bass purchased Offilers and closed it down, there were just a few publican brewers left as relics of the past. Gradually they fell by the wayside. When the Exeter Arms turned to Marston's, Derby became a non-brewing city.

In 1988 Midsummer Leisure, new owners of the Firkin chain, converted a former car sales building into a beer hall. The Flamingo and Firkin is typical of the former David Bruce style of pubs. It is lively, basic and full of humour. The awful puns are there and there is a Watney's Red Barrel suspended over the urinal in the gents' lavatory. Live music maintains the atmosphere on many evenings. On a Saturday night the large bar is thronged with youngsters moving to and from Derby's pubs, wine bars and night clubs.

The brewery can be seen from the rear of the bar. It is a full-mash system producing two house beers, which are stored in cellar tanks and dispensed under top pressure. Derby is rapidly becoming one of the best watering-holes for the real-ale enthusiast and the Flamingo and Firkin provides yet another choice of tastes. As well as the house beers there are always guest ales available.

REAL ALES
Flamin Ale (OG 1038) – a session bitter
Dogbolter (OG 1060) – a rich strong ale

## Fox and Hounds
Single-pub and Free-Trade Brewers
Stottesdon, Shropshire

The Fox and Hounds is a no-frills pub, serving honest food and good ale. It is set in an attractive location in the Shropshire countryside between Bridgnorth and Cleobury Mortimer. Like many of the village pubs of old England it was originally the home of a publican brewer. Malcolm Downing was always interested in decent real ale – at one time his pub provided the second outlet for John Roberts' beers from the renowned Three Tuns at Bishops' Castle.

After the Three Tuns changed hands, Malcolm decided to try brewing for himself in the old brewery buildings at the back of the pub. He installed a four-barrel stainless-steel full-mash plant and began with Dasher's Draught and then Super Dash (Dasher being his not-too-serious nickname). The pub has changed hands since then but the small plant is still in use, turning out an increasing quantity of beer for the Fox and Hounds and for guest beer appearances in the free trade. A mild has been added in recent times and you will also occasionally find Hound's Bitter, which has replaced Super Dash.

REAL ALES
Foxy's Mild (OG 1036) – a well-rounded mild
Dasher's bitter (OG 1040) – a sweetish light bitter

**Hanby Ales**
Free-trade Brewers
Unit C9, Wem Industrial Estate, Wem, Shropshire

When Greenall Whitley closed the Wem Brewery, head brewer Jack Hanby was not of a mind to desert the area. In March 1989, with his partner and their wives, he established Hanby Ales in a temporary unit on the Wem Industrial Estate. That put a smile back on the faces of the local population.

He built a full-mash plant of stainless steel to his own design and began brewing beers, eventually settling on two ales – Drawwell Bitter (named after the famous old draw-well at the Wem Brewery) and Treacle Miner Bitter (Wem was always known locally as the 'Treacle Mine' and Jack was entitled to the title of head treacle miner). Soon he was producing fourteen or fifteen barrels per week for the free trade and there was no need to look for customers. The free trade came to him.

By the end of his first summer Jack had established himself as a successful independent and was ready to find a permanent home in order to maintain expansion. He reassembled a second-hand concrete-framed building as Unit C9 and moved the operation there. Hanby Ales are available in several free houses in the locality and further afield through wholesalers. Their presence is likely to spread as Jack moves forward from his sound beginnings.

REAL ALES
Drawwell Bitter (OG 1039) – a malty session bitter
Treacle Miner Bitter (OG 1046) – a full-flavoured premium bitter

FREE TRADE
*Cheshire*
Malpas: Red Lion

*Shropshire*
Burlton: Burlton Inn
Hammerhill: Bridgewater Arms

# Hardy and Hanson's Limited
Independent Regional Brewers
Kimberley Brewery, Nottingham, Nottinghamshire

The story of Hardy and Hanson's is one of a couple who consorted but resisted marriage for many years. The two families ran separate businesses on opposite sides of the street (at a mere 50 yards' distance) from 1850 until 1930. They then decided to become engaged – an amalgamation of interests which gave the brewing responsibilities to Hardy's Kimberley Brewery Limited and left the bottling to Hanson's Limited. It was not until an AGM in February 1972 that the shareholders blessed proper wedlock and the two companies at last became fully entwined.

Kimberley has a long history of brewing, which began because of the ample water supplies from Holly Well. Records of the early years are lost, but it is known that before 1850 there were two small breweries in operation. The larger of them, opened in 1847, had a Mr R. G. Hanson as one of its partners. Within a few years he had assumed full control. Nearby, in 1857, William and Thomas Hardy acquired the smaller four-quarter brewery and began trading from there.

Since the full amalgamation of those old businesses, Hardy and Hanson's has established itself as a major force in Nottingham brewing. Kimberley ales have taken their share of prizes at brewers' exhibitions, including the Gold Medal as Runner-up for the Best Draught Beer in 1952 and 1968 and a similar award in the year of the amalgamation. The good honest ales are available in around 200 public houses, mainly in Nottinghamshire, Derbyshire and Leicestershire.

REAL ALES
Best Mild (OG 1035) – a dark fruity mild
Best Bitter (OG 1039) – a full-flavoured Nottingham bitter

TIED HOUSES
Try the real ale in any of the following:

*Derbyshire*
Alfreton: Robin Hood, Waggon and Horses
Belper: White Hart
Bonsall: Barley Mow
Buxton: Devonshire Arms
Codnor: Lord Byron

Crich: Cliff Inn
Darley Dale: Grouse
Derby: Duke of Clarence,
    Sun Inn
Fritchley: Red Lion
Heanor: Sir John Warren

Ilkeston: Mundy Arms,
    Traveller's Rest
Little Eaton: Queen's Head
Lower Hartsay: George Inn
Pleasley: Nag's Head
Tideswell: George Hotel
Wirksworth: Black's Head

*Leicestershire*
Bottesford: Red Lion
Hathern: Dew Drop

Loughborough: Crown and
    Cushion, Old Pack Horse

*Nottinghamshire*
Awsworth: Gate Inn
Beeston: Commercial
Blyth: Angel
Brinsley: Durham Ox
Eastwood: Greasley Castle
Fiskerton: Bromley Arms
Harworth: Galway Arms

Kimberley: Lord Clyde,
    Queen's Head
Mansfield: Crown and Anchor
Nottingham: Lord Nelson
Warsop: Hare and Hounds
Westwood: Gate

**Heritage Brewery Limited**
Contract and Free-trade Brewers
Anglesey Road, Burton upon Trent, Staffordshire

For visitors to Burton upon Trent there are two 'musts' – the Bass Museum in Horninglow Road and the Heritage Brewery Museum in Anglesey Road. The Heritage is both a museum and a working brewery. It is open to tour parties by appointment and to casual visitors.

The typical Victorian tower brewery was built in 1881 for Thomas Sykes, a Liverpool brewer who wanted to take advantage of Burton's special waters. In 1881 it was sold to Everard's and by 1931 was producing the whole of the Leicester-based company's output. When Everard's decided to return to its home base in 1985, there was great concern that yet another of Burton's Victorian breweries would be lost.

Heritage Brewery Limited was formed by the combined efforts of the local authority, Burton businessmen and beer enthusiasts. Their progress has been remarkable. A deal was agreed with Everard's whereby Tiger Bitter and Everard's Mild would still be brewed under contract at Anglesey Road. A restoration

appeal was launched and the first two phases raised £800,000 to purchase the site and to repair and restore the buildings. The project included preservation of cottages, stables, waggon sheds and a cooper's shop. A new visitors' centre and museum shop were added. Perhaps most impressively, the original Buxton and Thornley stationary steam engine, which had been scrapped in 1969, was recovered and restored to working order on its original plinth in 1987.

Besides the two beers brewed for Everard's, a bitter and a strong ale are now in production for general sale. They are found in an increasing number of free houses as guest ales. At the museum you can buy commemorative beers made both for the general public and to order for local businesses.

Heritage is a flourishing place. It is a tribute to the volunteers there and to the team who made a dream become a reality – an impressive old brewery restored, in full production and actually welcoming visitors. The contract to brew for Everard's was lost in the spring of 1990 and the future of Heritage put in jeopardy.

REAL ALES
Everard's Mild (OG 1033) – a dark mild of character
Tiger Bitter (OG 1035) – a distinctive session bitter
Heritage Bitter (OG 1045) – a balanced premium bitter
Thomas Sykes (OG 1100) – a very strong and rich old ale

**Holden's Brewery**
Independent Regional Brewers
George Street, Woodsetton, Dudley, West Midlands

The call for a pint of 'Holden's Golden' is a familiar sound in
the Black Country. The company's logo depicts a solid working
man thrusting forward a foaming pint at the end of a hard
day. A modest estate of eighteen pubs within a limited range
of Dudley is extended by a considerable presence in the free
trade throughout the Midlands.

Edwin Holden, the son of a Rowley Regis boot and shoe
maker, married a publican's daughter in 1898. He was drawn
into the trade and ran several public houses before he purchased
the Park Inn, George Street, Woodsetton, in 1920, shortly before
his death. A dark strong mild was brewed in the small brewery
which occupied a building at the rear and part of the cellars.
Gradually production was expanded and a second pub was
purchased – the Painter's Arms at Coseley. Both houses are
still owned by the company. The Park Inn remains the brewery
tap and is now a well-modernised comfortable pub.

Holden's is a true family firm. It has passed from father to
son through three generations and the present Edwin Holden is
involved in running the business on a daily basis. He is assisted
by a trade brewer, whose job is to make regular checks on beer
installations and the beers themselves in the public houses. In
this way consistency of quality is ensured from the brewery to
the glass.

The single strong mild has grown into a full range of six beers
which are enjoyed throughout the Black Country and beyond.
The main period of expansion was in the 1950s and 1960s. That
small pub brewery has become a sizeable unit behind the Park
Inn and there is currently a capacity of 250 barrels per week.
It is fortunate indeed that Edwin Holden married a publican's
daughter all those years ago. Lucy Blanch Round was that lady's
name and a new premium ale was launched in 1989 to celebrate
her memory.

REAL ALES
Mild (OG 1038) – a dark tasty mild
Black Country Bitter (OG 1038) – refreshing and of good flavour
Lucy B (OG 1043) – a new premium ale
Special (OG 1051) – a full-bodied premium bitter

Old Ale (OG 1080) – a strong rich old ale
Black Country XL (OG 1092) – a winter ale of great strength

TIED HOUSES
*West Midlands*
Bilston: Britannia, Trumpet
Brierley Hill: Elephant and
    Castle, Rose and Crown
Coseley: New Inn, Old Bush,
    Painter's Arms
Cradley Heath: Swan Inn
Darlaston: Prince of Wales
Gornal: Miner's Arms,
    Old Mill
Oldswinford: Shrubbery
    Cottage
Sedgley: Bull's Head
Tipton: Royal
Wednesbury: Cottage Spring
West Bromwich: Wheatsheaf
Wolverhampton: Great
    Western
Woodsetton: Park Inn

## Holt, Plant and Deakin
Subsidiary Regional Brewers
91 Station Road, Oldbury, West Midlands

Holt's is part of the giant Allied Breweries combine but it
deserves individual mention because of its unique contribution
to Black Country drinking. It was established in 1984 as a
small chain of public houses served by a modest brewery at
one of them, the Brewery Inn, Oldbury. The brewing equipment
is visible through a window at the pub and for most of the year
it produces a single beer – the esteemed Holt's Entire, which the
company describes as 'pure Black Country'.

The number of public houses in the Holt's estate has grown
steadily since 1984, mostly by transfer from Ansell's. Holt's
Brewery Tap, Dudley Road, Wolverhampton, now provides a
second brewhouse for the chain and is also an interesting place
to visit. You will find everything from cosy corner taverns to
large town drinking establishments under the Holt's banner.
The other Holt, Plant and Deakin beers sold in them are in
fact brewed at Tetley Walker, Warrington. It is the Entire
which should be the main focus of your attention.

REAL ALES
Holt's Entire (OG 1043) – a distinctive tasty premium ale
Deakin's Downfall (OG 1060) – a seasonal warming strong ale

HOLT'S BLACK COUNTRY HOUSES

Blackheath: Shoulder of
 Mutton
Brewood: Admiral Rodney
Brierley Hill: Bell, Brockmoor
 House, Red Lion
Bushbury: Wentworth
Claverley: Old Gate
Coseley: Horse and Jockey
Daisy Bank: White House
Dudley: Hill Tavern, Old
 Priory
Dudley Wood: Bunch of
 Bluebells
Halesowen: Loyal Lodge
Hasbury: Rose and Crown
Kingswinford: Cross
Langley: Crosswells
Lower Gornal: Bush, Old Bull's
 Head
Netherton: Elephant and
 Castle

Oldbury: Brewery Inn, New
 Navigation
Pensnett: Fox and Grapes
Quarry Bank: Church Tavern
Rowley Regis: Beech Tree,
 Cock Inn, Malt Shovel
Sedgley: Mount Pleasant
Stourbridge: Plough and
 Harrow
Tipton: Crown and Cushion,
 Dudley Port, Fountain
Tividale: Barley Mow
Wednesfield: Pheasant
West Bromwich: Great
 Western, Hawthorn Tavern
 Old Hop Pole
Wolverhampton: Brewery Tap,
 Fox and Goose, Posada,
 Swan, Warstones
Wordsley: Gladstone Arms,
 Queen's Head

## T. Hoskins Limited
Independent Local Brewers
Beaumanor Brewery, Beaumanor Road, Leicester

When Jabez Penn moved to Leicester from Warwickshire, he purchased Hope Cottage in Beaumanor Road and set up in business as a shop-keeper. By 1895 he had begun brewing ale there, so establishing one of the most famous cottage brewhouses in the country. The original premises were extended three times as Jabez demonstrated that he was a very capable common brewer.

Tom Hoskins married Penn's daughter and was taken into partnership in 1901. Within five years he had gained sole control. During his fifty-odd years in charge Tom produced some splendid ales. He won medals at four brewers' exhibitions between 1922 and 1936 and his greatest achievement came in 1938 when he carried off the Diploma of Excellence and Gold Plate for his IPA and strong ale.

After his death the Hoskins family kept on trading, but they missed Tom's skill and energy. Eventually they sold the business in 1983 to Barrie and Robert Hoar. Since that day Hoskins has prospered, growing into a major force in East Midlands brewing. A considerable cash injection has enabled the tied estate to refurbish and expand. Output from Beaumanor has increased steadily under head brewer N. Burdett. The brewery itself, the oldest surviving reminder of a small common brewer, is a working museum and the company encourages organised brewery trips. Many historical brewing items are on display there.

REAL ALES
Mild (OG 1033) – a dark Midlands mild
Beaumanor Bitter (OG 1039) – a hoppy session bitter
Penn's Ale (OG 1045) – a distinctive premium ale
Premium (OG 1050) – a strong full-flavoured bitter
Old Nigel (OG 1060) – a deceptively light winter warmer

TIED HOUSES
*Derbyshire*
Heanor: Ray's Arms
Shardlow: Hoskins' Wharf

*Leicestershire*
Cropston: Bradgate Arms        Market Bosworth: Red Lion
Leicester: Rainbow and Dove    Melton Mowbray: Mash Tub

*London*
N1 (King's Cross): Waterside Inn

*Warwickshire*
Claverdon: Ardencote Hotel


**Hoskins and Oldfield**
Free-trade Brewers
North Mills, Frog Island, Leicester

When the original Hoskins' Brewery was sold to the Hoars, two of the family showed that they had brewing in their blood. Philip and Stephen Hoskins, together with Simon Oldfield, began a new operation in Leicester. In 1984 they leased premises in the city and installed plant from the Hawthorne Brewery in Gloucester (the same source as that used by Premier Midland Ales). It took three months to adapt and refurbish the equipment to their requirements. What had been part of a lateral brewery became a tower system using only a single pump.

The brewery on Frog Island is approached by a road alongside a canal and is set among many older industrial premises. From it emerges a splendid range of ales. Philip is mainly employed in brewing while Stephen is often on the road. The beers are normally brewed in ten-barrel batches but there is a twenty-barrel-brew-length potential if required. Output can reach fifty barrels at certain times of the year; the average, however, is twenty to thirty barrels per week. HOB Bitter is the best-seller, but look out for Christmas Noggin (affectionately known as 'Brain Damage') in the winter months.

HOB Ales are sold in several free-trade outlets in Leicestershire and beyond. Stephen will tell you that they have been enjoyed from Inverness to Falmouth. Wholesalers make sure that the beers from Frog Island are given a presence as guest ales throughout the country. Instead of disappearing in 1983, the old T. Hoskins Limited gave birth to two quite separate and successful new enterprises.

REAL ALES
HOB Mild (OG 1035) – a dark sweetish Midlands mild
HOB Bitter (OG 1041) – hoppy and refreshing
Little Matty (OG 1041) – a dark bitter
Tom Kelly's Stout (OG 1043) – a dry black stout
EXS Bitter (OG 1051) – a distinctive well flavoured bitter
Old Navigation (OG 1071) – dark, strong and warming
Christmas Noggin (OG 1100) – lighter but deceptively
    awesome

FREE TRADE
  *Leicestershire*
Hose: Rose and Crown            Loughborough: Albion Inn
Leicester: North Bridge         Walcote: Black Horse
                                Tavern


**Sarah Hughes' Brewery**
Home-brew Pub
Beacon Hotel, Bilston Street, Sedgley, West Midlands

Sarah Hughes brewed her famous strong mild at the Barley Mow in Bilston before moving to the Beacon Hotel at Sedgley in 1921. She brewed there until 1958, using the miniature tower brewery which was built around 1860. Her grandson

John Hughes found the precious recipe and modernised the brewery so that he could revive the brew. Sarah Hughes' Dark Ruby reappeared in 1987 and it was an instant success with a new generation of drinkers.

Is it a mild or is it a strong ale? Dark Ruby is neither or both. When it appears at beer festivals, it still attracts a great deal of attention. You will hear speculation that there must be an additive of spirits to give it that special flavour. Demand for the output of five barrels per week is so great that little Dark Ruby is available for the free trade – the customers of the Beacon Hotel make sure of that.

If you are in the Black Country, do call in at the Beacon Hotel, because the place complements the drink. Do not expect the Hilton – you will find a modest pub in an ordinary setting. But if you take a seat in the Snug and listen to the Black Country humour of the regulars as they play crib, you will experience a great warmth. Try a couple of pints of Sarah Hughes' Dark Ruby (making certain that you have transport arranged for closing time) and that warm glow will spread all over you. It is one of the great experiences of Black Country drinking.

REAL ALE
Sarah Hughes' Dark Ruby (OG 1058) – a dark strong mild, quite superb

FREE TRADE
You will find the odd sample of Dark Ruby cropping up in unexpected places. For instance, customers of Bernie's Off-licence in Solihull often carry it home. The most regular free-trade outlets are:

*West Midlands*

| | |
|---|---|
| Halesowen: Wagon and Horses | Tipton: Court House |
| Shifnall: White Hart | Willenhall: Brewer's Droop |

## The Mansfield Brewery Company
Independent Regional Brewers
Littleworth, Mansfield, Nottinghamshire

The Mansfield Brewery is situated about half a mile from the town centre, just outside the ring road. Its mixture of buildings of different ages reveals something of its odd history.

The Victorian tower is still there – Mansfield dates back to 1855 – but it has become almost enveloped in modern buildings which testify to the influence of keg and lager upon the company.

Mansfield was one of the first regionals to abandon traditional beers and move into keg and lager with a large-scale financial investment in the necessary plant. It was about the last to respond to the real-ale revolution and turn its attentions back to proper stuff. The company held out until 1982 before returning to a traditional ale (4XXXX Bitter), which it first introduced into selected houses in a rather half-hearted manner. Mansfield publicans had forgotten how to handle real ale. Happily, nowdays there are three good beers, and they are becoming more evident, backed by some prominent poster advertising. Old Baily, the strong bitter, is named after William Baily, one of the three founders of the firm.

The company is a lively and ambitious one. It acquired North Country Breweries of Hull in 1985 and has a considerable presence in many clubs in Nottinghamshire, Derbyshire and South Yorkshire. You can find Mansfield pubs from Whitby in the North to Leicester in the South and from Bakewell in Derbyshire through to the East Coast. The beers also reach the South East of England through agencies. If you wonder about Canterbury Ale and Buff's Bitter sold at Canterbury Brewery houses in Kent, there is no active Canterbury Brewery – the beers are brewed by Mansfield.

One of the company's policies in recent years has been to become involved in a great deal of local sponsorship. The favoured parties include Mansfield Town Football Club, Hull Kingston Rovers and Hull Rugby League Clubs, Hull City Football Club and Chesterfield Football Club. Mansfield has made certain that it is a part of the social life of its trading area.

Although the company owns 320 managed and tenanted houses its products are available in over 1,000 other outlets, the real ales are not yet dominant. Fortunately, however, they are beginning to become more obvious as their popularity grows.

REAL ALES
Riding (OG 1035) – a tasty session bitter
Old Baily (OG 1045) – a distinctive full-bodied premium
   bitter
A draught mild was added in late 1989.

TIED HOUSES
Many outlets do not yet sell real ales but the following
examples will serve as a guide:

*Derbyshire*
Belper: Tavern
Chesterfield: Blue Bell, Punch
  Bowl, St Helen's

Derby: Crown and Cushion,
  Strutts

*Nottinghamshire*
Blidworth: Bird in Hand
Edwinstowe: Dukeries,
  Robin Hood
Farnsfield: Plough, White Post

Mansfield: King's Head,
  Ladybrook Hotel, Oak Tree
  Inn, Old Ram, Queen's Head,
  Ravensdale, Victoria
Southwell: The Crown

*North Yorkshire*
South Milford: Black Bull
York: Hole in the Wall

## Marston, Thompson and Evershed Plc
Independent Regional Brewers
Shobnall Road, Burton upon Trent, Staffordshire

According to Marston's, Pedigree is the 'King of Bitters'. Few
would argue. The full-flavoured ale is the one premium bitter
left which has that superb flavour and character bestowed by
the Burton Union system of brewing. Marston's has continued
to entrust its future in the unique and historic method of fermenting and the immense success of Pedigree is a tribute to
the company's judgement.

The story of the business is a tale of three families. John
Marston, despite the fact that his father tried brewing and
became bankrupt, was a successful businessman in Burton. In
1825 he purchased the malthouse of Coat's Brewery to consolidate his interests in brewing and built up a flourishing business.
After his death his son, John Hackett Marston, continued the
good work until he retired in 1888.

John Thompson ran the Bear Inn, Horninglow Street, from
1765 and there was a small brewhouse at the rear. The enterprise was expanded by his two nephews, both also called John,

and by 1851 they employed fourteen men. The amalgamation with Marston's took place in 1898, John Thompson becoming the first chairman of the company.

The Eversheds were not locals, but originated from rural Surrey. Sydney Evershed trained at the Standsfield Brewery in London and came to the brewing capital to set up business in 1854. By 1861 his status was no better than that of a minor 'common brewer', operating from the Angel Inn in Bank Square. However, within a few years he had acquired two maltings and his business was expanding. He was elected Mayor of Burton in 1880 and became the constituency's MP. Evershed's was sold to Marston's in 1905, two years after his death, and his son joined the board of directors of the newly created Marston, Thompson and Evershed.

The bringing together of the skills of the three families resulted in one of the most traditional and yet progressive of the regional breweries. Its success has been based upon the foundation of some of the finest ales in England, which have given the company great strength within the brewing industry. When Marston's purchased the Winchester Brewery Company in 1923, it had already accumulated an estate of 600 public houses. Steady expansion has seen that number rise to over 850 today. There have been several other acquisitions, such as that of W.A. Smith and Sons of Macclesfield and of Border Breweries of Wrexham, to achieve an estate of such a size.

The story does not stop there. Marston's has a huge presence in the free trade – about 40 per cent of the output is sold beyond the company's tied estate. The flagship Pedigree Ale was the subject of an agreement with Whitebread in 1989, ensuring that the famous beer will be made available in selected Whitbread outlets in many areas. The success of the expansion scheme in recent years has been marked. In 1988/9 profits rose by over 15 per cent to £14.9 million.

REAL ALES
Border Mild (OG 1031) – a traditional dark mild
Mercian Mild (OG 1032) – a refreshing malty mild
Border Exhibition (OG 1034) – a light session bitter
Border Bitter (OG 1034) – a well-rounded bitter
Burton Bitter (OG 1036) – a light delicate bitter of character
Pedigree (OG 1043) – the excellent full-flavoured premium bitter
Merrie Monk (OG 1043) – an unusually strong dark mild
Owd Rodger (OG 1080) – a powerful strong ale

Holly Bush, Church Broughton

TIED ESTATE

A full list of Marston's houses would form a book in itself. The following are interesting examples in the Midlands and Wales:

*Clwyd*
Abergele: Gwindy
Caerwys: Traveller's Inn
Hanmer: Hanmer Arms
Wrexham: Nag's Head

*Derbyshire*
Ashbourne: Smith's Tavern
Breaston: Bull's Head
Broadholme: Fisherman's Rest
Church Broughton: Holly Bush
Derby: Exeter Arms
Etwall: Hawk and Buckle
Horsley: Coach and Horses
Knockerdown: Knockerdown Inn
Matlock Bath: County and Station
Morley: Three Horse Shoes
Old Brampton: George and Dragon
Shardlow: Malt Shovel
Smalley: Nag's Head
Wirksworth: Malt Shovel

*Leicestershire*

Long Whatton: Royal Oak
Loughborough: Boat Inn
Lount: Ferrer's Arms
Shepshed: Bull and Bush

Sutton Bonnington: Anchor
Swannington: Fountain Inn
Whitwick: Forester's Arms
Worthington: Malt Shovel

*Shropshire*

Aston Newport: Wheatsheaf
Dawley: Three Crowns
Haybridge: Summer House

Leegomery: Malt Shovel
Moreton: Rising Sun

*Staffordshire*

Abbots Bromley: Bagot Arms
Burton: Albion Hotel,
   Oddfellow's Arms
Horninglow: Plough Inn
Shenstone: Railway Inn

Stanton: Gate Inn
Swadlincote: Angel Inn
Tamworth: Bull's Head
Uttoxeter: Lime's House
Yoxall: Crown Inn

*West Midlands*
Burntwood: Trident


**Old Swan**
Renowned Home-brew Pub
Halesowen Road, Netherton, Dudley, West Midlands

In an inconspicuous row of shops near the centre of Netherton there is a painted sign on the wall declaring 'Pure Home Brewd Ales'. The Old Swan does not seem of great significance at first glance. A flush-fronted old pub in a rather drab setting is not normally likely to arouse too many emotions. But this is the famous 'Ma Pardoe's', a Black Country institution. Real-ale lovers still make pilgrimages to Dudley in order to visit it.

Doris Pardoe and her husband Fred purchased the pub and brewery in 1932. Beers had probably been brewed on the premises for over 100 years. It was destined to become the last of the Black Country publican breweries – a sole legacy of a near-forgotten age. By the end of the takeover and keg massacre, the Old Swan was one of only four remaining home-brew pubs in the country. When Fred died in 1952, his widow carried on the tradition by

brewing the single bitter in the small brewery at the rear. The
place became known, with utmost affection, as Ma Pardoe's.

For thirty-two years Doris produced a consistent, very drinkable pint. On her death in 1984 there was a temporary lapse
but, with the help of CAMRA, the business continued. A merger
with Hoskins of Leicester in 1987 ensured that the single beer
was still brewed to the old recipe and sold on the premises. An
adjoining shop was purchased to enlarge the Old Swan with a
new two-room bar. Hoskins then sold the business on to the
Wiltshire Brewery Company.

To some extent, and probably inevitably, the character of
the place has altered with the changes of management and
with the extension. However, the original Victorian bar (with
its enamelled ceiling and old stove) is still there and so is the
small snug at the rear. The house bitter now shares the bar
with a full range of Wiltshire Brewery beers, but Ma Pardoe's
remains an historic and interesting place.

REAL ALE
Bitter (OG 1034) – honest and refreshing

Parish Brewery

## Parish Brewery
Home-brew Pub
Stag and Hounds, Main Street,
Burrough-on-the-Hill, Leicestershire

In a tidy village not far from Melton Mowbray the Stag and
Hounds stands in rolling Leicestershire countryside. You will
find a restaurant there which serves good inexpensive food
and you will hear the usual banter from the locals. Everything
seems what you might expect of a village pub – predictable and
pleasant. But do not be deceived: landlord-turned-brewer Barrie
Parish has a surprise for you.

On the other side of the car park entrance at the side of
the pub is a neat little brewery converted from an old stable. In
that brewhouse Barrie conjures up Baz's Bonce Blower, which
is most definitely capable of sending your scalp into orbit. With
a staggering original gravity of 1105-10, Bonce Blower is to be
treated with the utmost respect. It is more powerful than many
wines.

The brewery was established in 1986, as a hand-painted
sign on the rear of the pub proudly testifies. Originally Barrie
used a tiny plant, hardly more sophisticated than that used by

a home-brewer. However, he soon saw the potential for his beers and installed a five-barrel plant in the former stable in order to cope with demand. These days he produces a range of four beers for the 400-year-old public house. Occasionally samples of Parish Ales can be found in the free trade.

REAL ALES
Dark Mild (OG 1032-4) – a traditional dark mild
Parish Special (OG 1035-8) – a sweetish bitter
Poacher's Ale (OG 1058-62) – a powerful strong ale
Baz's Bonce Blower (OG 1105-10) – a dark, sweet, head-banging ale

## Premier Midland Ales
Independent Local Brewers
Stourbridge Industrial Estate, Stourbridge, West Midlands

Premier is principally a pub-owning company which runs a chain of real-ale establishments. Since 1983 the company has been providing welcome choice for West Midlands drinkers by offering a range of beers from around the country. There has been a considerable amount of buying and selling of licensed premises but there are currently seven outlets, including a representative in Gloucestershire.

In 1988 it was decided to add a range of Premier Ales to those offered over the bars. A Robert Morton mini-tower brewery (similar to the one which was set up in the Falklands to brew Penguin Ale) was installed in a modern warehouse unit. The equipment had previously been employed by the Leicester Brewing Company and by Hawthorn Brewery. Jonathan Stancill operates the plant now and he produces a splendid range of beers for the company's pubs and for the free trade. With a ten-to-eleven-brew-length and a range of sixteen ten-barrel fermenters he turns out up to forty barrels per week of the various beers. Jonathan is hoping to add a low-gravity mild and a session bitter to his range.

Premier is one of those pub-and-brewery operations which is to be applauded. The company refurbishes run-down pubs and creates havens for real-ale lovers. It is also active in the off-licence trade, selling draught beers from the Bewdley Beer Shop, for example. Look out for PMA pubs and for the beers in the free trade.

REAL ALES
Old Merlin (OG 1040) – a dark well-hopped mild
Knightly Bitter (OG 1044) – a refreshing hoppy bitter
Black Knight Stout (OG 1050) – an Irish-style stout of medium
    dryness
Maiden's Ruin (OG 1075) – lightish in colour but dangerous

PREMIER PUBS
*Gloucestershire*
Stroud: Queen Victoria

*West Midlands*

| | |
|---|---|
| Blackheath: Traveller's Rest | Stourbridge: Moorings Tavern |
| Darlaston: Three Horseshoes | Walsall: Oak |
| Enville: Cat Inn | West Bromwich: Oddfellows |

**Rising Sun**
Home-brew Pub
Knowle Bank Road, Shrayley Brook, Audley, Staffordshire

Sam Holland transformed the Rising Sun from a quiet country
pub into a vibrant free house. He did it by introducing a range
of guest beers, concentrating upon small independents (often
from the Black Country). With seven handpumps the former
blacksmith's shop provides welcome variety in a locality which
is dominated by Ansell's houses.

After seven years in the Rising Sun Sam had extended
and improved the property until it had become one of the most
popular pubs in the district. There was one further improvement
which he could make – he could add some home-brewed ales to
his range. When the Unicorn Inn at Ketley, Telford, stopped
brewing in 1989, Sam purchased the equipment. He obtained
planning permission to enclose a yard at the rear of the pub and
the brewery was installed there. It has a five-barrel brew-length
with a single fermenter, but interest from the free trade suggests
that Sam will soon be installing a second vessel to allow him to
increase production. Like the Brunswick Tavern in Derby, the
Rising Sun is an example of an enterprising free trader adding
his own house beers to an already extensive range to produce
the complete public house.

Rising Sun Bitter (OG 1040) – hoppy and full-flavoured
Setting Bitter (OG 1048) – darker and fruity
Total Eclipse (OG 1060) – a rich strong ale


## James Shipstone
Subsidiary Regional Brewers
Star Brewery, New Basford, Nottingham

Shipstone's was founded in 1852 by the father of the company,
James, and the Star Brewery was built by Stovin Bradford, one
of the best Victorian brewery architects. It was deliberately sited
on sandstones so that wells and cellars could be incorporated with
ease. The brewery tower, which dominates the premises, was
added in 1900, together with an additional fermentation room.

The rise of Shipstone's followed the familiar pattern of a
successful nineteenth-century family brewery. James was in
control for almost thirty years. He was joined by his two sons,
who eventually succeeded him, and the company made steady
progress. Small breweries were accumulated and their pubs
added to the tied estate. The Carrington Brewery was acquired
in 1898 and the Beeston Brewery in 1922. George Hooley's
Wheatsheaf of Radford followed in 1926 and T. Losco Bradley's
Midland Brewery on Northgate in 1955. The former Beeston
Brewery is now one of two maltings owned by Shipstone's.

At one time the company was well known for its colourful
horse-drawn drays. Splendid shire horses plodded the streets
of Nottingham at the turn of the century. Many of them were
conscripted into the army during the First World War, but that
was not the end of the tradition. Shipstone's continued to use
horses until the early 1970s.

In 1978 Shipstone's merged with Greenall Whitley of Warrington but it has retained an independent identity. The merger
resulted in a welcome injection of funds, investment being made
both in the public houses and in the brewery itself. A new copper
house and bulk-malt-handling plant were installed. The modern
laboratories at Warrington became available to the Shipstone's
brewers for improving quality and control. The closure in 1989
of another Greenall subsidiary, Davenport's of Birmingham,
resulted in several of the Davenport's and Wem beers being
moved to Nottingham. In fact Shipstone's had been brewing
some of Davenport's beers for a while. Whether the full range of

Shipstone's Brewery

the beers from those lost breweries will be maintained for long is open to question.

REAL ALES

Shipstone's
Mild (OG 1035) – a hoppy dark mild
Bitter (OG 1038) – a sharp distinctive bitter

Davenport's
Mild (OG 1035) – a balanced dark mild
Bitter (OG 1038) – a tasty session bitter

Wem
Best Bitter (OG 1037) – a distinctive bitter
Special Bitter (OG 1042) – a sweetish premium bitter

TIED HOUSES

Shipstone's houses number over 260. The vast majority are in Nottinghamshire and Leicestershire, where the brewery's presence is obvious.

*Derbyshire*

Near the border with Nottinghamshire, the town of Ilkeston has sixteen 'Shippo's' pubs. Elsewhere in the county you can try:

Alfreton: Devonshire Arms
Alvaston: Cornishman
Belper: Martha's Vineyard
Bolsover: Cromwell's
Breaston: Chequers Inn
Brimington: Great Central Hotel
Cotmanhay: Brick and Tile, Peacock Inn
Derby: Sitwell Tavern
Dronfield: Gorsey Brigg
Heanor: Nottingham House, Queen's Head

Leabrooks: Three Horseshoes
Long Eaton: Old Bell
Pinxton: George Inn, New Inn
Riddings: Greenhill Hotel
Ripley: Gate Inn, Hollybush, Talbot Inn, 1874 Brewery Co.
Somercotes: Rifle Volunteer
South Normanton: Hawthornes, New Inn
Stanton-by-Dale: Stanhope Arms
Swanwick: Steampacket Inn

*Lincolnshire*

Boston: Martha's Vineyard Still
Grantham: Royal Oak
Heighington: Turk's Head
Horncastle: Red Lion

Lincoln: Martha's Vineyard, Roebuck Hotel
Skegness: Shade's Hotel, Welcome Inn
Washingborough: Royal Oak

*Northamptonshire*
Kettering: Mikado Pheasant
Northampton: Standen's Inn

*Warwickshire*
Coventry: Tiger Moth

*South Yorkshire*
Doncaster: Coach and Horses,
    St Leger Tavern
Sheffield: Eversley House

**The Steamboat**
Home-brew Pub
Trent Lock, Long Eaton, Derbyshire

Barry Churchill began brewing on the premises in 1987. From
his tiny brewery adjoining the cellar – 'you can hardly turn
round', he admits – Barry produces a range of six beers which
include one claimed to be the strongest brewed in Britain. His
Broadside at OG 1150 certainly seems to be destined for a place
in the *Guinness Book of Records*. It is sold at £4.50 a pint, or
more realistically at £1.50 a nip, and Barry says that it tastes
like Madeira.

The Steamboat is beside the canal at Trent Lock, not far
from the River Trent. To reach it you will have to cross the
canal by footbridge, but there is plenty of car parking in the
vicinity. The delivery problem was one of the reasons for the
beginning of the home-brew operation, which has proved to be a
great success. As you would imagine, there is a nautical flavour
about the place and the names of the beers match that image.
On sunny days you can enjoy the unusual ales at a table on the
large patio. Inside there is a restaurant (the Captain's Table),
two bars and a function room.

The beers are brewed with malt extract and the mini-plant has
a ten-to-eleven-barrel capacity, using four fermenting vessels. As
well as the draught beers listed below there is a Master's Lager
(OG 1036), which is filtered but not pasteurised. Barry drinks the
lager himself and claims that it is far superior to the nationally
advertised brands from the 'big boys'.

REAL ALES
Seaman's Mild (OG 1033) – a dark mild

Frigate Bitter (OG 1038) – a malty rounded bitter
Bosun's Bitter (OG 1050) – a well-hopped premium bitter
Destroyer (OG 1080) – a rich strong ale
Broadside (OG 1150) – a devastating malt wine

## John Thompson Brewery
Free-trade Brewers
John Thompson Inn, Ingleby, Derbyshire

If you turn off just before the historic bridge at Swarkestone,
a little south of Derby, you will find the John Thompson Inn.
The building itself has a place in history, because it was there
that brewing in Derbyshire was revived in 1977. John Thompson
named the brewery after himself and began producing JTS for
his pub, which is on the banks of the River Trent. It is a popular
venue, providing a range of ales and good food. In the summer
it is a favourite country haunt for thirsty families.

The brewery is just to the rear of the John Thompson Inn.
In 1978 Colin Lloyd, a former employee of Bass, allowed John
to concentrate on running the pub and took over the brewing
duties. Colin marketed Lloyd's Country Beers in the free trade.
The present brewer, Chris Voyce, had worked at Marston's (but
not on the brewing side) before he arrived in 1980 to assist Colin
and learn the art of brewing. By 1983 he was ready to take over
and in 1989 Chris went into partnership with Bob Dummons of
the Wagon and Horses, Halesowen, with a view of expansion of
trade. Not only do they supply free houses with the ales from
Ingleby but they also handle beers from other breweries around
the country.

The John Thompson is a full-mash brewery but recipes have
always been adventurous, creating beers of distinctive flavour.
Chris has a talent for naming beers as well as brewing them.
VIP is short for Very Important Pint. The Derby Bitter is sold
as John Thompson Special in the 'brewery tap' and as Monsal
Head Bitter at the Monsal Head Hotel. In 1989 Chris anticipated
the birth of his first child by producing a bottled Little Nipper
(proceeds to the Children in Need Appeal) in a limited edition of
1,000 bottles. The recipe used for that commemorative ale was
adjusted only slightly to create the new Lloyd's Overdraught,
launched at the Nottingham Beer Festival in the autumn of the
same year.

REAL ALES
Derby Bitter (OG 1042) – the standard fruity bitter
VIP (OG 1048) – a distinctive premium bitter
Skullcrusher (OG 1065) – a dark heavy winter warmer
Lloyd's Overdraught (OG 1070) – a pale but strong ale

OUTLETS
*Derbyshire*
Chinley: Squirrels
Ingleby: John Thompson Inn
Monsal: Monsal Head Hotel

*Staffordshire*
Marston: Fox

*West Midlands*
Halesowen: Wagon and Horses

**Three Tuns**
Renowned Home-brew Pub
Bishop's Castle, Shropshire

It is well worth searching out the Three Tuns at Bishop's Castle, which is south of Shrewsbury and close to the border with Wales. In the picturesque village stands an historic four-storey brewery by its pub. The beers brewed there are some of the best 'small beers' you will find. One of the famous four surviving home-brew establishments of the early 1970s, the Three Tuns occupies a prominent position in the history of British brewing.

Beers have been mashed in Bishop's Castle for over 350 years. The one remaining brewhouse was built around 1890 and is an example of a Victorian tower brewery in miniature. The building stands prominently, across the yard and car park from the pub. Three generations of the Roberts family were involved in running the business and it was the last of them, John Roberts, who stood firm when most other small brewers were falling to the 'keg revolution'. He did it by producing quality beers.

When the backlash of the real-ale revolution arrived, John was well placed to receive the visitors from far and wide who wanted to taste his famous beers. He even led the way in producing memorabilia, including beer-making kits, so that those visitors could go home and try to brew their own version of XXX Bitter. Those heady days may have passed but the Three

Three Tuns

Tuns, an attractive pub with plenty of room, is still sought out by beer lovers.

John Roberts sold the business to Peter Milner in the late 1970s. The brewery and pub are now under the control of James, Jack and Robert Wood, themselves from a well-known local brewing family.

REAL ALES
Mild (OG 1035) – a traditional dark mild
XXX (OG 1042) – a well-rounded bitter
Castle Steamer (OG 1045) – a distinctive premium bitter
Old Scrooge (OG 1054) – a rich winter warmer

**Titanic Brewery**
Free-trade Brewers
Dain Street, Middleport, Stoke-on-Trent, Staffordshire

Stoke's major brewery is situated in a nursery industrial unit near the centre of Burslem. It was opened in 1985 by John Pazio, who ran the Traveller's Rest in Newcastle Street. When John was forced to sell up in April 1988, one of his employees, Keith Bott, and his brother David stepped in to save the sinking ship.

Phil Salt is the head brewer at Titanic. He has charge

of a seven-barrel-brew-length operation with three fermenters and produces fifteen to twenty barrels per week. The flagship ale is Titanic Premium but Captain Smith's (named after the Stoke-on-Trent officer who had charge of the ill-fated vessel) is also very popular. The session bitter is brewed rather less frequently and the powerful Christmas Ale hits the mash tun just once a year. Titanic beers are sold in the free trade and they slip down nicely.

REAL ALES
Titanic Bitter (OG 1036) – a well-hopped session bitter
Titanic Premium (OG 1042) – a full-flavoured premium bitter
Captain Smith's (OG 1050) – darker and of good strength
Christmas Ale (OG 1080) – a very potent winter warmer

FREE TRADE
*Staffordshire*
Burton upon Trent: Stud Baker
Cobridge: Pot O' Beer
Eccleshall: Old Smithy
Newcastle-under-Lyme: Cask and Mallet
Stafford: Stafford Arms

**The Wolverhampton and Dudley Breweries Plc**
Independent Regional Brewers
Bank's Park Brewery, Lovatt Street, Wolverhampton, West Midlands
Hanson's Dudley Brewery, High Street, Dudley, West Midlands

Bank's and Hanson's beers are abundantly available in the Black Country and West Midlands, where they are much loved. In recent years the company has entered into a policy of expanding its territory and you will find the Bank's sign in unexpected places. It is refreshing to see the way in which Wolverhampton and Dudley Breweries has put the emphasis of its advertising expenditure on beers rather than lager. The bitter and the light mild, both 'unspoilt by progress', are equally popular.

Henry and John Banks formed a partnership as maltsters at Newbridge in 1840. By 1875 they were well established and decided to venture into brewing. They opened the Park Brewery at Chapel Ash to produce 'October brewed ales'. The traditional Banks beers have been brewed there ever since, using malts from the company's own maltings. In 1890 the

Wolverhampton and Dudley Breweries Company was formed from an amalgamation of three local businesses: Banks and Company, George Thompson and Sons and C.C. Smith. After relatively slow beginnings the company began acquiring other Midland breweries around the time of the First World War. During this hectic period in the company's history eleven different breweries were purchased and, of course, the estate of public houses grew rapidly.

The development of the company's second brewery owes much to the determination of Julia Hanson. Her husband Thomas had come from farming stock at King's Bromley, near Lichfield. He involved himself in building up a thriving business in the wines and spirits trade. When he died, Julia was left to handle affairs. With the help of her son she expanded the firm to the point where, in 1889, they were able to purchase the Peacock Hotel and the brewery behind it. The Hansons involvement in brewing began there in Dudley – the Peacock was sited on what is now the brewery cellar.

Julia Hanson died five years later at the age of seventy-eight, leaving the younger members of the family to build on her hard work. Her son Thomas Piddock Hanson took control of the flourishing enterprise. It remained an independent family business until 1943, when it was purchased by Wolverhanpton and Dudley. There has never been any question of closing Hanson's and the two breweries have continued, just 8 miles apart, ever since.

About 85 per cent of Wolverhampton and Dudley's tied estate lies within a 20-mile radius. However, the trading area now extends as far south as Bristol, as far north as Manchester, as far west as Aberystwyth and as far east as Coalville. The excellent ales are enjoyed wherever they are sold.

REAL ALES
Bank's beers
Mild (OG 1035) – a well-flavoured light mild
Bitter (OG 1038) – a rounded well-hopped bitter
Hanson's beers
Mild (OG 1035) – rather darker but full of flavour
Black Country Bitter (OG 1035) – a refreshing light bitter

TIED ESTATE
Leaving aside the hundreds of pubs which are not far from the breweries, the following are some examples from seventeen counties of England and Wales:

*Avon*
Bristol: Bristol Bridge
Churchill: Stag and
  Hounds

Stoke Gifford: Parkway
  Tavern
Thombury: Knot of Rope

*Buckinghamshire*
Finmere: King's Head
Milton Keynes: Globe

*Cheshire*
Broxton: Durham Heifer
Great Barrow: White Horse

*Clwyd*
Wrexham: New Inn

*Derbyshire*
Derby: Jonty Farmer, Needles
Long Eaton: Tapper's Harker

*Dyfed*
Talybont: White Lion

*Gloucestershire*
Charlton Keys: Clock Tower
Quedgley: Basket Maker

*Hereford and Worcester*
Hereford: Cock of Tupsley
Kempsey: Talbot
Malvern: New Inn
Ombersley: Reindeer

Redditch: Golden Cross
Tenbury Wells: Crow
Wadborough: Mason's Arms
Whittington: Swan

*Leicestershire*
Cosby: Huntsman
Gilmorton: Talbot
Hinkley: Tin Hat

Market Harborough: Sun
Wigston Magna: Meadow
  Bank

*Greater Manchester*
Belle Vue: Longsight
Bumage: Milestone

Cheadle: Station
Old Trafford: Toll Gate

*Northamptonshire*
Naseby: Royal Oak
Old: White House

*Nottinghamshire*
Wollaton: Milestone

*Oxfordshire*
Banbury: North Arms
Bicester: Fox and Hounds
Oxford: Victoria

*Powys*
Machynlleth: Slater's Arms,
    White Lion

*Shropshire*
Bayston Hill: Beeches
Dawley: Wrekin View
Ironbridge: Boat
Madeley: Cuckoo Oak

Oswestry: Punch Bowl
Shrewsbury: Acorn
Upton Magna: Corbet Arms

*Staffordshire*
Brocton: Chetwynd Arms
Hanley: Albion
Leek: Bird in Hand

Lichfield: Feathers
Penkridge: Star
Stafford: Bear

*Warwickshire*
Coventry: Leg and Cramp
Kenilworth: Tiltyard
Leamington Spa: Gristmill

Nuneaton: Crow's Nest
Rugby: William Webb Ellis
Warwick: Crown

**The Wood Brewery Limited**
Single-Pub And Free-trade Brewers
Winstanstow, Craven Arms, Shropshire

The small Wood Brewery is situated across the yard from the
Plough Inn, Winstantow, in the south of Shropshire. It was set
up by Basil Wood and his two sons in 1980 and has proved to be
an enduring and enterprising member of the breed. One of the
sons, Anthony, played a large part in establishing the business
but it is his brother Edward who is in charge these days. With
the help of a small staff he brews the beers and makes local
deliveries.

He uses a modern nine-barrel-brew-length plant (which
was specially designed for the family) with five fermenters
and the normal output is twenty-five to thirty barrels per
week. Edward is proud of the fact that he uses a 100 per
cent malt grist mash and Herefordshire hops in the boil. Care
is taken at all stages of the 'Wood Process' to ensure beers of

consistent quality which will suit a wide range of palates. Special brews are made to order and bottled commemoratives have been produced on several occasions for local businesses and for groups such as the Horsehay Steam Trust at Telford.

REAL ALES

Parish Bitter (OG 1040) – a light hoppy bitter
Wood's Special (OG 1043) – a full-flavoured premium bitter
Wood's Wonderful (OG 1050) – a dark strong bitter
Christmas Cracker (OG 1060) – a tasty winter warmer

FREE TRADE

At any one time Wood's beers are available in around forty free houses, often as guest beers. The following are some of the most regular outlets:

*Hereford and Worcester*
Alvechurch: Coach and Horses
Eaton Bishop: Ancient Camp

Greater Malvern: Royal Malvern Hotel
Yarpole: Bell Inn

*Powys*
Llandysl: Upper House

*Shropshire*
Brockton: Feathers Inn
Clun: Sun Inn
Hengoed: Last Inn

Hopton Wafers: Crown Inn
Little Stretton: Green Dragon
Yorton: Railway Inn

Remember also that the family's Plough at Winstanstow is the brewery tap.

# CHAPTER TEN

# The North East

## Big End Brewery
Independent Local Brewers
Otley Road, Harrogate, North Yorkshire

Bill Witty opened the Big End on the edge of Harrogate in May 1988. It is housed in old stables which at one time were used as a milk delivery depot. He has built up a steady trade from the sound base of two tied public houses in Ripon.

Bill's brewer is Bernard Linley. He operates a five-barrel full-mash system of stainless-steel construction. The equipment came from a lost brewery in Wales (as did Piston, the name of the bitter brewed in it) and the original fermenter was a converted milk tank. Two more modern vessels were added and in autumn 1989 Bill and Bernard began installing a David Bruce-style system, including a new copper. This enabled Bernard to build from his usual ten barrels a week towards fifteen. Big End is likely to expand even further into the free trade, where it has already made quite an impact.

You will find Piston and Old Lubrication in several of Cameron's Tap and Spile houses. If you are drinking Oliver John's Bitter at the Golden Lion in Leyburn, you have not found yet another brewery (despite the claim on the owner's van outside) – the beer is brewed by Big End and sold under the house name.

REAL ALES
Piston (OG 1038) – a light refreshing bitter
Old Lubrication (OG 1042) – a darker premium bitter, hoppy
  and well-balanced

TIED HOUSES
   *North Yorkshire*
Ripon: One Eyed Rat,
   Water Rat

FREE TRADE
   *North Yorkshire*
Brearton: Malt Shovel              Leyburn: Golden Lion
Harrogate: Tap and Spile           Middleham: Black Bull

## Big Lamp Brewery
Independent Local Brewers
Summerhill Street, Westgate Road, Newcastle-Upon-Tyne,
Tyne and Wear

Big Lamp was the first brave venture to introduce a measure
of choice for drinkers around Newcastle-Upon-Tyne. It was
established in 1982 and has gradually built up into a minor
force in the North East. When Terry Hanson stepped down from
his role as brewer in October 1988 to return to teaching, John
Ingham took over the job. He has maintained the high quality
of the beers.
   The brewery is in a three-storey Victorian building which
in its time had been home to a firm of undertakers and to a
sports manufacturer. The ten-barrel plant is installed on the
tower principle with the copper on the top floor, the fermenting
vessels beneath and the settling tanks on the ground floor. The
three regular beers are supplemented by a skull-crushing Black-
out strong ale (OG 1100), which is brewed only for the Newcastle
Beer Festival, and by other occasional special brews when they
are commissioned.
   Currently Big Lamp has two tied houses near Newcastle.
The remainder of the output comes and goes as guest beers
in the free trade. Agencies distribute the beers over a wide
area, so there is a fair chance of finding Big Lamp making
an appearance in a multi-beer free house.

REAL ALES
Big Lamp Bitter (OG 1040) – a fresh well-hopped bitter
Prince Bishop Ale (OG 1048) – a light premium bitter
Old Genie (OG 1070) – a rich strong ale

TIED HOUSES
Felling: Wheatsheaf
Hebburn: Albert

## J. W. Cameron Limited
Subsidiary Major Brewers
Lion Brewery, Hartlepool, Cleveland

In the dark days before the real-ale revolution Cameron pubs offered the best chance of finding real ale in the far North East. In particular Strongarm Bitter, which was introduced in 1955 in direct contrast to the overwhelming trend towards keg beers, provided ale enthusiasts of the area with a welcome traditional drink. The territory supplied was mainly North Yorkshire and South Durham but there were plenty of Cameron pubs in the vicinity. The estate was expanded to around 750, reduced for a while by sales off and then built up again through purchases from other breweries.

Cameron's was established in 1865 and is a Victorian brewery with many modern additions. Best Bitter (currently Traditional Bitter) was introduced in 1961 after the acquisition of Russell and Wrangham, and was at one time called Lion Bitter (a name now used by Matthew Brown). The independence of the family firm was lost in 1977 when Ellerman Lines, the shipping company, purchased the business. Two years later a second brewery, that of Tollemache and Cobbold (Tolly Cobbold), Ipswich, was purchased by the new owners. Both breweries were allowed to operate as pseudo-independents until 1989, when Ellerman sold out to the massive Brent Walker empire. George Walker closed the Ipswich brewery and moved the whole operation to Hartlepool. This extended the output of the Lion Brewery to an impressive 500 000 barrels.

Tolly Cobbold had an interesting history. Thomas Cobbold began brewing on a site behind the Cups Hotel in 1723, fifty years before the Boston Tea Party and seventy-five before the first confrontation with Napoleon. One of the coppers from that original brewery was still in use until 1989. Because he had been forced to transport his prime raw material, water, by boat, he moved to a site on the cliff near Holy Wells in 1746. The business prospered from that day and soon the Cobbold family owned a fleet of twenty ships which traded with the East.

The Tollemache family arrived on the scene in 1888 when they purchased the 'Ipswich Brewery'. For a period the two businesses were in direct competition. Cobbold's Cliff Brewery was rebuilt around the turn of the century, and when the companies merged in 1957 it was natural that all brewing was moved there. Tolly Cobbold was Suffolk's principal bulk brewer.

There is no doubt that the loss of the Cliff Brewery was one of the greatest blows to the industry during 1989. It is perhaps ironic to consider that it was the Lion Brewery which had seemed likely to close in 1984, when it was the subject of a bid from Scottish and Newcastle which was thwarted only by a timely objection from Vaux. Although the intention of Brent Walker is to supply Tolly houses with beers which the local palate will find acceptable, there have been initial problems with quality and it seems likely that changes will be made. However, George Walker has promised to market his beers in Europe and some comfort can be taken from the fact that the future of the Lion Brewery seems assured.

REAL ALES
Cameron Beers
Traditional Bitter (OG 1036) – a distinctive session bitter
Strongarm (OG 1040) – a full-bodied malty premium bitter
Tolly Cobbold Beers
Tolly Mild (OG 1031) – a dark slightly sweet mild
Tolly Bitter (OG 1034) – a light well-rounded bitter
Original Bitter (OG 1037) – slightly stronger, with a tang
　　from dry hopping
XXXX (OG 1046) – a full-flavoured premium bitter
Old Strong (OG 1046) – a dark not-too-powerful winter ale

TIED ESTATE
J. W. Cameron, Tolly Cobbold and Brent Walker Inns number around 1,200. They are centred around the active and the defunct breweries, of course, and the following list provides some examples over a widespread area.

CAMERON PUBS
Look out for the company's Tap and Spile outlets, which carry a range of guest beers. Otherwise try any of the following Cameron locals:

*Cleveland*

Bilingham: Smith's Arms

Brotton: Green Tree

Guisborough: Globe

Hartlepool: Causeway

Stainton: Stainton Inn

Stockton: Wild Ox

*Durham*

Bishop Auckland: Newton Cap

Darlington: Central Borough

Shildon: King William

Spennymoor: Mason's Arms

*Humberside*

Langtoft: Ship Inn

North Frodingham: Star

*North Yorkshire*

Camblesforth: Black Dog

Faceby: Sutton Arms

Kirklington: Black Horse

Lockton: Fox and Rabbits

Lythe: Red Lion

Malton: Gate Inn

Muston: Ship Inn

Northallerton: Durham Ox

Norton: Railway Tavern

Pickering: White Swan

Robin Hood's Bay: Ye Dolphin

Scarborough: Angel Inn, Black
Lion, Shakespeare

Staithes: Royal George

Thornton-le-Dale: Buck Hotel

Welburn: Crown and Cushion

Whitby: Dolphin, First In
Last Out

York: Little John, Old Ebor,
Yorkshire Hussar

TOLLY COBBOLD PUBS

You will have no difficulty in finding Tolly Cobbold pubs in Cambridgeshire (there are thirty-three in Cambridge alone), Essex (of which seven are in Colchester) or Suffolk (there are fifty-six Tolly houses in Ipswich). Elsewhere the tied houses are less easily found:

*Bedfordshire*

Barton in the Clay: Speed the
Plough

*Buckinghamshire*

Milton Keynes: Suffolk Punch

*Norfolk*

Norwich: Four Leafed Clover,
Hog in Armour, Pickwick,
Wild Man

Thetford: Norfolk Terrier

Weasenham: Ostrich

## H. B. Clark and Company (Successors) Limited
Independent Local Brewers
Westgate Brewery, Wakefield, West Yorkshire

'The Drinks Specialists since 1905' have many interests besides brewing, including the sale of minerals, wines, spirits and tobacco. When the keg revolution slashed the profits of the traditional brewing side of the enterprise, those wholesale and retail interests were strong enough to keep the company in business. The brewery was closed in 1960 and did not reopen until 1982.

Brewing began on the site in 1905 and shortly afterwards two Wakefield families, together with Henry Boon Clark, founded H. B. Clark and Company. Henry was sacked in 1912 and the company was wound up. The current successors emerged in the following year and presided over the brewery until its temporary closure in 1960.

The Westgate Brewery site houses the full range of Clark's business interests, including wholesale and cash-and-carry facilities. The purpose-built brewing plant there is fifteen-to-thirty barrel brew-length and has a capacity of 100 barrels a week. Clark's Traditional Bitter is the mainstay of the company, selling well to the free trade. Within two months of the reopening it had carried off the Best Bitter Award at the Great British Beer Festival in Leeds.

In 1983 Clarks purchased some property next to Westgate and converted it into the first tied house, named Henry Boon's after the founder. The pub is a very interesting one where you can play many pub games or even watch silent films – it is worth the trip if you are anywhere in rugby-league country. Two further Boon pubs have since been opened and the company has now acquired the eighteenth-century King's Arms on Heath Common.

REAL ALES
Clark's HB (OG 1034) – a light refreshing bitter
Garthwaite's SB (OG 1035) – a new session bitter
Clark's Traditional (OG 1038) – hoppy and distinctive
Burglar Bill's (OG 1044) – a full-flavoured premium bitter
Winter Warmer (OG 1044) – a new ale to add a glow
Hammerhead (OG 1056) – a rich strong ale

## Cropton Brewery
Single-Pub and Free-Trade Brewers
The New Inn, Cropton, Pickering, North Yorkshire

The New Inn, an attractive Yorkshire free house near Pickering, is quite normal in appearance. But if you place your empty pint pot on the bar and ask the landlord to put two pints in it, he will not be at all surprised. The best bitter brewed on the premises is actually called '2 Pints', which can confuse the casual visitor.

David Mullins began the Cropton Brewery there in September 1984 with a capacity of a mere two and a half barrels per week for the bars of his public house. The business was purchased by Michael and Sandra Lee and their partner Bernard Sherry in January 1986.

The brewery, which was extended in 1987, is situated to the rear and beneath the New Inn. Extensions and alterations became necessary because of the rising popularity of the ales and the resultant increase in the number of enquiries from the free trade. The capacity is now ten barrels per week.

Beers from the Cropton Brewery are available in the free trade, both as guest beers and on a more regular basis. Michael Lee supplies some of his customers directly from Cropton, but the majority of sales are through beer agencies in the North East. This allows 2 Pints and Special Strong to reach a much wider market than has been the case in the past.

REAL ALES
2 Pints (OG 1042-4) – a well-flavoured rounded premium bitter
Special Strong (OG 1058-60) – a rich and warming strong ale

OUTLETS
The New Inn is probably the best place to order your 2 Pints but the following are regular customers:

Ailesby: Blacksmiths
Whitby: Stakesby Manor

Cropton Brewery

**Franklin's Brewery**
Free-Trade Brewers
Bilton Lane, Bilton, Harrogate, North Yorkshire

Franklin's is a story of romance and perfection. Sean Franklin, a Master of Wine, was working in France when he met a girl from Harrogate. He fell in love and returned to England with her. Employment in the wine industry was not as easy to find in England. Sean had time on his hands and he hit upon the idea of brewing a beer with a wine-like character – a beer to make you inhale its bouquet and smack the lips.

The result was the splendid Franklin's Bitter, described by most writers as 'fruity and aromatic'. When Sean eventually settled back into the wine trade, Tommy Thomas and Jane Osborne, two devotees of the beer, were on hand to take over the operation. Since 1985 they have continued to brew the distinctive ale for the free trade. The most prestigious outlet is the Duke of Devonshire at the famous Bolton Abbey, where thousands of visitors from home and abroad have an opportunity to sample 'a brew from the Dales'.

The small brewery is at the rear of the Gardener's Arms, but that particular free house is not one of the outlets. Tommy and Jane produce seven barrels per week and Franklin's reaches the far North East and Scotland through agencies. Long may they continue to brew the unique beer.


REAL ALE
Franklin's Bitter (OG 1038) – distinctive in its fruity flavour
    and bouquet


FREE TRADE
   *North Yorkshire*
Wharfedale: Duke of
    Devonshire
York: John Bull

   *West Yorkshire*
Leeds: Duck and Drake, Eagle

## Frog and Parrot
Subsidiary Home-Brew Pub
Division Street, Sheffield, South Yorkshire

Sheffield's representative of the Whitbread home-brew chain is situated not far from the City Hall and there is plenty of car parking in the area. The speciality is strong ale, so be careful.

As usual the brewing method employs malt extract rather than a full mash and the pub is very popular with young drinkers. Roger Nowill is the brewer and he enjoys seeing the effect of his dangerous brews on unsuspecting customers. To be fair, there is a clever warning system for those tackling his famous Roger & Out. This ale is brewed to an original gravity of 1125 and is claimed to be the strongest draught beer in Britain. It is sold only in nips and warning cards are handed out to the innocents who try it. Other special brews around 1100 OG are sometimes produced.

REAL ALES
Old Croak Ale (OG 1036) – a hoppy session bitter
Roger's Reckless (OG 1047) – a full-flavoured premium bitter
Old-Fashioned Porter (OG 1057) – dark, rich and strong
Roger's Conqueror (OG 1066) – a full-bodied strong ale
Roger & Out (OG 1125) – dangerously powerful, more like a wine

## Hadrian Brewery
Free-Trade Brewers
Foundry Lane Industrial Estate, Byker, Newcastle-Upon-Tyne, Tyne and Wear

Like Big Lamp, Hadrian has tackled the problem of the North East's tight brewery tie with a good measure of success. Trevor Smith and his brother Gary have established a sound business in hostile territory. Gary does the brewing and Trevor is usually out on the road making deliveries or finding new outlets.

In a small factory unit not far from the city centre they began with a five-barrel plant in 1987. Within a year they found it necessary to expand by increasing the capacity to an eight-barrel brew-length and adding an eight-barrel fermenting vessel to the two original five-barrel fermenters. Average weekly output is fifteen barrels.

Hadrian beers find their way into a scattered free trade.

They are also regularly available in a dozen of Cameron's Tap and Spile real-ale houses. The three beers provide a refreshing change from the normal diet for beer lovers in the North East.

REAL ALES
Gladiator Bitter (OG 1039) – a hoppy session bitter
Centurion Best Bitter (OG 1045) – a light premium bitter
Emperor Ale (OG 1050) – a rich dark strong ale

FREE TRADE
*Durham*
Darlington: Turk's Head

*Tyne and Wear*
Newcastle: Crown Posada,
    Rose and Crown

*West Yorkshire*
Leeds: Pig and Whistle

## Leeds Brewhouse Company
Subsidiary Home-Brew Pub
The Fox and Newt, Burley Road, Leeds, West Yorkshire

Much like the Lass O'Gowrie in Manchester, the Fox and Newt provides a little extra choice for locals. It is also a Whitbread-owned malt-extract pub and the beers are again brewed in the cellar. Burley Road is near the inner ring road and the pub is popular with students.

Part of the Rutland Hotel until Whitbread purchased it in 1982, the house is full of simple character and idiosyncrasies. Rather than through the usual window, the brewery equipment is viewed through an adapted peep-show machine. The place is worth a visit to sample the atmosphere. As well as the malt extract beers there are several of Whitbread's better-known offerings and a monthly guest beer is available.

REAL ALES
Rutland Mild (OG 1032) – a dark sweetish mild
Burley Bitter (OG 1036) – a light hoppy extract bitter
Old Willow (OG 1046) – a sweetish premium bitter
Kirkstall Ruin (OG 1063) – a rich malty winter warmer

**Linfit Brewery**
Home-Brew Pub
Sair Inn, Lane Top, Linthwaite, Huddersfield, West Yorkshire

If you want a different experience in drinking, go to Linthwaite
on the outskirts of Huddersfield. The Linfit Brewery is rather
special and so is Ron Crabtree. He is one of the true characters
of modern brewing.

The Sair Inn is a multi-roomed public house which nestles on
the side of a hill next to a mill and overlooks the Colne Valley. It
is an attractive stone-built property with an interesting history.
In the nineteenth century it was the home of several publican
brewers but it is doubtful whether those particular gentlemen
had the versatility of Ron, who learned his skills with the old
West Riding Brewery. Using a tiny one-and-a-half-barrel plant
he regularly turns out at least six different full-mash beers.
They are all of excellent flavour and character. Ron built the
equipment to his own design and the secret of his ability to
produce such a wide range of ales is the quick transfer of the
new beers from the fermentation vessel into storage tanks. This
enables him to mash at frequent intervals.

Ron has been brewing at Linthwaite since 1982. The names
of some of his beers have a flavour of local history about them
and there is no doubt that the mini-brewery of the Sair Inn has
itself a place in the history of the new beer revolution. It is well
worth a visit.

REAL ALES
Linfit Mild (OG 1032) – a dark refreshing mild
Linfit Bitter (OG 1035) – the standard session bitter
Linfit Special (OG 1041) – a full-flavoured premium bitter
English Guineas (OG 1041) – a dark dry stout
Old Eli (OG 1050) – a rich strong bitter
Leadboiler (OG 1063) – a heavy distinctive strong ale
Enoch's Hammer (OG 1080) – lightly coloured but dramatic

**Malton Brewery Company Limited**
Independent Free-Trade Brewers
Crown Hotel, Wheelgate, Malton, North Yorkshire

Malton is a racing town and it is perhaps not surprising that
the brewery's premium bitter is named after a racehorse. Double

Chance was a chestnut gelding of uncertain parentage who, after an undistinguished career, suddenly developed the ability to win in the 1924–5 season. He won six-races, the last of them being the Grand National of 1925. For some time he was a resident of Malton and was in fact stabled in the very building that is now the Malton Brewery's fermenting room. They will tell you that the building 'has produced both a National winner and a local favourite'.

As well as stabling famous racehorses, Malton has brewed good ales for many years. Russell's and Wrongham's was one of the town's breweries with a fine reputation which lost its independence and was closed down in the 1960s, as was Roses. The smell of malt and hops was absent from the local air for nearly twenty years until Geoff Woollons, Colin Sykes and the late Bob Suddaby opened the new Malton Brewery.

They converted the derelict stable block and coach house at the rear of the Crown Hotel, Wheelgate, into a splendid fourteen-barrel-length full-mash brewing plant. The conversion work took five months, the first mash being in February 1985. Since that date the reputation of the company's four beers has spread, helped by a Best in Show award at the Newcastle Beer

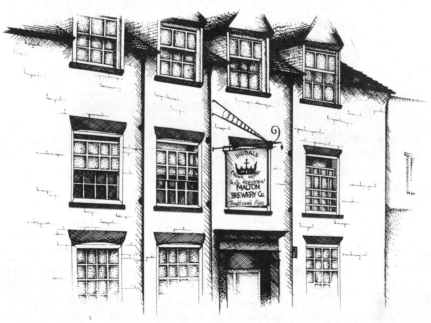

Malton Brewery

Festival. Potentially the small brewery can produce over seventy barrels a week.

Beers from Malton may be enjoyed in several parts of England and Scotland. Agencies supply to the free trade from Newcastle, Edinburgh and Lincoln. There are also several regular outlets in North Yorkshire which are supplied directly from the brewery.

REAL ALES

Malton Pale Ale (OG 1034) – a light session bitter, full of flavour

Double Chance Bitter (OG 1037–8) – a distinctive bitter from Yorkshire malts

Pickwick's Porter (OG 1042) – dark, stout-like and dry

Owd Bob (OG 1055) – a rich ruby and smooth strong ale

OUTLETS

*North Yorkshire*

Egton Bridge: Horse Shoe Inn
Goathland: Mallyan Spout
Keighley: Grinning Rat
Low Marishes: School House Inn
Malton: Crown Hotel
Scarborough: Hole in the Wall

**Marston Moor Brewery**
Single-Pub and Free-Trade Brewers
Kirk Hammerton, York, North Yorkshire

The Marston Moor Business was first established on a former Second World War airfield in Tockwith. That was in 1984 and there was a pause in brewing in 1987 while Peter Smith looked for more suitable premises. Happily he found a new home in 1989. He relocated to a former forge building at the rear of the Crown Inn at Kirk Hammerton.

The equipment used is a full-mash brewery which Peter designed himself. It is capable of a six-to-eight-barrel brew length. Malt is supplied by Fawcett's Maltsters of Castleford and the hops used are a mixture of Kentish Goldings and Challenger. Two beers are produced, Cromwell Bitter and the cheekily named Brewer's Droop, mainly for the 'brewery tap', but Peter is gradually gaining a foothold in the free trade.

REAL ALES
Cromwell Bitter (OG 1037) – a hoppy clean-tasting bitter
Brewer's Droop (OG 1050) – a premium bitter with special
  powers

## Newcastle Brewhouse Company
Subsidiary Home-Brew Pub
Dog and Parrot, Clayton Street West, Newcastle-Upon-Tyne,
Tyne and Wear

Whitbread's representative from its in-house brewing chain
is situated in central Newcastle. As in the case of its sister
establishments, the beers are brewed from malt extract rather
than from a full mash. It is a very basic pub, full of music and
hubbub. This is especially the case when the youngsters are on
the town at weekends.

The Dog and Parrot began brewing in 1982 and produces
a wide range of beers from its small plant. You can see the
brewing equipment from the interior of the pub. If you like a
'spit and sawdust' atmosphere, drop in and try the unusual beers.

REAL ALES
Mild (OG 1035) – a dark sweetish mild
Scotswood Bitter (OG 1036) – a light session bitter
Wallop (OG 1046) – a full-flavoured premium bitter
Porter (OG 1055) – a dark dry porter
Christmas Cracker (OG 1080) – a strong winter warmer

## North and East Riding Brewers
Single-Hotel and Free-Trade Brewers
The Highlander, The Esplanade, South Cliff, Scarborough,
North Yorkshire

The beers under the William Clark's banner reflect the family's
origins in Scotland. Both Scottish-style ales and Yorkshire-type
beers are produced at the Highlander. William Clark brought
his family down from Falkirk and his son Jamie, an engineer
by trade, built his own brewery at the family hotel.

Jamie constructed the plant to his own design, the mash
tun being the only purchase he had to make. It has a ten-
barrel-brew-length potential, although the normal mash is of

5 barrels. Using three fermenters, 15 barrels of the William Clark beers is the usual weekly output. The ales are sold in the bars of the Victorian hotel, which overlooks Scarborough's South Bay.

In 1989 Jamie handed over the brewing duties to his son Tim so that he could concentrate on his other interests, which include night clubs. He is converting the former Stresa Hotel into flats and opening a gaslight bar in its basement. The Highland is also in the Stresa so there will be a choice of two different atmospheres in which to enjoy the unusual beers. You can also find them in the free trade, where they are distributed by agencies. North and East Riding beers are obviously most likely to be encountered as guest beers in the North East but they are becoming evident in Lincolnshire. It may well be that when Tim has settled into his role of head brewer he will start delivering to a few regular outlets in the vicinity.

REAL ALES
Thistle Mild (OG 1034) – a refreshing dark mild
Thistle Bitter (OG 1040) – a Scottish-style bitter
EXB (OG 1040) – a well-balanced bitter
68 (OG 1050) – a well-flavoured premium bitter

## Northern Clubs' Federation Brewery Limited
Independent Regional Club Brewers
Lancaster Road, Dunston, Tyne and Wear

If you walk into a club in the North of England and ask for a pint, the chances are that you will be given a pint of 'Fed'. The brewery has a unique place in British brewing: it supplies about 1,300 different clubs with their ales. These outlets are situated in south-west Scotland, Cumbria, Northumberland, Durham, north Lancashire, Yorkshire, the Midlands, Hemel Hempstead, Tilbury, Loughton in Essex, Chadwell St Mary and other areas between the Midlands and north London. Supplies are even distributed in the St Austell area of Cornwall and the company is proud of its role as the major supplier of beer to the House of Commons and the National Theatre.

The story began in 1919 when a group of clubmen came together in Northumberland to consider the possibilities of brewing for themselves. They felt that they were not getting a good deal from brewers. Local clubs were circulated to discover if they would participate and a federation was formed. The new company purchased the Alnwick Brewery but it had been ill advised: Alnwick had been out of use for too long – it proved impossible to restore it to working order and a new plant was required. The members hired a horse and cart and decorated it with posters, inviting investment as they proceeded from village to village. In this way they raised sufficient funds to buy a brewery plant which was available in Hedley Street, Newcastle-Upon-Tyne. It was moved to Alnwick and the federation was in business.

The inevitable battles with private brewers ensued. The opposition reduced its prices and offered inducements but the Federation became firmly established. More and more clubs took the beers. In 1957 a new brewhouse costing £$^1/_2$ million came into production in Hanover Square under the guidance of the dynamic chairman, Syd Lavers.

To celebrate the Golden Jubilee of the company a further £2 million was spent, this time on an extension, and the brewery's registered office was moved to Forth Street. These building works created some problems when it was discovered that the site had been occupied by the Romans. Besides coins and pottery, two coffins which contained human remains were

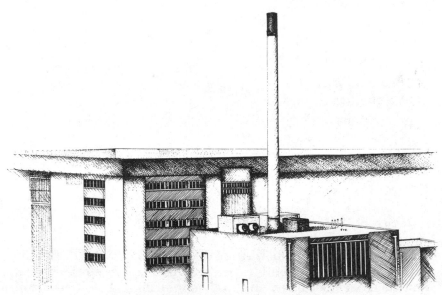

Northern Clubs Federation Brewery

discovered. However, the new Dunston complex opened in 1975.

Shortly afterwards plans were made for a massive extension to the brewery itself. When negotiations with the planning authority broke down, Federation decided to build a completely new brewery close to the Dunston complex. This new brewery was officially opened on 17 June 1980. It is a very modern unit with computer controls and extensive laboratories, built at a cost of £18 million. The initial output was 20,000 barrels a week but there is scope for twice this amount. 'Fed' has won many awards for its beers over the years and is well placed to continue serving the clubs of England and Scotland into the future.

REAL ALES
Best Bitter (OG 1036) – a refreshing session bitter
Special Ale (OG 1041) – a well-balanced tasty premium bitter

OUTLETS
Almost all Federation ales are sold in clubs, but there are a few other outlets:

*London*
Thamesmead: Cutty Sark

*Northumberland*
Acomb: Miner's Arms

*Scotland*
Friockheim: Star Inn
Lossiemouth: Beach Bar

*Tyne and Wear*
South Shields: Ashley

*West Yorkshire*
Castleford: Langree Park


**Old Mill Brewery**
Independent Local Brewers
Mill Street, Snaith, Goole, Humberside

Bryan Wilson and Paul Wetherall set up the Old Mill Brewery at Snaith in 1983 in a building which, during the course of its life, had been used both as a mill and as maltings. After the derelict premises had been completely reroofed and cleaned out ready for a stainless-steel brewing plant from SPR of Lancashire, Bryan and Paul began by producing a traditional bitter and Bullion under the low ceilings.

When Bullion won the award for the best beer from a new brewery at the Great British Beer Festival of 1985, the success of the business was assured. Bryan Wilson now has a staff of four, including two salesmen pursuing outlets in the free trade, and he has built up a firm base of five tied houses in the North East.

The plant has a twenty-barrel brew-length and the normal weekly output is a commendable 100 barrels. Seven fermenting vessels are available for use. Richard Eyton-Jones, well qualified with a degree from Heriot-Watt of Edinburgh, is the brewer these days and he maintains a very high standard. About two thirds of his output finds its way into the free trade. As well as the three splendid beers listed below, he produces Altmuhle Lager, which is filtered but not pasteurised.

REAL ALES
Dark Mild (OG 1034) – a traditional Midlands-style mild
Traditional Bitter (OG 1037) – a refreshing well-hopped bitter
Bullion (OG 1044) – a well-rounded premium bitter

TIED HOUSES
*Humberside*
Grimsby: Rutland Arms
Scunthorpe: Riveter
Snaith: Brewer's Arms

*South Yorkshire*
Sheffield: Mill Tavern

*West Yorkshire*
Bradford: Crow's Nest

FREE TRADE
The three best customers for Old Mill Traditional Bitter are:

*West Yorkshire*
Bradford: Fighting Cock
Brighouse: Red Rooster
Halifax: Woodcock

**Robinwood Brewery**
Free-Trade Brewers
Burnley Road, Todmorden, West Yorkshire

Robinwood has made rapid strides since its birth in September 1988. Freddie Sleap and Tim Fritchley hatched the idea of brewing their own beers on a novelty basis at their pub, the Staff of Life. They had been running the free house for four years before they decided upon the venture. Looking about the place, they could not find a room large enough to house the enterprise. Eventually they purchased an ex-builder's yard about half a mile away. The site happened to be next to the old Lydgate Brewery, which closed around the turn of the century.

They installed a stainless-steel full-mash plant from Brew Eng Consultancy of Luddendenfoot with a five-barrel brew-length and began producing some of the most admired ales from a new brewery. The three regular beers have once been supplemented by Hospital Porter, which was brewed for the 1989 Halifax Beer Festival (the proceeds going to the local Bodyscanner Appeal).

The possibility of making the Porter a regular product, or indeed of increasing production generally, depends upon future investment in more fermenting vessels and other equipment. Tim and Freddie are hopeful that this can be achieved. They also intend to begin bottling.

There is certainly plenty of demand for Robinwood. The beers are delivered throughout Yorkshire and Lancashire and wholesalers make certain that there are many guest-beer appearances further afield. The partners are looking for their first tied house, though for the time being they are content to supply up to seventy free-trade accounts at any one time. These include the local cricket club and the Hippodrome Theatre. You will often find Robinwood in the Cameron Tap and Spile pubs.

The strangely titled strong ale was named after an imaginary beer in a Private Eye cartoon.

REAL ALES
Best Bitter (OG 1036) – a refreshing lightly hopped bitter
XB (OG 1046) – lightly hopped and malty
Old Fart (OG 1060) – a traditional dark old ale

FREE TRADE
Most of the regular outlets are not far from the brewery:

*West Yorkshire*
Halifax: Brewer's Delight        Widdop: Packhorse
Todmorden: Coach House Inn,
   Fountain, Sportsman's Arms,
   Staff of Life


**Selby Brewery**
Single-Pub and Free-Trade Brewers
Millgate, Selby, North Yorkshire

Selby Brewery was a significant catalyst in the new brewery revolution. The Sykes family had brewed there since the nineteenth century, but eventually bowed to the pressures of keg and closed down in 1954. Martin Sykes became one of the leaders of the real-ale revolution when he cleaned up the old equipment and began brewing again in 1972.

Sadly, Selby's major role has been as an encouragement to other brewers, because its beers have never really established themselves as a force in North Yorkshire. Tetley's has a strong hold in the vicinity and there are also the beers from Tadcaster to provide stiff opposition. Martin's one tied house is a considerable distance from the brewery at Howden, Humberside. If you are in Selby, you can call at the Brewery Tap Off Licence, which is opposite a petrol filling station on Millgate. It is a tiny place, standing unpretentiously in front of the Victorian brick-and-slate brewery building and yard. The draught beers can be purchased there in self-conditioned form in the bottle (Best Bitter in bottle is, quite rightly, called 'No. 1').

Martin can justifiably claim to have been a prophet of the new brewery generation – a prophet of doom so far as the all-embracing ambitions of the Big Six were concerned. These days he has several other business interests but the modern plant which he installed to replace the family brewing equipment in 1980 is still in operation within that old building. Selby Brewery will always have an important place in the history of the industry.

REAL ALES
Best Bitter (OG 1039) – a well-hopped refreshing beer
Old Tom (OG 1069) – a powerful winter strong ale

TIED HOUSE
  *Humberside*
Howden: Board Inn


## Samuel Smith
Independent Regional Brewers
The Old Brewery, Tadcaster, North Yorkshire

Tadcaster gained its fame as a brewing centre because of the skills of the Smith family and the hard well-water there, which is particularly suitable for brewing bitter beers. The two Smith breweries stand just across the road from each other. A split in the family in the 1880s created two separate businesses. Sam Smith's is fiercely independent, while John Smith's was swallowed by Courage (now Elders) in 1970.

A family by the name of Beaumont owned the Old Brewery at Tadcaster before Stephen Hartley purchased it in 1758. He erected a brewing tower and sank the well which is still in use today. The Hartley family perhaps had too many interests in the area (in particular they ran the local posts and coaches) and the brewery struggled.

When Samuel Smith purchased the company in 1847, it was close to bankruptcy. Samuel acquired the place for his son John and funded him in the early years. Until John died in 1879 there was only one Smith brewery in Tadcaster. John had been a bachelor and the Old Brewery, together with its pubs, passed to his nephew, the third Samuel Smith. Shortly afterwards John's brother William built a new brewery nearby, to be called John Smith's, and the family was split. The Old Brewery was reopened in 1886 by Samuel and has been a family business ever since.

Samuel Smith's still uses Yorkshire slate squares in the fermenting room and is the only brewery which manufactures its own oak casks. It is a traditional brewery in every sense, with splendid grey shire horses stabled on the premises. While most of the world has turned to mass production, Sam Smith's, the oldest brewery in Yorkshire, has remained proudly defiant in concentrating upon proven, unadulterated real ales brewed in the Yorkshire way.

REAL ALES
Old Brewery Bitter (OG 1039) – a malty sweetish bitter of
  character

Museum Ale (OG 1047) – smooth, strong and well-rounded

OUTLETS
There are over 300 pubs in the Samuel Smith estate. The following are some interesting houses where you will find the ales from Tadcaster:

*London*
Bermondsey: Anchor Tap
Bucklersbury: Shades
Fleet Street: Ye Olde
  Cheshire Cheese
Great Portland Street: Cock
High Holborn: Cittie of York
Trafalgar Square: Chandos

*North Yorkshire*
Askham Richard: Buckles
Bishopthorpe: Ebor Hotel
Carlton: Forester's Arms
Catterick: Oak Tree
Fairburn: Wagon and Horses
Haxby: Tiger
Killinghall: Greyhound Inn
Knaresborough: Wellington
  Inn
Long Marston: Sun Inn
Moor Monkton: Alice
  Hawthorne
Oswaldkirk: Malt Shovel
Rufford: Tankard
Saxton: Greyhound
Selby: Cricketer's Arms
Skelton: Blacksmith's Arms
Spofforth: Railway Inn
Stutton: Hare and Hounds
Tadcaster: Britannia, Howden
  Arms, Royal Oak
Tockwith: Boot and Shoe
Tunstall: Bay Horse
Whitby: Jolly Sailors
York: Brigadier Gerard,
  Crystal Palace

*South Yorkshire*
Doncaster: Corporation
  Brewery Taps
Edenthorpe: Ridge Wood
Grenoside: Cow and Calf
Kirk Sandal: Holly Bush
Kiveton Park: Saxon
Maltby: Lumley Arms, Manor
Mexborough: Star
Rossington: White Rose
Rotherham: New Broom
Sprotborough: Ivanhoe
Ulley: Royal Oak
Worsborough: Edmund's Arms

*West Yorkshire*
Bradford: Brown Cow, Red
  Lion, Shoulder of Mutton
Elland: Collier's Arms
Featherstone: White Horse
Huddersfield: Jug and Bottle
Leeds: General Elliott
Wragby: Spread Eagle

## Stock's Doncaster Brewery
Independent Local Brewers
The Hallcross, Hall Gate, Doncaster, South Yorkshire

Cooplands (Doncaster) Limited is a family-run bakery and fresh-food business with over forty shops. In 1981 a decision was taken to add an order for brewers' yeast to that for the more familiar bakers' yeast. The Hallcross pub was converted from the company's original home-made sweet shop and the brewery is on the side of the beer garden at the rear.

Soon the ambitions of the family extended beyond the single pub outlet of the early years. The Turnpike in High Street, Bawtry, was acquired in 1986 and in 1989 the Lion Hotel, Bridge Street, Worksop, was added. Renovation of the Lion, a fifteenth-century listed building, was soon begun with a budget of around £1 million to build a further twenty-three en-suite bedrooms and expose a section of the medieval roof.

All three Stock's beers are brewed from Marris Otter malt and a mixture of Golding and Fuggles hops. Brewer Jim Butcher presides over a potential output of forty barrels a week and pays particular attention to temperature control in order to keep the beers in peak and consistent condition.

Besides the three tied houses, there are a number of outlets in the free trade which are mainly supplied through agencies. The company also has reciprocal arrangements from time to time with other brewers. Stock's ales have been sold through the Tap and Spile houses in the North East and the powerful Old Horizontal was voted Beer of the Year by the customers of that chain of Cameron pubs in the face of competition from 113 other brews.

REAL ALES
Stock's Best Bitter (OG 1037) – a light hoppy bitter
Stock's Select (OG 1044) – a smooth slightly malty premium ale
Old Horizontal (OG 1054) – a nutty strong ale with good body

TIED HOUSES
**Bawtry: Turnpike**
**Doncaster: Hallcross**
**Worksop: Lion Hotel**

## Timothy Taylor and Company Limited
Independent Regional Brewers
Knowle Spring Brewery, Keighley, West Yorkshire

In the mid-nineteenth century the great man Timothy was indeed a tailor. Fortunately he decided that his true vocation lay beyond the lapel and, in 1858, he turned his attentions to malting and brewing. It was then that he established the famous family business in Keighley, and Yorkshire has been proud of Timothy Taylor ales ever since.

The family has remained independent and very true to tradition over the years, both in its style of operation and in its methods of brewing. The deep artesian well which Timothy sank is still used to draw the liquor for a splendid range of beers. It is no exaggeration to say that they cannot be surpassed in the North of England. As a testimony to that claim many championships have been won by the ales from the Knowle Spring Brewery. However, the company is not one to shout the odds. With admirable reticence it maintains a small but stable estate of pubs within close range of the brewery and releases about half of its production to the free trade. You will find Timothy Taylor beers in free houses all around the country.

Landlord is the major prize-winner and is much revered among those with educated palates. It is a distinctive well-flavoured bitter which is very individualistic as a result of the use of Styrian Golding hops. At times the company produces a delicious sweet porter, which is also worth searching out for its singular flavour.

REAL ALES
Golden Best (OG 1033) – a tasty light pale ale
Dark Mild (OG 1033) – the same beer with added caramel
Best Bitter (OG 1037) – a well-hopped standard bitter
Landlord (OG 1042) – the distinctive full-flavoured premium
  bitter
Porter (OG 1043) – a dark sweetish porter
Ram Tam (OG 1043) – a dark version of Landlord, usually
  sold in the winter

OUTLETS
The following offer the best chance of finding a range of Taylor beers:

*North Yorkshire*
Glusburn: Dog and Gun
York: Brown Cow

*West Yorkshire*
Bingley: Brown Cow
Bradford: Oakleigh
Dewsbury: John F. Kennedy
Haworth: Fleece Inn
Hebden Bridge: Cross Inn,
   Hare and Hounds

Keighley: Albert Hotel,
   Boltmaker's Arms, Brown
   Cow, Cricketer's Arms,
   Eastwood, Fountain, Globe,
   Royal Hotel, Volunteer's
   Arms
Leeds: Eagle Tavern
Thornton: Blue Boar

**Trough Brewery**
Independent Local Brewers
Louisa Street, Idle, Bradford, West Yorkshire

The brewery with a porcine theme is situated in a suburb of Bradford. Graham Coates has thirty-five years of experience in brewing, having worked for Thwaites', Webster's and Heys' (where his father was head brewer). Since it opened in 1981, Trough has taken the sensible step of basing its operation on a small tied estate, so that its prosperity has not been totally exposed to the vagaries of a difficult and limited free trade. This sound foundation of captive outlets has served the business well.

After eight years of brewing from malt extract, Graham installed a stainless-steel full-mash system in the summer of 1989. With a maximum brew-length of fourteen barrels the company is set to expand its production and to increase its tied estate. The beers are brewed in a Victorian stone building which began life as a plaster factory and has been used for several other purposes over the years.

A new third beer was added to the range in autumn 1989 under the name of Hog's Head. The theme very clearly is that of pigs, taken from Bradford's city crest, and the distinctive emblem of the brewery depicts an amiable young porker with more than a hint of moisture around his chops. Despite this strange image Trough is one of the more enterprising and successful of the new breweries in the North East, as you would expect from a man of Graham Coates' experience and expertise. Try any of the company's tied houses or watch out for the piggy beers in the free trade.

REAL ALES
Trough Bitter (OG 1035) – a refreshing session bitter
Wild Boar (OG 1040) – a well-balanced bitter
Hog's Head (OG 1045) – a new premium bitter

TIED ESTATE
Bradford: Castle, Flagship          Idle: Brewery Arms, Brewery
Dewsbury: Flying Pig                     Tap
Greengate: Hog's Head               Keighley: Red Pig


## S. H. Ward and Company Limited
Subsidiary Regional Brewers
Sheaf Brewery, Eccleshall Road, Sheffield

Ward's arrived in Sheffield by a happy accident. A young
man rode into town in the 1880s, his mission to collect a
debt for his father-in-law, a corn merchant. Best-quality malt
had been supplied but the account had not been settled. The
brewer concerned, a Mr Kirby, could not pay up and the young
man, George Wright, did not fancy returning empty-handed to
Lincoln. Instead he stayed at the brewery and assisted Kirby
in putting his affairs in order. Soon the two men formed a
partnership.

Just as George had helped Kirby out of financial difficulties, it
was Septimus Ward who some years later was needed to rescue
George from a similar problem. The latter had unwisely acted
as guarantor for a relative in the shipping business and, when
a clipper sank, it was his turn to fall on hard times. Septimus
dipped into his pocket in exchange for a stake in the brewery.
S. H. Ward and Company Limited was formed in 1890.

Originally the beers were brewed at the Sheaf Island Brewery
in Effingham Road and the two adjoining breweries, the Albion
and Bradley's Soho, were acquired by the company. For a time
both the original Sheaf and the Albion were used but a new plant
was installed at the Soho site and the firm's activities have ever
since, despite considerable interference from road widening, been
carried out on the Eccleshall Road site.

The brewery has changed with the times – Yorkshire stone
squares gave way to slate vessels, then aluminium, followed by
open stainless-steel and now enclosed stainless-steel vessels with
in-built cleaning systems. This attention to detail and progress

has served the Sheaf (renamed from Soho) Brewery well over the years. Before 1950 there were a number of breweries in Sheffield but it was Ward's alone which survived the hard times of the post-war period.

The independent family firm was confronted with the prospect of takeover in the early 1970s. Facing up to the reality of the situation, chairman Wilfred Wright accepted the inevitability of it and gave a lot of thought to the choice of company which he should join. In 1972 Ward's became part of the Vaux Group of Sunderland. The decision which Wilfred took then has proved to be a sound one, for Ward's has been allowed to continue trading under its own name and to retain its established range of products. The excellent Sheffield Best Bitter is as good today as it ever was and the new Kirby Ale is very popular.

REAL ALES

Darley Dark Mild (OG 1032) – a traditional dark mild
Darley Thorne Best Bitter (OG 1037) – a pleasant rounded bitter
Sheffield Best Bitter (OG 1038) – a splendid full-flavoured bitter
Kirby Ale (OG 1049) – a distinctive strong bitter

TIED HOUSES

*Derbyshire*

Bakewell: Peacock
Chesterfield: Barley Mow, Cricketers' Inn, Devonshire, Junction Inn, Somerset House, Steelmelter's Arms, Trumpeter
Dronfield: Blue Stoops
Eckington: Bird in Hand, Duke of York

Froggatt Edge: Chequers
Holmesfield: Rutland Arms
Horsley Woodhouse: Jolly Colliers
Ilkeston: Durham Ox
Riddings: Seven Stars
Ripley: Three Horse Shoes

*Humberside*

Barton-upon-Humber: Wheatsheaf

Brigg: King William IV, Wheatsheaf, White Horse

*Lincolnshire*

Gainsborough: Marquis of Granby
Lincoln: City Vaults

Louth: Turk's Head
Retford: Black Boy, Turk's Head

Phoenix Inn, Highlane, Sheffield

## Yorkshire

You do not need to walk far in any direction from Sheffield city centre to find a Ward's pub – there are forty-four of them. Outside Sheffield there is plenty of choice:

Aston: Roland Arms
Barnsley: Furnace Inn, Royal Albert, Royal Hotel
Chapeltown: Norfolk Arms, Prince of Wales, Thorncliffe Arms
Doncaster: Three Horse Shoes, White Swan
Dore: Devonshire Arms
Ecclesfield: Greyhound
Greasborough: Alpine
Greetland: Star Inn
Grenoside: Norfolk Arms
Highlane: Phoenix Inn

Mortomley: Market Inn
Mosborough: George and Dragon, Queen
Oxspring: Traveller's Inn
Rotherham: Crinoline Bridge, Crown Inn, Turner's Arms, White Lion
Sowerby Bridge: Puzzle Hall Inn
Stannington: Crown and Glove
Thorpe Green: Hawk and Dove
Thurcroft: Double Barrel
Totley: Cricket Inn
Worrall: Wharncliffe Arms

## Whitby's Own Brewery Limited
Free-Trade Brewers
St Hilda's, The Ropery, Whitby, North Yorkshire

'Have beer – will travel' is the motto of brewer Duncan Evans.
It is one of the quirks of the mini-brewery revolution (and a
sad commentary on the tightness of the tie in the North East)
that Whitby's Own Brewery does not have an outlet in Whitby.
He has been forced to seek outlets further afield for his beers,
despite the fact that his strong Force Nine ale won the Supreme
Champion Award at the Leeds Beer Festival in late 1988.

This was no mean achievement for a brewery which began
production only in June 1988. With a full-mash plant designed
to his own requirements and recipes of his own creation, Duncan
brews three beers and his equipment gives him a potential
output of twenty barrels a week. No sugars or chemicals of
any kind are used in the brewing process.

Whitby beers can be found in a scattered free trade from
Newcastle down to Hull or Leeds, particularly in country free
houses during the summer season, and they are sold to a number
of universities and polytechnics. Joan Evans will tell you that
the opening of the brewery was a big step for her husband to
take. However, all parties concerned are enjoying the challenge
as they work towards achieving the small brewery's full potential
of twenty barrels per week of fine traditional ales.

REAL ALES
Ammonite (OG 1036–40) – a refreshing bitter
Wobble (OG 1043–7) – a premium bitter which can affect
  the knees
Force Nine (OG 1053–7) – the prize-winning strong ale

FREE TRADE
  *Cleveland*
Middlesbrough: Strap and Garter,
  Tap and Barrel
Moorsholm: Toad Hall
Redcar: New Bigging

  *North Yorkshire*
Lealholm: Board
Ugthorpe: Black Bull

## Vaux Breweries PLC
Independent Major Regional Brewers
The Brewery, Sunderland, Tyne and Wear

The story of Vaux is one of determination and strength. Cuthbert Vaux started it all when he progressed from brewery apprenticeship to the establishment of his own company, C. Vaux and Sons, in 1837. He purchased a brewery in Union Street, Sunderland, and traded there successfully until 1875, when the site was required by the North Eastern Railway Company to build the Central Station. C. Vaux and Sons then moved to its present site between Castle Street and Gillbridge Avenue.

The Castle Brewery began production in June 1875 and the move provided the company with a perfect opportunity for expansion. Cuthbert's two sons took over control on his death in 1878 and the business grew under their management until, by the end of the nineteenth century, it had become one of the largest brewery businesses in the North of England.

The founder's grandson, Major Cuthbert Vaux, studied at the Ny Carlsberg Brewery in Copenhagen and elsewhere on the Continent. He was able to use this experience to anticipate the new demand for bottled beers. Vaux was to the forefront of the pioneers of bottled beers, while at the same time continually increasing its tied estate. The small Victorian brewery grew to become an industrial complex covering two acres. Bottling plants were set up in several cities of the North.

The growth of the company continued after the First World War. Several smaller breweries were gobbled up and the number of tied houses thereby increased. Lorimer and Clark of Edinburgh was acquired in 1919, to be followed by several others. In 1927 C. Vaux and Sons Limited amalgamated with its former rival, North Eastern Breweries. The name was later changed to Vaux and Associated Breweries and eventually in 1973 to Vaux Breweries Limited.

During this period other breweries were falling to Vaux – Berwick Brewery in 1937, Blythe and Tyne and Newcastle's Ridley Cutter and Firth in the following year, Hepworth's of Ripon and Whitwell Marks' of Kendal in 1947. Two of the most significant purchases were Thomas Usher and Sons of Edinburgh in 1959 and S. H. Ward and Company Limited in 1972. Vaux has purchased more breweries than many breweries have purchased public houses.

In 1986 Darley's was closed and the same fate was to befall Lorimer and Clark in the following year. Lorimer's, happily, was the subject of a management buyout and now brews under the Caledonian banner.

REAL ALES
Lorimer's Best Scotch (OG 1036) – a light hoppy ale
Vaux Bitter (OG 1038) – a light session bitter
Samson (OG 1041) – a full-flavoured premium bitter

TIED ESTATE
Vaux is the second-largest independent in the country and a list of the tied houses would resemble a mini telephone directory. The beers are easily found in the North East but check that there are real ales available – less than half of the 400-odd houses sell cask-conditioned beers.

CHAPTER ELEVEN

# The North West

### Boddington's Breweries
Subsidiary Regional Brewers
Strangeways Brewery, Manchester

Boddington's has been the ambitious brewery of the North West. Oldham Brewery was purchased in 1982 (to be closed in 1988) and Higson's of Liverpool in 1985, making the company one of the major 'regionals' in Britain. Like most of the larger members of the industry, Boddington's diversified from its sound base of beer production by purchasing both Village Leisure and Thornham Construction in 1987 and by setting up a distribution company (Brewery Link) in 1988.

When Caister and Fray founded Strangeways Brewery in 1778, they sited it just outside the town boundary so that they would be exempt from grain taxes (duties liable to be paid by the residents of the City on any purchase of malted barley). The Boddington family first became involved in the business in the early 1830s and soon showed that 'Boddie's' trait of ambition by acquiring outlets from Crewe to the Fylde. They even purchased the Bridge Brewery at Burton-on-Trent in 1872, not selling it until they were happy that the special properties of the waters at Burton could be simulated at Strangeways by chemical liquor treatment.

Many other breweries were purchased and absorbed by Boddington's over the years. The tables were turned in 1969 when the company itself faced an unwelcome approach from Allied Breweries and seemed at one time likely to fall. Only the company's determination and the help of major shareholders Whitbread and Britannic Assurance held off Allied and allowed a further twenty years of independence.

The company trades mainly within a seventy-mile radius
of Manchester and there are over 530 Boddies' houses. Beer
sales have been promoted by expensive television commercials
(featuring Bill and Alan – 'If you don't get Boddie's, you'll
just get bitter'). Having built up trade in this modern style,
the company (which had a turnover of £96 million in 1988)
resolved in late September 1989 to sell its brewing interests.
A deal was negotiated to sell the breweries to one of its major
shareholders, Whitbread, for £51 million. Fortunately a feature
of the negotiations was to ensure that Boddington's Bitter would
continue to be brewed for at least five years.

REAL ALES
OB Mild (OG 1031) – a dark fruity mild
Mild (OG 1032) – the original Boddie's mild, dark and rich
Bitter (OG 1035) – exceptionally light, hoppy and distinctive
OB Bitter (OG 1037) – the light tasty former Oldham bitter

TIED HOUSES
Boddington's beers are available in about 450 pubs in the
North West. The main concentrations are in Manchester (227
outlets), Merseyside (sixty-four outlets) and Cheshire (twenty-
two in Macclesfield alone). Elsewhere there is plenty of choice:

*Derbyshire*
Glossop: Drover's Arms,
   Grapes Inn, Manor Inn,
   Plough Inn, Star, Surrey
   Arms, Victoria Vaults

New Mills: Grove Inn
Whaley Bridge: White Horse

*North Lancashire and Fylde*
Blackpool: Buccaneer, Cliffs
   Hotel, Dunes Hotel, Park
   House Hotel
Carnforth: Longlands, Melling
   Hall Hotel, Shovel Inn,
   Warton Grange, West View
   Hotel
Fleetwood: Mount Hotel

Lancaster: Hest Bank Hotel,
   Horse and Farrier,
   Lancastrian
Lytham St Anne's: County and
   Commercial, Fairhaven
   Hotel, Victoria Hotel
Morecambe: Bath Hotel, New
   Inn

*South Lancashire*
Preston is excluded from this list as Boddington's is easily
found there – it boasts 35 tied houses.

Accrington: Commercial Hotel,
Duke of Wellington,
Mister Miller's, Royal Oak,
Spinning Jenny
Chorley: Cardwell Arms, The
Dresser's Arms, Euxton
Coaching House, Halfway
House

Darwen: Crown Inn
Rossendale: Buck Inn
Skelmersdale: Busy Bee

*Staffordshire*
Leek: Jester Hotel
Newcastle-under-Lyme:
Borough Arms

Stoke: Gitanas, Huntsman,
Lloyd's Tavern

*Wales*
Abergele: Harp Inn

*Yorkshire*
Batley: Black Labrador
Bradford: Fighting Cock,
Metropole
Brighouse: New Tavern, Red
Rooster
Castleford: Crimea Tavern
Elland: George and Dragon
Halifax: Woodcock
Huddersfield: Bull's Head,
Royal Oak

Leeds: Duck and Drake,
Golden Lion, Painter's Arms
Liversedge: Swan Inn
Marsden: Carriage House
Mirfield: Navigation Inn
Ossett: Park Tavern
Pontefract: Kinsley Hotel

Boddington's ales are also available in all of the Higson pubs listed later in this chapter under that brewery.

**Burtonwood Brewery PLC**
Independent Regional Brewers
Burtonwood, Warrington, Cheshire

They will tell you at Burtonwood that Northerners are very discriminating about what they drink and that it is no accident that the 'Big Taste of Burtonwood' has stood the test of time. Certainly the company has developed into a major regional brewer with around 300 tied houses mainly because of the popularity of its draught ales. 'Burtonwood Country' now stretches from Lancashire down to Powys and from Staffordshire across to the Welsh coast.

James and Jane Forshaw founded the business at Burtonwood in 1867. In a rural setting they produced 4 $1/2$-gallon casks (called 'Tommy Thumpers' by the locals) for licensed premises in the vicinity. By 1884 forty barrels a week were being produced and progress has been maintained ever since. By 1937 it had become necessary to rebuild a great deal of the original premises to increase output and modernise the equipment there.

Burtonwood is another example of a brewery whose owners' past is linked closely with that of local life. Members of the family have held high office in the community and have been involved in many charities. The aim of the company's pubs is to provide a full range of facilities, from quiet country inns to bustling city hotels.

Burtonwood Inns Hotel Group offers quite a range of hotels, providing from seventy-four bedrooms to a mere ten. The company has its own wine and spirit division – J. B. Almond of Standish. On a more historic note, the steam locomotive *Burtonwood Brewer* is on loan to the Llangollen Railway Society and can be seen on Sundays chugging along the line between Llangollen and Pentrefelin.

REAL ALES
Dark Mild (OG 1032) – a rich easy-drinking mild
Bitter (OG 1036.5) – a pale smooth bitter

TIED HOUSES
There are 105 Burtonwood pubs in Lancashire and Greater Manchester and a further 100 in Mid- and North Wales. In areas less well served with the 'Big Taste' the company's real ales can be found at the following:

*Cheshire*

Barthomley: White Lion
Burtonwood: Bridge Inn,
　The Elm Tree
Chester: King's Head,
　Rake Hall
Glazebury: Chat Moss Hotel,
　Raven
Hazel Grove: Royal Oak
Nantwich: Vine

Norley: Carrier's Inn,
　Tiger's Head
Stalybridge: Stamford Arms
Stockport: Golden Lion
Tarporley: Crown Hotel
Warrington: Penny Ferry
Weaverham: Leigh Arms
Winsford: Brighton Belle,
　Raven

*Derbyshire*
Hayfield: George

*Merseyside*

Billinge: Forester's Arms, Holt Arms
Birkenhead: Caledonia
Earlestown: Houghton Arms
Garswood: Stag
Haydock: Chasers
Hoylake: Green Lodge
Liscard: Royal Oak
Liverpool: Bootle Arms, Cambridge, Stanley Arms
Lydiate: Scotch Piper
Newton-le-Willows: Vulcan, Wellington
Rainhill: Manor Farm
Southport: Zetland Hotel
St Helen's: Glassblower

*Shropshire*

Marton: Sun Inn
Shrewsbury: Halfway House, Seven Stars
Whitchurch: Victoria Hotel

*Staffordshire*

Burston: Greyhound
Cheadle: Miner's Rest
Cresswell: Isaac Walton
Eccleshall: Royal Oak
Hilderstone: Roebuck
Ipstones: Red Lion
Kingsley Holt: Blacksmith's Arms
Leek: Red Lion
Meaford: George and Dragon
Rushton: Golden Lion
Salt: Holly Bush
Sandon Bank: Seven Stars
Sheldon: Wharf Inn
Talke: Swan Inn

Holly Bush Inn, Salt

**Bushy's Brew Pub**
Independent Local Brewers
Victoria Street, Douglas, Isle of Man

Bushy's, which used to be Zhivago's, is a bustling pub in the centre of Douglas. It has three bars and live music is often heard from one of them. The boisterous atmosphere is supplemented by the heady aroma of brewing from the cellars. Martin Brunnschweiler has a three-barrel-brew-length malt-extract plant beneath the pub.

Since 1986 he has been turning out two bitters for Bushy's, despite problems with flooding in the cellar when there is a high tide. The premium bitter is known as Old Bushy Tail for most of the year but it becomes Piston for the duration of the TT Races and the Manx Grand Prix.

When Isle of Man Breweries began attempting to sell off forty pubs in 1989, Martin managed to acquire a small second outlet for his beers and, perhaps more importantly, he saw the potential of an expanding free trade on the Isle. He purchased the full-mash equipment from the defunct Brighton Brewery and set about establishing a new brewery in the south of the island. The malt-extract beers at Bushy's are likely to be phased out as Martin concentrates upon a range of full-mash ales from his new brewery. He intends to add a lager, similarly brewed within the constraints of the Manx Pure Beer Act. It should be an interesting time for the drinkers on the Isle of Man.

REAL ALES
Bushy's Bitter (OG 1037) – a light moderately hopped session bitter
Old Bushy Tail (OG 1045) – a sweetish dark premium ale

TIED HOUSE
Douglas: Rover's Return


## Greenall Whitley Plc
Major Regional Brewers
Wilderspool Brewery, Warrington, Lancashire

Greenall's has come very close to joining the Big Six national brewers by virtue both of its size and of its approach to the industry over recent years. The company has pursued a policy of expansion coupled with rationalisation, brushing aside protests as it has closed down regional breweries which it has acquired (notably Wem and Davenport's). The extensive brewing activities have now been concentrated at just two sites.

Realistic observers of the industry do not waste too much of their time bemoaning mergers or takeovers in themselves – it is usually the whim of the independent company as to whether it wishes to take a lucrative offer or not. However, when the inevitable outcome of such a transaction will be loss of a range of local ales, they see plenty of justification for making their complaints. Although Greenall Whitley promises to retain the flavour of beers which are to be brewed elsewhere after the closure of the original brewery, the locals will tell you that something has changed, as they stare forlornly into their pint pots.

Greenall's now brews at the Wilderspool Brewery in Warrington and at Shipstone's in Nottingham. The latter is dealt with in Chapter Nine.

Thomas Greenall and his successors have been brewing at Wilderspool since 1787 but the family actually started in the business in 1762 at St Helen's, 12 miles away. In the eighteenth century it was common for workers to be given beer, a significant element of their diet, as part of their wages. In good times, or as a

particular reward, they would be allowed a more expensive beer
than usual and given 'Allowance Ale' notes. There was plenty of
scope to supply these requirements of a growing population when
Thomas Greenall moved from his job as manager of Parr Stocks'
Brewery in St Helen's and built his own premises in Hardshaw
nearby. By 1786 he was despatching beers to Liverpool, Bolton
and Wales.

It was the need for easy transport to these markets which led
him to Warrington and the River Mersey. He took two partners
into a twenty-five-year deal and they purchased the Saracen's
Head Brewery at Wilderspool for £15,000. The boom in the cotton
industry was bringing more and more mill workers into the area
and they had appreciable thirsts.

Thomas also purchased a small brewery in Liverpool and
his son managed that part of the business. This expansion
proved a little premature, however. During the French wars
there were temporary difficulties at home and increases in
food prices reduced the demand for ale. The Liverpool brewery
suffered badly and was closed down around 1814 – Greenall's'
first venture into rationalisation. Times were certainly hard for
brewers around that period. Thomas had followed the example of
the London brewers and begun producing porter. He also looked
at diversification and took financial stakes in the cotton industry, in a nail-making firm and in a colliery near his Hardshaw
Brewery.

After his death in 1807 the scientific advances of the
industrial revolution were soon to bring prosperity to the
community and thus stability to the brewing industry. He
had seen the company through the worst of the hard times
and it was left to his three sons to begin the expansion. The
partnership at Wilderspool became Lyon and Greenall. Thomas
Lyon was also a partner in Parr, Lyon and Company (which
was to become National Westminster Bank) and the stage was
set for the progress which had seemed inevitable. The company
has never looked back since that day.

A list of mergers and major acquisitions since the First
World War makes interesting reading. Spirits and mineral-
water manufacturers, hoteliers and leisure companies have
been purchased. The major brewing acquisitions have been
Chester Northgate in 1949, Shrewsbury and Wem in 1951,
Magee Marshall of Bolton in 1958, Groves and Whitnall of
Salford in 1961, Wrekin in 1966, Shipstone's in 1978 and
Davenport's of Birmingham in 1986.

Today Greenall's owns thirty-five hotels in the UK (including the De Vere chain), eight in the USA, the Belfry Golf Complex and about 1,900 public houses. It has interests in virtually every aspect of the drinks and leisure industries. In 1988 the company's turnover was more than £243 million.

Despite the closure of Davenport's in 1989 the company did take one step which real-ale drinkers will applaud. A new premium bitter, named after the founder of the firm, was introduced. Thomas Greenall Original was put on sale in a selected 140 flagship pubs.

REAL ALES

Mild (OG 1033.7) – a dark sweetish mild
Local Bitter (OG 1036.5) – a light session bitter
Original (OG 1038.5) – a well-rounded bitter
Thomas Greenall Original (OG 1045) – the new smooth premium
  bitter

TIED STATE

If you are in 'Greenall Country', you will know it (and bear in mind that the territory now extends well into the North Midlands with the acquisition of the Wem and Davenport's estates). There should be little difficulty in finding one of the 1,900 pubs under the various banners. Shipstone's pubs are dealt with separately in Chapter Nine.

The Former Wem Brewery

**Hartley's (Ulverston) Limited**
Subsidiary Regional Brewers
The Old Brewery, Ulverston, Cumbria

Of all the takeovers in the industry in recent years the
purchase of Hartley's by Frederic Robinson Limited of Stockport
in 1982 was perhaps the most friendly. It was a case of one
family brewery acquiring another family brewery. The result
has been that Hartley's has been allowed to continue brewing
its distinctive beers for its customers in Cumbria.

Ulverston, a charter market town since 1280, is an interesting
place to visit, full of nooks and crannies and pleasant discoveries.
The Old Brewery's chimney is a prominent landmark in the
town. A stone plaque built into the blue brick base indicates
that the chimney was erected in 1755 and enlarged in 1882.
Every few years it is repointed and rubbed down with linseed oil.

The Hartley family purchased the brewery in 1896 and
gave its name to the firm shortly after the First World War.
Brewing from Kent and West Country hops and British sugar
and malt, Hartley's soon became famous for its 'beers from the
wood' throughout Lakeland and beyond. Great attention has
always been paid to good cellarmanship in Hartley's tied houses
and you will invariably find a well-nurtured pint in your glass.

When making his maiden speech in the House of Commons in
1983, Cecil Franks MP referred to Ulverston as the birthplace of
Stan Laurel and Hartley's beer: 'For many years much pleasure
has been given to a great number of people by the happy combination of Laurel and Hartley'.

REAL ALES
Mild (OG 1031) – a dark gentle mild
Bitter (OG 1031) – a distinctive session bitter
XB (OG 1040) – a full-flavoured premium bitter

TIED HOUSES
Hartley's houses are compactly placed in Lakeland. As you
might expect there are plenty of them in Ulverston – twenty-
one to be exact. Outside the historic market town you will find
them at:

Ambleside: Golden Rule,
  Outgate, Queen's Head,
  Unicorn

Barrow-in-Furness: Crown,
  Farmer's Arms, King's
  Arms, Ormsgill, Robin Hood,
  Victoria

Bowness: Albert, New Hall
Carnforth: Lunesdale Arms,
  New Inn
Cleator Moor: New Crown
Coniston: Crown, Ship
Dalton-in-Furness: Cavendish
  Arms, Golden Ball, Miner's
  Arms, Prince of Wales
Egremont: Blue Bell

Grange-over-Sands: Crown,
  Hope and Anchor, Pig and
  Whistle, Rose and Crown
  Royal Oak
Kendal: Sawyer's Arms,
  White Hart
Lancaster: Waggon and Horses
Millom: Castle, Red Lion
Milnthorpe: Cross Keys
Whitehaven: Lowther Arms,
  Welsh Arms

And a recent incursion into Yorkshire:

Bentham: Coach House

## Hesket Newmarket Brewery
Home-Brew Pub
Old Crown Barn, Hesket Newmarket, Cumbria

A unique taste of Lakeland can be enjoyed at the Old Crown
Inn, Hesket Newmarket, which is deep in fell country about 10
miles south of Carlisle. Jim Fearnley and Liz Blackwood took
over the pub in December 1986, selling Thwaites' beers. There
was a derelict barn at the back which had obvious potential and
they applied for planning permission to develop it as a brewery
and craft workshops.

Their first brew, in March 1988, was named Blencathra
Bitter after the Saddleback mountain which is not far away.
Sales in the pub of that original beer were so encouraging that
they soon added a very delicate bitter, Wrynose Light Bitter
(named after a Lakeland pass), which Jim says is 'intended for
the safety-conscious'. As a contrast Old Carrock, a strong ale,
followed in December 1988. That beer celebrates the local fell
which can be seen from the fermenting room and it has proved
to be popular all year round rather than just as a winter warmer.

The Hesket Newmarket beers are brewed from malt extract
and crystal malt in a five-and-a-half-barrel-brew-length plant
with mash tun and four fermenters. Currently ten barrels or
more a week can be brewed. There are plans to produce a fourth

ale, an all-mash bitter with an original gravity of 1045, and to begin bottling Old Carrock. The next step will be to expand production so that Jim and Liz can move into the free trade.

Hesket Newmarket is signposted from both the B5305 and the B5299. It is at the quieter northern end of the Lake District in an area of great interest to geology students. As well as the natural beauty of the fells there is an abundance of abandoned mineral workings in the locality to attract visitors. Drop in at the Old Crown for a taste of its distinctive beers in a splendid setting.

REAL ALES

Wrynose Light Bitter (OG 1027) – one of the lightest session beers brewed

Blencathra Bitter (OG 1035) – a full-bodied bitter with good hop content

Old Carrock (OG 1060) – a rich fruity strong ale

## Higson's Brewery
Subsidiary Regional Brewers
Stanhope Street, Liverpool, Merseyside

The only remaining brewery on Merseyside lost its independence in 1985. It is perhaps ironic that the main reason for the takeover by Boddington's was to acquire the lager production potential of the firm. Fortunately the real ales from Higson's are still available, often side by side with 'Boddie's' on the bar.

When William Harvey founded the Cheapside Brewery in Liverpool, it was really as a sideline to his main business of building and bricklaying. The modest brewery was passed down the Harvey family line until 1875 when Daniel Higson, who had been a book-keeper with the company, purchased the business. When the lease of the brewery came up for renewal in 1909, the family set about looking for new premises and five years later moved to a new site in Upper Parliament Street.

At the end of the First World War, Higson's was acquired by a firm of wine and spirits merchants, J. Sykes and Company. The following years saw a period of rapid expansion based upon the purchase and closure of small local breweries – Spragg's of Wallasey and Jones' of Knotty Ash, for example. In 1937 Sykes, Higson's and Jones were wound up and the assets used to launch a new public company, Higson's Brewery Limited. A major redevelopment scheme to modernise the brewery and increase lager production was begun in 1978. The new lager brewhouse which was built on land adjacent to the brewery attracted attention from Manchester and in 1985, shortly after celebrating 200 years of brewing, Higson's was acquired by Boddington's.

Higson's beers will survive only if the parent company is satisfied that they are holding or improving their market position – try a couple of pints if you are in the area, to help the cause. The takeover of the group by Whitbread in 1989 casts even more doubt on the future of the Liverpool brewery.

REAL ALES
Mild (OG 1033) – a clean-tasting dark mild
Bitter (OG 1038) – a refreshing well-hopped bitter

OUTLETS
There are still 100 outlets for Higson's beers. As you might expect they are most common on Merseyside (there are thirty in Liverpool alone). There are also plenty of pubs for the holiday-maker in North Lancashire (eight in Blackpool). The remainder are listed below:

*Cheshire*
Chester: Bull and Stirrup, Bunbury Arms, Offa's Dyke
Crewe: Raven Inn
Macclesfield: Cock and Pheasant, Crown, Fool's Nook

Mobberley: Chapel House Inn
Nantwich : Malbank Hotel
Warrington: Bewsey Farm, Britannia Bell
Wilmslow: Boddington Arms, Railway Hotel

*South Lancashire*
Blackburn: Brewer's Arms, Forrest Arms, Quarryman's, Sam's Bar
Ormskirk: Ring O' Bells, Royal Coaching House, Yew Tree

Oswaldtwistle: Golden Cross
Preston: Continental, Legh Arms, Lord Nelson

*Greater Manchester*
Altrincham: Gardner's Arms
Bolton: Anchor Inn, Churchill's
Manchester: Brewer's Arms, Gardener's Arms, Half Moon, Old Garratt

Middleton: Albion Inn
Ramsbottom: Railway Hotel
Wigan: Plough and Harrow

*Staffordshire*
Newcastle-under-Lyme:
 Mainwaring Arms
Stoke: Coach House

*Yorkshire*
Batley: Rose of York
Huddersfield: Scapehouse Inn,
 Spinners


**Joseph Holt Plc**
Independent Regional Brewers
Derby Brewery, Empire Street, Manchester

Holt's Derby Brewery, near Victoria Station, is solidly part
of Manchester and its fortunes have ebbed and flowed with
those of the city. From humble beginnings in a small brewhouse
behind a pub, originating in 1849, the company has grown into
a strong regional brewer.

Joseph Holt supplied local pubs from his small brewery
until 1855, when he took over the Dulcie Bridge Brewery
on what was then York Street. He was able to expand his
trade, providing financial assistance to his customers in return
for outlets for his ales and porter in much the same way as
the major brewers operate today. Soon after the Dulcie Bridge
premises had become inadequate for his needs he purchased a
piece of land near York Street in 1860. The Derby Brewery was
erected and the family has been there ever since.

The increases in the company's tied estate and the improvements and extensions to the brewery have followed the economic
surges of the past 130 years. By 1871 there was a staff of eight
and in 1872 a new boiler was installed for steam power. Joseph
passed control to his son Edward ten years later and the business
continued to prosper. In the late 1880s twenty-seven new tied
houses were purchased and a period of great prosperity was
experienced.

Edward Holt was in control of the Derby Brewery for
forty-six years until his death in 1928. He was a prominent
public figure, having the rare distinction of being lord mayor
of the city for two consecutive years. In 1916 he was made a
baronet. His son Sir Edward steered the company through the
difficult period of the Depression in the early 1930s, avoiding

making any redundancies despite the fact that demand for
beer had dropped by about a third. When he died in 1968,
he had been working at the brewery for no less than sixty-four
years.

Holt's was one of those stalwart breweries which stood firm
in the face of the keg beer 'revolution'. Traditional beers were
brewed throughout the 1960s, regardless of national trends, and
when real ale reacquired its popularity the company was able to
profit from that foresight. In 1983 the firm turned its attention, in
true Joseph Holt style, to the free trade, and the well-loved beers
from the Derby Brewery have become more and more common
in the North West.

REAL ALES
Mild (OG 1033) – dark and rich but with a good hop content
Bitter (OG 1039) – a distinctive and well-hopped bitter

TIED HOUSES
Holt's own fifty-nine managed houses and a further thirty-six
occupied by tenants. Unlike several brewers in the region the
firm has retained a geographically compact estate. In Greater
Manchester you will find a Holt's pub in most localities. Try
also:

Bolton: Black Dog, Rosehill
  Tavern
Bury: Blue Bell
Cheadle: Griffin Hotel,
  Junction Hotel
Heaton Mersey: Griffin Hotel

Hollingwood: Bridgewater
  Hotel, King's Arms
Padgate: Millhouse
Rochdale: Cross Yates,
  Navigation
Westhoughton: White Lion

In Manchester the two most recent acquisitions are the Crown
and Cushion in Corporation Street and the Hibb in Lathbury
Road.


**Hyde's Anvil Brewery Limited**
Independent Regional Brewers
46 Moss Lane West, Manchester

Annie Hyde might sound like a character from the Wild West
but she was a famous lady of the North West. The prosperity of
this, the smallest of the old Manchester breweries, owes a lot to
Annie's determination. She ran the company for fifty-six years

from 1880 when her father died. With her brother William she built up a solid business with an expanding estate of public houses.

The early history of Hyde's was a troubled one. Thomas Shaw, a wealthy colliery owner from Sheffield, purchased the Audenshaw Brewery for his two youngest sons in 1860 but they did not make a success of it. Within a few years the business was transferred to two of his grandsons, Alfred and Ralph Hyde. Because of an inferior water supply the Hyde brothers fared little better there. Recognising the problem, they moved to the Mayfield Brewery, Ardwick. Ralph left the partnership in 1877. When Alfred died, his wife Emma was left to run the business until her children came of age. Annie and William took over as soon as they were old enough and the company at last began to establish itself as a force in Manchester brewing.

Even so, more moves were necessary. The Mayfield Brewery was showing signs of decay and smaller premises were taken in Fairfield Street. This proved to be a mistake because demand for Hyde's was increasing. The next home was Rusholme Street, but that lasted only ten years. In 1899 the family business at last settled at the Queen's Brewery in Brooks Bar – the present site. The property had been built around the time when Thomas Shaw first introduced his sons to brewing.

In 1944 the name was changed from Hyde's Queen Brewery to Hyde's Anvil Brewery. The buildings may be Victorian but modern stainless-steel equipment has been installed in recent years. The brewhouse was completely re-equipped in 1981 yet the methods of production remain entirely traditional. Hyde's is one of the distinctive tastes of Manchester and is one of the few regional breweries still to provide a choice of two milds.

REAL ALES
Mild (OG 1032) – a dark fruity mild
Light (OG 1034) – a refreshing light mild
Bitter (OG 1037) – a well-balanced bitter
Strong Ale (OG 1080) – a powerful warming drink

TIED HOUSES
The two areas where you will find Hyde's are Greater Manchester and around Wrexham in North Wales. Examples are given below:

*Clwyd*
Bwlchgwyn: King's Head
Cymau: Olde Talbot
Moss: Bird in Hand
Summerhill: Crown Inn

*Greater Manchester*

Affetside: Pack Horse
Altrincham: Baker's Arms
Ashton-on-Mersey: Old Plough
Cheadle: Star
Didsbury: Gateway
Duckinfield: Newborough

Gatley: Horse and Farrier
Hulme: Hope Inn
Little Lever: Horseshoe Inn
Manchester: Grey Horse
Timperley: Quarry Bank

**Isle of Man Breweries Limited**
Independent Regional Brewers
Falcon Brewery, Douglas, Isle of Man

The Manx way of doing things has always been rather different from that of the mainland. With a tax rate of 15p in the £ and cats of reduced length, there is an insular non-conformity about the place, a singular image that has been apparent in the brewing industry. The Manx Pure Beer Act permits the use of only malt, hops and sugar in brewing. This German-style approach has maintained a high standard and almost all of the beer sold has been traditional and dispensed without pressure. However, the relationships between breweries and their tenants have sometimes been described as feudal.

Two breweries served the island until 1986. The Castletown Brewery of Victoria Road, Castletown, owned thirty-six pubs and produced for them a standard hoppy bitter and a mild fashioned out of the same ale by the addition of caramel. Okell and Sons brewed a mild and a best bitter in the impressive Victorian Falcon Brewery for about seventy public houses. This healthy competition ceased in 1986 when the two companies merged to form Isle of Man Breweries Limited.

In 1989 the chairman of the new company, John Cowley, cast a sideways glance at the MMC Report on the mainland (although it did not directly affect him) and decided that Manx men also deserved more choice. He took the decision to sell off half of his 100 or so pubs and allow them to go to the free trade. At the same time he announced that Isle of Man Breweries would be floated as a public company.

There was comparatively little interest in his surplus public houses, even from brewers, and they sold only slowly. Nevertheless, the licensed trade on the island was thrown into understandable confusion. The pubs marketed were mostly of low turnover – the island is generally considered to have too many pubs. It remains to be seen how the trade on the Isle of Man settles down after such turmoil.

REAL ALES
Okell's Mild (OG 1035) – a dark refreshing mild
Okell's Bitter (OG 1036) – a hoppy session bitter
Castletown Bitter (OG 1036) – a more malty standard bitter

TIED ESTATE
When on the island, you should find the local beers without difficulty. However, with half of the estate either sold or for sale, there can be no certainty of the company's outlets for some time.

## Jennings Brothers Plc
Independent Regional Brewers
Castle Brewery, Cockermouth, Cumbria

Jennings' Brewery stands at the confluence of the rivers Derwent and Cocker. It was on that site that William de Meschines, brother of the Earl of Cumberland, built his castle shortly after the Norman Conquest. One of the attractions for him was that there was an ample water supply for times of emergency. About 800 years later the Jennings family, who brewed not far away at Lorton, sampled that water from a well and decided that they too would profit from establishing themselves at Cockermouth.

Their original business had been in operation in the Vale of Lorton since 1828 and the move to the new premises took place in 1890. The operation was set up as a complete one, with an impressive sandstone maltings nearby (now, sadly, closed). Cumbrian ales have been brewed on the site ever since.

Over the decades the company's estate of tied houses has gradually been increased. Between the wars licensed premises were purchased from Faulder's Brewery of Keswick and in 1972 the closure of the Carlisle State Management Scheme (Britain's famous 'nationalised' brewery) brought further acquisitions. The tied estate now numbers seventy-seven pubs, which are listed below. Naturally such expansion attracted the vultures of the industry. In 1973 it required family determination and loyalty from the shareholders to enable the company to resist takeover overtures.

The original brewhouse, with its 100-barrel length and 1936 Briggs mash tun, was replaced by a modern version in the 1980s. These days the brewery in the market-town setting has a 150-barrel copper and a hopback to match, as well as plenty of other up-to-date equipment.

Besides the company's own tied houses, some Tetley pubs sell Jennings' ales and there is an increasing presence in the free trade.

REAL ALES

Mild (OG 1034) – a clean-tasting dark mild
Bitter (OG 1034) – a refreshing bitter with good hop content
Marathon (OG 1041) – a well-balanced premium bitter

TIED HOUSES

Appleby: Crown and Cushion
Aspatria: Fox and Hounds, Letters Inn
Bassenthwaite: Sun Inn
Bothel: Greyhound, Queen's Head
Bowness-on-Solway: King's Arms
Braithwaite: Royal Oak
Brigham: Wheatsheaf Inn
Camerton: Black Tom
Carlisle: Maltster's Arms, Woolpack
Cockermouth: Bowling Green, Bush Hotel, Grey Coat Huntsman Hotel, Rampant Bull, Roundabout, Swan Inn, Tithe Barn
Crosby-on-Eden: Stag Inn
Cumwhinton: Lowther Arms
Deanscales: Beehive
Dovenby: Ship Inn

Drigg: Victoria Hotel
Eaglesfield: Black Cock
Egremont: Horn of Egremont, Ship Launch Inn
Embleton: Wheatsheaf Inn
Gilcrux: Mason's Arms
Great Broughton: Brewery House, Punch Bowl
Greystoke: Sportsman Inn
Harrington: Golden Lion, Station Hotel
Hensingham: Sun Inn
High Harrington: Galloping Horse
Ireby: Sun Inn
Keswick: Bank Tavern Central Hotel, Four in Hand, Lake Road Vaults Oddfellow's Arms, Pack Horse Inn, Pheasant, Two Dogs Inn
Kirkbride: Bush Inn

Black Cock, Eaglesfield

Kirby Lonsdale: Red Dragon
Lorton: Wheatsheaf Inn,
    Horseshoe Inn
Lowca: Ship Inn
Maryport: Crown, Golden Lion
Monkhill: Drover's Rest
Newlands: Swinside Inn
Oulton: Bird in Hand
Penrith: Salutation Hotel
Portinscale: Farmer's Arms
Rowrah: Stork Hotel
Scales: White Horse

St Bees: Oddfellow's Arms
Threlkeld: Horse and Farrier
Whitehaven: Anchor Vaults,
    Dolphin, Golden Fleece,
    Jubilee Inn, Puncheon Inn,
    Royal Hotel, Royal Standard
Wigton: Lion and Lamb,
    Victoria Hotel
Workington: Coastguard Inn,
    Commercial Inn, George IV,
    Nag's Head, Sailor's
    Return, Steam Packet

THE NORTH WEST 253

## Lass O'Gowrie Brew House Company
Subsidiary Home-Brew Pub
Lass O'Gowrie, Charles Street, Manchester

This is one of Whitbread's ventures into small beer. The Manchester city centre pub has an Inn Brewing malt-extract plant installed in the cellar. As is the fashion, the equipment can be viewed from the bar while you sip your pint of the distinctive beer.

The ales are brewed in four-barrel batches for the Lass O'Gowrie alone and provide yet another choice for the well-served drinkers of Manchester. Opened in 1983, the operation has proved to be one of the more successful examples of the occasional incursion into the home-brew scene by national brewers.

REAL ALES
LOG 35 (OG 1035) – a distinctive malt-extract bitter
LOG 42 (OG 1042) – a well-rounded malty premium bitter
LOG 56 (OG 1056) – an occasional rich strong ale

## J.W. Lees and Company Ltd
Independent Regional Brewers
Greengate Brewery, Middleton Junction, Manchester

In true Lancashire tradition J.W. Lees was born out of the cotton industry. John Lees had been a cotton manufacturer all his life but when he retired in 1828 he fancied trying his hand at something different. He purchased several cottages and a parcel of land at Middleton Junction and went into business as a brewer of ales and porter.

By 1888 the business had flourished to such an extent that it was necessary to build the larger Greengate Brewery nearby. It was then considered to be one of the finest breweries in the land. Greengate is still the company's headquarters but it has been modernised, extended and improved to keep pace with changes in the industry.

John Willie Lees is proud that its beers are brewed in the time-honoured way, using first-class malt and hops – just as they were more than 160 years ago. Several prizes have been won at Brewex exhibitions and at the 1981 Great Western Beer Festival Moonraker Strong Ale was judged first in its class. Lees' lager was one of the first beers of its type to be brewed in Britain and you can sometimes find it, the only cask-conditioned lager on the stands, at beer festivals.

Greengate is very much a community brewery. Sponsorship of the local football club and a famous brass band are well established and other deals involve the company in supporting rugby league, tennis, cricket and squash. Over 100 local clubs are supplied with beers from Lees. The company owns the renowned Willoughby's in Cross Street, Manchester, where you will find about 11,000 bottles of wine and spirits on the shelves (with a further 60,000 in the cellar). Customers travel from all over the country to explore this Aladdin's Cave of wines and spirits.

One of the more interesting places to sample the beers of John Willie Lees is the White Grouse. No, it is not in Manchester – it can be found among the snow-capped mountains of France in the skiing resort of Flaire. The popular story is that a Lees company director who holidays in the area could not bear to be without his pint of Lees', so he built a pub. The truth is that the management of the Flaire complex asked a Lees director to provide a social centre. A brewery architect designed the pub and Lees' beers are shipped there regularly by container.

REAL ALES
GB Mild (OG 1032) – a light mild brewed to the local taste
Bitter (OG 1038) – smooth with a creamy head
Moonraker (OG 1074) – a powerful rich winter ale

TIED HOUSES
Lees' beers are common in and around Manchester, extending into Cheshire. There are also a number of tied houses in North Wales which are popular with holiday-makers – those selling real ale are listed below:

Abergele: Bee Hotel, Bull Hotel
Almwch: Bull Bay Hotel
Benilech Bay: Glanrafon Hotel
Brymbo: George and Dragon
Bryntrillyn: Sportsman's Arms
Carrog: Grouse Inn

Cerrig-y-Drudion: White Lion
Colwyn Bay: Imperial Hotel
Corwen: Owain Glyndwr Hotel
Denbigh: Old Vaults
Gyffylliog: Red Lion
Halkyn: Britannia Inn

Llanbedr-y-Cennin: Ye Olde
  Bull
Llandegla: Crown Hotel
Llandudno: Links' Hotel
Llandulas: Dulas Arms
Llanfihangel: Crown Inn
Llangefri: Railway Inn
Llansannan: Red Lion

Menai Bridge: Anglesey Arms
Newbridge: Black Lion
Rhosneigr: Maelog Lake Hotel
Rowen: Ty Gwyn Hotel
St Asaph: New Inn
Trearddur Bay: Trearddur Bay
  Hotel
Tyn-ye-Groes: Red Lion


## Mitchell's of Lancaster (Brewers) Limited
Independent Regional Brewers
Moor Lane, Lancaster, Lancashire

'Born in 1880 and still brewing strong. Brewed by the family, run by the family and enjoyed by the family.' Such is the proud boast of Mitchell's. It was William Mitchell who founded the firm in the nineteenth century and his Central Brewery was much admired in Victorian circles. To have his business described by a contemporary commentator as 'one of the most perfect and complete establishments of its kind in the Kingdom' must have been satisfying for the founder.

The brewery flourished quickly and William built up an estate based upon Lancaster but soon extending into the towns and countryside beyond. He used an exceptionally deep well to draw up water, which analysis showed to be comparable with that of Burton-upon-Trent. A double-action (ram-and-suction) pump was used with the capability of raising 1,600 gallons per hour. Soon William extended into adjoining premises so that he could employ some of the abundant liquid resource for an aerated water manufactory.

Great emphasis was placed upon purity. William used the most up-to-date equipment available and had impressive laboratories for quality control. Only pure malt and hops were employed for making the beers with 'no deleterious chemicals whatever entering into their composition'. This determination to produce quality ales has served the family well over the years. Mitchell's was one of the independents well able to hold its own against the tide of acquisitions and mergers which swept across the country.

The present company is run by William's two grandsons and now operates from the old Yates and Jackson Brewery. A tied estate of fifty pubs is served and Mitchell's promises you 'great traditional ales served with old-fashioned hospitality'. This is no idle publicity banter from one of the most respected independents in England.

REAL ALES
Mild (OG 1035) – a dark satisfying mild
Bitter (OG 1036) – a well-balanced malty bitter
ESB (OG 1050) – a rich strong premium bitter

TIED ESTATE
Not surprisingly, Mitchell's is well represented in Lancaster itself (where there are twenty pubs). Otherwise there are plenty of the company's houses to choose from in Cumbria and North Lancashire:

*Cumbria*
Burton-in-Kendal: King's Arms
Hale: King's Arms

Milnthorpe: Coach and Horses
Ulverston: Bay Horse
Whittington: Dragon's Head

*Lancashire*
Arkholme: Bay Horse
Bolton-le-Sands: Blue Anchor, Royal Hotel
Carnforth: Cross Keys, Royal Station
Clifton: Windmill Tavern
Cockerham: Manor Inn
Dolphinholme: Fleece Hotel
Galgate: New Inn
Glasson Dock: Victoria Hotel
Halton: White Lion
Heaton-with-Oxcliffe: Golden Ball

Heysham: Old Hall, Royal Hotel
High Bentham: Brown Cow, Royal Oak
Hornby: Castle Hotel
Low Bentham: Punch Bowl
Morecambe: Bradford Arms, Clarendon Hotel, William Mitchell, York Hotel
Over Kellet: Eagle's Head
Preston: Bay Horse
Warton: Black Bull
Wray: George and Dragon

## Moorhouses
Single-Pub and Free-Trade Brewers
Moorhouse Street, Burnley, Lancashire

Moorhouses is not so much a new brewery as a revitalised old one. The company had concentrated upon producing hop bitters (used in the manufacture of shandy) for some years before Michael Ryan became one of the revivalists by beginning to brew beers in 1979. Within two years the firm was taken over by a leisure concern. A further change of ownership in 1985 was followed by the purchase of the brewing side by Bill Parkinson. Since then stability has been apparent and the spread of Moorhouses' beers through the free trade has been marked.

By 1988 the original plant, of ten-barrel capacity, had become insufficient for the growing demand and a new twenty-five barrel plant of stainless steel was installed. The brewer is Richard Wintle and he maintains an average output of eighty barrels per week, although there is potential to increase that to 125 barrels if required. The Premier Bitter is a very popular tasty standard bitter, whereas Pendle Witches' Brew (with its emblem of a witch astride her broomstick) has gained quite a reputation among strong-ale lovers. Six times a year an even stronger Old Ale is mashed to make them still happier.

The brewery is quite inconspicuous, situated within a row of old terraced properties, but from it the company delivers to a large number of free houses. Moorhouses is found in an area stretching from Lancaster to Manchester and from Blackpool to Leeds. In addition there is one tied house – the General Scarlett in Accrington Road, Burnley.

REAL ALES
Premier Bitter (OG 1036) – well-rounded and tasty
Pendle Witches' Brew (OG 1050) strong and full of flavour
Old Ale (OG 1065) – an occasional dark winter ale


TIED HOUSE
*Lancashire*
Burnley: General Scarlett


FREE TRADE
*Lancashire*
Blackpool (Clevelys): Royal Hotel
Croston: Black Horse
Newchurch: Lamb Inn
Whitewell: Inn

*Greater Manchester*
Rochdale: Cemetery

**New Fermor Arms**
Home-Brew Pub
Station Road, Rufford, Lancashire

The New Fermor Arms, built in 1975, is a large public house with seating for 300 in its olde-worlde-style interior. It's car park can accommodate 200 vehicles. Rufford is on the A59 north of Ormskirk.

Alan Mawdsley began brewing his Fettler's Bitter there in 1976. In 1981 he was tempted by an offer from the brewing giant Allied's Tetley-Walker division and he sold the place, including the brewhouse. He was back again in 1985 after a spell as a non-brewing publican.

To all appearances nothing much has changed since the mid-1970's. Alan still brews two and a half barrels a week for the pub with a malt-extract plant. You will have to stop at the prominent public house if you want to try the distinctive beer, which is brewed with the specific intention of keeping the customers there in good fettle.

REAL ALE
Fettler's Bitter (OG 1038) – light but fruity

**Oak Brewery**
Free-Trade Brewers
Merseyton Road, Ellesmere Port, Cheshire

The latest addition to Tony Allen's impressive range of full-mash ales is called Wobbly Bob. It is the only beer named after a cat. Bob was the resident feline at the Riverside Hotel, Chester. Do not believe anyone who tells you that he only had three legs – the truth is that he suffered from a nervous disorder which caused him to fall over whenever he tried to turn a corner. You might develop a similar affliction, if you over-indulge in the strong ale named after poor Wobbly Bob.

Tony worked on the production side of the brewery industry at Sheffield and Runcorn before he decided to set up his own business. He took some industrial space at Ellesmere Port in 1982 and began brewing for the free trade. There is a maximum fourteen-barrel brew-length and he has three fermenting vessels which enable him to brew up to forty barrels per week. Even so, with free-trading conditions improving all the time in the North West, Tony is looking to move to larger premises.

When West Riding Brewery closed after its second fire, it was decided that the prize-winning Tyke Bitter should not disappear. Tony Allen now brews it under licence and delivers it (together with other ales from his range) over the Pennines to the Barge and Barrel in West Yorkshire. In addition he supplies a number of free houses over a wide geographical area and several steam railway concerns sell Oak Brewery beers.

REAL ALES
Oak Best Bitter (OG 1038) – a light well-hopped bitter
Tyke Bitter (OG 1038) – a Yorkshire-style bitter
Old Oak Ale (OG 1044) – a sweetish premium bitter
Double Dagger (OG 1050) – a full-flavoured stronger bitter
Porter (OG 1050) – a dark fruity porter
Wobbly Bob (OG 1060) – a rich strong ale: walk only in
    a straight line!

FREE TRADE
    *Greater Manchester*
Manchester: Marble Arch

    *Merseyside*
Liverpool: Ye Cracke

    *South Yorkshire*
Thurlstone: Huntsman
Wentworth: George and Dragon

    *West Yorkshire*
Elland: Barge and Barrel

**Frederic Robinson Limited**
Independent Regional Brewers
Unicorn Brewery, Stockport, Cheshire

The familiar unicorn of Robinson's trade mark derives from the first pub which William Robinson purchased in September 1838 – the Unicorn Inn, Lower Hillgate. Although he ran the pub as a retail outlet only, his son Frederic entered the business in 1865 and began to brew for the bar, as was then the fashion.

Within a short period Frederic had expanded from the role of a publican brewer to that of a common brewer. He purchased his first licensed house, the Railway at Marple Bridge, and supplied several others. The old Unicorn Inn has long gone but the Railway, now known as the Royal Scot, is still in the company's estate.

By the time that Frederic's eldest son William joined his father, the firm was proudly in possession of two pubs and a horse and dray. From that point expansion was steady. When Frederic died in 1890, there were twelve public houses. Subsequently Schofield's Portland Brewery of Ashton-under-Lyne and Kay's Atlas Brewery of Ardwick were acquired and the regional nature of the business had become established.

William's son, another Frederic, was one of the first brewers in the country to hold a science degree. He set up the family firm's first laboratory and constructed a new brewhouse. Quality control was introduced to ensure that Robinson's beers are consistent and to the company's exacting requirements. The fact that they are served in many delightful country pubs can be attributed to Sir John Robinson, who, much against the trend, pursued a policy of buying rural pubs in the 1930s.

In 1973 work began on a new bottling and packaging complex on land in Bredbury and a kegging plant followed in 1981. The traditional beers were not neglected and the company was well able to respond to the increasing demand for real ales.

Robinson's beers are available over a large area of the North West and from North Wales across to parts of the Midlands. The most northerly outpost in North Lancashire was extended when Hartley's of Ulverston was acquired in 1982.


REAL ALES

Best Mild (OG 1032) – a light refreshing mild
Bitter (OG 1035) – a hoppy session bitter
Best Bitter (OG 1041) – sharp and hoppy but of fuller flavour
Old Tom (OG 1080) – a rich and very strong ale


TIED HOUSES

Away from the heartland of Robinson country (which includes thirty-one pubs in North Wales) you will also find the beers in Derbyshire and North Lancashire.

*Derbyshire*

Ashton-in-the-Water: Bull's Head
Ashwood Dale: Devonshire Arms
Bakewell: Manners
Buxton: Grove Hotel, New Inn
Castleton: Bull's Head
Chapel-en-le-Frith: Jolly Carter, New Inn, Old Pack Horse, Shoulder of Mutton
Darley Dale: Square and Compass
Dove Holes: Wheatsheaf
Flagg: Duke of York
Glossop: Friendship, Surrey Arms
Great Longston: St Crispin, White Lion
Hurdlow: Bull i' th' Thorn
Longnor: Ye Olde Cheshire Cheese
Peak Dale: Midland
Sparrowpit: Wanted Inn
Tideswell: Anchor Inn

*North Lancashire*

Balderstone: Myerscough
Catforth: Running Pump
Garstang: Royal Oak
Preston: Black Horse

## Daniel Thwaites PLC
Independent Regional Brewers
Star Brewery, Blackburn, Lancashire

Daniel Thwaites was an excise officer who in the course of his duties visited many small breweries in the Blackburn area. He decided that rather than levying taxes on the local beers he ought to see if he could brew a better pint himself. The original Thwaites Eanam Brewery dated from 1807. Daniel chose a site which had a natural well, so that he could be guaranteed a source of water for the brewing process.

Having studied the publican and common brewers at first hand, Daniel Thwaites set about trying to brew the perfect pint. The company has adhered to this simple philosophy ever since. It has remained an independent family concern, with control being handed down from one generation to the next. The present chairman, John Yerburgh, is the great-great-grandson of the founder.

Many awards have been won by Thwaites' beers. In 1983 the bitter won the ultimate accolade of the British brewing industry when it was voted Britain's Best Beer at Brewex. In 1986 the company became the first ever to win the title of Britain's Best Mild for a third time at the CAMRA British Beer Festival.

Traditions die hard at Thwaites'. The famous shire horses are still employed in a working capacity, delivering to local houses as they did over 180 years ago and on display as show horses at major events around the country. A vintage 1935 Bedford dray-lorry can also be seen at selected functions.

The Star Brewery is one of the most up-to-date in Europe. When new fermenting vessels were installed in 1986 HRH Princess Anne was at the brewery to commission them. A subsidiary company, Shire Inns, was formed to control the residential side of the business and Thwaites Inns was set up to handle the managed house estate in 1985.

REAL ALES
Mild (OG 1032) – a dark tasty mild
Best Mild (OG 1034) – the famous rich prize-winning mild
Bitter (OG 1036) – a well-balanced hoppy bitter

TIED HOUSES
Thwaites' houses are not difficult to find. There are over 400 of them and the concentration is in Lancashire. A few examples are listed below:

*Cheshire*
Bunbury: Dysart Arms
Congleton: Lion and Swan
Rainow: Highwayman

*Lancashire*
Accrington: Boars Head
Bartle: Sitting Goose
Blackburn: Havelock Inn
Blackpool: Empress
Burnley: Queen's Head
Clitheroe: Buck
Darwen: Golden Cup
Eaves: Plough
Elswick: Boot and Shoe
Forton: New Holly
Glasson Dock: Caribou
Lancaster: Brown Cow
Middleton: Old Roof Tree
Morecambe: George
Osbaldeston: Bay Horse
Paythorne: Palmer's Arms
Pilling: Golden Ball
Preston: George
Tarleton: Cock and Bottle
Weir: Weir

*West Yorkshire*
Bradford: Horse and Farrier
Brighouse: Bandsman
Dewsbury: Aletasters
Thornton: Great Northern

## West Coast Brewing Company Limited
Single-Pub and Free-Trade Brewers
King's Arms, Helm's Shaw Walk, Charlton-on-Medlock,
Manchester.

Brendan Dobbin is one of the great new characters of British brewing. After qualifying with a master's degree in brewing and malting at Heriot-Watt, Edinburgh, he gained his practical experience around the world. On his return he first looked at the possibility of setting up his own business on the west of Ireland – hence the name of his company. Soon he realised that there was insufficient demand for his considerable talents there and he settled instead at the fire-damaged King's Arms in a suburb of Manchester.

The large Victorian pub was carefully refurbished to his own taste – very traditional, with plenty of brass and copper. Brendan installed his brewing equipment in the roomy cellars there. Although he has been brewing only since May 1989, it looks as if he will quickly outgrow the makeshift brewery.

His experience of brewing was gained in many countries, including the USA, China and Africa, and it has given him the expertise to produce an amazing range of international beers. Using a filtration plant which he designed himself, he can produce at least half a dozen different lagers within a two-week period. Traditional tastes are catered for with a mild, two bitters and a stout. It is all achieved with a maximum five-barrel-brew-length full-mash down there in the cellars. Brendan says that he is reversing the trend of the big boys by 'making beer interesting'. You cannot argue with that!

The King's Arms is a true family pub. It is also the only pub where you will find a Dobbin Health Warning on prominent display. Brendan's bottled beers carry on their labels a caution against the perils of over-indulgence. The same warning stands boldly behind the bar: 'The products, while entirely wholesome in nature, contain alcohol, excessive intake of which is not recommended.' The industry could do with a few more colourful characters like Brendan. West Coast beers are likely to make quite a splash in the free trade as they become better known.

REAL ALES
Mild (OG 1035) – a subtle mild of medium colour
Best Bitter (OG 1038) – well-hopped and refreshing
Extra Special (OG 1060) – a pale full-bodied strong ale

FREE TRADE
Keighley: Grinning Rat
Manchester: Crescent, Marble Arch
Stockport: Old Vic

## Yates' Brewery
Free-Trade Brewers
Ghyll Farm, Westnewton, Aspatria, Cumbria

Carole and Peter Yates have an idyllic life not far from the coast in north Cumbria. Their brewery is the only industry of any kind other than farming in Westnewton and they combine it with a smallholding which specialises in goats' milk. Peter had gained experience in brewing in Wolverhampton, Leicester, Burton upon Trent and Warrington before he joined Jennings of Cockermouth. When he left that post in 1986, he decided to keep his farm and to try his hand at brewing for the free trade. It was a happy decision.

Peter moved some goats out of the old barn and built his own brewery. He picked up second-hand equipment from here and there and assembled an efficient twelve-barrel-brew-length stainless-steel system. Old cellar tanks which each take four barrels are used as fermenting vessels and there are nine of them there. Average output is twenty-four barrels per week but this can be increased to thirty-six when the thirsty summer visitors are in the area.

Ghyll Farm is in a tranquil location. Peter and Carole can watch everything that happens in the village as they go about their daily business. It is not uncommon for the villagers to drop in for a chat and perhaps to cadge a drink. Although the backdrop is of a gentle pace of life, Yates' Brewery is a busy and successful place. The splendid beers are very popular in the free trade.

REAL ALE
Bitter (OG 1035) – a subtle well-balanced bitter
Best Cellar (OG 1052) – a tasty strong mild of character

FREE TRADE
*Borders*
Bailey: Dog and Gun

*Cumbria*

Allonby: Ship Inn
Appleby: Royal Oak
Aspatria: Grapes Hotel
Barngates: Drunken Duck
Braithwaite: Coledale Inn
Bromfield: Greyhound
Keswick: George Hotel

Langdale: Old Dungeon Ghyll
Nether Wasdale: Screes Hotel
Sandwith: Dog and Partridge
Strawberry Bank: Mason's
  Arms
Wasdale: Wasdale Head Inn
Yanwath: Yanwath Gate Inn

CHAPTER TWELVE

# *Wales*

## S.A. Brain and Company Limited
Independent Regional Brewers
The Old Brewery, Cardiff

Samuel Arthur Brain and his uncle Joseph Benjamin Brain purchased the old Brewery together with the Albert Hotel, which stood in front of it, in October 1882. The buildings dated back to 1713. Today nothing other than a section of wall remains of that original brewery, the last part having been demolished in 1919.

Brain's is one of those companies whose history is entwined with that of its city. S.A. Brain was mayor of Cardiff in 1899-1900 and was a keen supporter of many local charities. His prowess as a brewer is best evidenced by the expansion of the company under his direction. In 1882 beer was supplied to just eleven pubs and output was around 100 barrels a week. By 1900 1,000 barrels a week were being distributed to over eighty public houses. Such a rapid expansion had been made possible by the construction in 1887 of what was then the largest brewing plant in South Wales.

The 1887 brewery is now flanked by large additional developments. Inside modern stainless-steel plant has replaced the old wooden vessels but the method of producing the ales has not really altered since those old days. Traditional brewing is concentrated in the Old Brewery, whereas keg beers, bottled beers and lagers are the province of the 'New Brewery', which was built just before the First World War on a site between Nora Street and Helen Street, Cardiff.

Brain's is very active in the free trade. In the late nineteenth century many working men's clubs sprung up as a result of the Sunday Closing Act and a large number of them were supplied with Brain's beers. Jack Brockway, 'the Father of the Free

Brain's Brewery

Trade', worked for the company from 1905 until 1965 and did a great deal to expand this side of the business, which still flourishes today.

REAL ALES
Red Dragon Dark (OG 1034) – a lightly hopped, smooth but not too sweet mild
Bitter (OG 1035) – a well-hopped distinctive bitter
S A Bitter (OG 1042) – a stronger, highly hopped premium bitter

TIED HOUSES
You do not need to walk far in any direction in Cardiff to find a Brain's pub. There are more than sixty of them, around half of the company's tied estate. Outside the city are the following:

Barry: Castle Park, Windsor Hotel
Beddau: Bowman
Blackweir: Hope
Bonvilston: Old Post, Red Lion
Bridgend: Railway Inn
Caerphilly: Boar's Head
Canton: Admiral Napier, Duke of Clarence
Cogan: Station
Cowbridge: Duke of Wellington
Coychurch: White Horse

Cwmbran: Blinkin' Owl
Cyncoed: Hollybush
Cyntwell: Culverhouse,
    Highfields Inn
Dinas Powis: Star, Station
Fairwater: Bulldog
Gibbonsdown: Master Mariner
Grangetown: Bird-in-hand,
    Cornwall, Grange, Inn
    on the River, Plymouth
Llandaff: Black Lion,
    Maltster's Arms, Mitre,
    Railway, Royal Exchange
Llandough: Merrie Harrier
Llanishen: Wolf's Castle
Maesteg: Sawyer's Arms
Penarth: Albion, Pilot
Pentyrch: King's Arms
Peterson-super-Ely: Three
    Horseshoes

Portcawl: Jolly Sailor,
    Newton, Pier
Radyr: Radyr Arms
Rumney: Cross Inn,
    Newbridge
St Brides: Church House Inn
Splott: Grosvenor
Skewen: Crown
Swansea: Adam and Eve,
    Vivian Arms
Taff's Well: Tynant
Thornhill: Pendragon
Tongwynlais: Lewis Arms
Trowbridge: Hendre
Tynewydd: Tynewydd Inn
Wenvoe: Wenvoe Arms
Whitchurch: Master's Arms,
    Plough

And one pub outside the principality:
Bath: Brain's Surgery


**The Bullmastiff Brewery**
Free-Trade Brewers
Anchor Way, Penarth, South Glamorgan

The Bullmastiff is a brave venture in an area dominated by
the big boys of brewing. Considering how short a time the
partnership has been in operation and the limitations of the
brewery which they use, it is a credit to Bob and Paul Jenkins
that they have made such an impact on the drinkers of South
Wales and beyond.

They began assembling their brewhouse in a waterfront
unit of about 500 square feet in June 1987, using equipment
purchased from the lapsed Monmouth Fine Ales Brewery. By
October they were in production and their first two customers
were the Coronation Club and the Royal Hotel in Penarth. Since
then they have spread through the free trade in South and South
East Wales and you will find Bullmastiff guesting (via distribu-
tors, of course) as far afield as the Borders of Scotland, Devon
and Cornwall, Somerset, Avon and parts of the Midlands.

The turnover of the first year's trading was doubled in the second. More equipment has been installed. At present capacity is twelve barrels a week, but Bob and Paul are looking for ways to squeeze more out of their tiny brewery. Four beers are produced, including the strongest cask ale brewed in Wales – the aptly named Son of a Bitch. Look out for these quality beers from Bullmastiff in the free trade.

REAL ALES
Brewery Bitter (OG 1036) – a light session bitter
Ebony Dark (OG 1041) – a dark ale rich from its sugars
Bullmastiff Best Bitter (OG 1042) – a full well-balanced bitter
Son of a Bitch (OG 1062) – a strong ale to mellow you

REGULAR FREE TRADE
Aberthin: Hare and Hounds
Brynmawr: Goose and Firkin
Llantwit Fardre: Crown

Penarth: Royal Hotel
Upper Llanover: Goose and Cuckoo

GUEST APPEARANCES
Abergavenny: Station Hotel
Bristol (Avon): Star
Cowbridge: Bear
Cwmavon: Westlake's Arms
Llancadle: Green Dragon
Llangynidr: Red Lion
Llantrisant: Barn
Machen: White Hart

Middlezoy (Somerset): George
Newport: Bailey's Bodega, Orange Tree
Penalt: Boat Inn
Pontypridd: Bunch of Grapes
Sebastopol: Open Hearth
Talybont-on-Usk: Star

**Crown Buckley PLC**
Subsidiary Regional Brewers
Gilbert Road, Llanelli, Dyfed

The merger of Buckley's Brewery PLC and Crown Brewery PLC in 1989 brought about the emergence of an ambitious new strength in Welsh brewing. Buckley's had seen some troubled times over the preceding few years. Following a successful fight against takeover in 1987, a sudden turn of events produced a new bidder and the company was purchased by the property and investment group Brodian. However, Gareth Thomas, managing director of Crown Brewery, Pontyclun, had always cherished the idea of creating a brewing force which could hold its own against the Big Six. With the backing of Harp Lager (a subsidiary of Guinness), he realised that ambition by merging the two breweries. Harp has the controlling interest in Buckley's but Crown runs all of the public houses.

Buckley's is the oldest brewery in Wales and it forms a dominant feature of the Llanelli skyline. It was established as far back as 1767 in what was then Carmarthenshire. For 220 years the independent family firm supplied the pubs of West Wales with distinctive traditional beers brewed for the local palate. An estate of around 150 tied houses was assembled over that period. Other outlets, particularly Allied houses selling Buckley's XXXX Mild as 'Ansell's Dark', had given it a firm foothold in the licensed trade of the region.

Crown Brewery had always specialised in supplying the club trade of Wales and the West Country and was producing around 25 million pints a year at the time of the merger. It had been established shortly after the First World War during a period when beer was in short supply, which understandably caused a certain restlessness among the members of the South Wales branch of the Club and Institute Union. They held an emergency meeting in Pontypridd in June 1919 and decided that the only way to alleviate the desperate situation was to buy a brewery for themselves. D. and T. Jenkins of Pontyclun was purchased in the name of the South Wales and Monmouthshire United Clubs' Brewery. A single beer, Clubs' Pale Ale, was produced at a rate of 200 barrels per week to slake the local thirst.

Demand increased over the years and a new brewery was built and opened in 1954 (the first new brewery in Wales since the Second World War). The exclusive link with the clubs was relaxed in 1976, when the free trade was allowed access to the beers. The award-winning Special Bitter had become far too palatable to be restricted solely to club outlets. Only the austere name of the business needed to be altered and that decision was taken in 1977 – Crown Brewery had been the name of the original building of D. and T. Jenkins.

The new Crown Buckley, under the guidance of Gareth Thomas, is pledged to place the emphasis upon traditional ales. With a sound base of tied houses, club outlets and a growing demand from the free trade, the company is investing heavily in promotion of its flagship ale, Buckley's Best Bitter. Production is being concentrated at Llanelli. There is a new image and the pubs are being renamed Crown Buckley Taverns. The only real

Crown Brewery

ale to be lost so far is Crown's Black Prince Mild, which has given way to Buckley's XXXX Mild.

REAL ALES
Buckley's Mild (OG 1032) – dark, hoppy and refreshing
Buckley's Best Bitter (OG 1036) – well-hopped and distinctive
Crown Special (OG 1036) – a smooth and well-flavoured bitter
Crown 1041 (OG 1041) – a well-malted premium bitter

OUTLETS
The beers can be found in around 750 varied outlets at any one time. The following are examples:

*Dyfed*
Ammanford: Cross Inn
Cardigan: Lamb
Lampeter: King's Head
Laugharne: New Three
  Mariners

Llandissilio: Bush
Meinciau: Black Horse
Tegryn: Butcher's Arms
Tresaith: Ship Inn

*Mid-Glamorgan*
Llantwit Fardre: Bush Inn
Maesteg: Beethoven's,
  Coytrahen Arms
Pontyclun: Brunel Arms

Porthcawl: Sandpiper
Treforest: Otley Arms
Treoes: Star

*South Glamorgan*
Cardiff: Lodge

*West Glamorgan*
Bishopston: Beaufort Arms
Crofty: Crofty Inn
Gorseinon: Tafarn-y-Trap
Gowerton: Commercial,
  Welcome to Gower
Neath: Welsh Bard
Newton: Ancient Briton

Ogmore: Craig Yr Eos
Pontardulais: King Hotel
Port Talbot: Burgess Green,
  Four Winds, St Oswald's
Swansea: Builder's Arms,
  Star Inn

*Gwent*
Pant-Yr-Est: Pant-Yr-Est Inn
Usk: Nag's Head

**The Felinfoel Brewery Company Ltd**
Independent Regional Brewers
Felinfoel, Llanelli, Dyfed

Felinfoel is a village in an area which has since the Industrial
Revolution had its roots in iron and steel. David John owned a
local iron and tinplate works and around 1840 he decided to
diversify his interests. He purchased the King's Arms, which
was situated opposite his home.

Like most pubs in the early nineteenth century the King's
Arms brewed its own beer. To buy a pub was, of necessity,
to become a brewer. David John took to the business, helped

Felinfoel Brewery

by fine spring water which ran nearby. Soon he was acquiring other public houses to supply with ale from the King's Arms. So quickly did the business prosper that the brewery which we see today had to be built in 1878 in the grounds of John's house. By 1906 a public company had been formed and the estate numbered around seventy-five pubs throughout Cardiganshire, Carmarthenshire and Pembrokeshire.

The mixed background of tinplate and beer which had been with the company since David John purchased the King's Arms came to the fore in the mid-1930s. 'Pioneers of Canned Ales' is a proud boast of Felinfoel. In fact the company came a very close second to an American brewery in the race to be the first to produce canned beers. If the brewery owed a debt to the tinplating industry for providing it with David John nearly a hundred years earlier, it was able to repay it by giving a boost to local businesses by placing orders for the cans which it needed.

At Brewex 1976, Felinfoel ales received their rightful accolade – a Gold Medal for the traditional draught bitter and a Gold Medal for Double Dragon, which also won the overall Challenge Cup.

Under the watchful eye of head brewer F. J. Keddie, the 'Champion Brewers' currently produce around 400 barrels a week for their tenanted houses in West Wales and for the free trade. The brewery itself is a mixture of old and new. Malt is still lifted by the original belt-driven hoist, but there is an ultra-modern stainless-steel 'copper' and in recent years much other up-to-date equipment has been installed. A new warehouse for the brewery now stands on the site of David John's house.

REAL ALES
XXXX Mild (OG 1031) – dark with a good flavour
Best Bitter (OG 1033) – pale full of flavour and lightly hopped
Double Dragon (OG 1040) – of fuller colour and well-hopped

TIED HOUSES
The company owns seventy-five public houses and leases seven clubs. Outlets are abundant in the Llanelli area, as you might expect. Elsewhere you will find the famous dragon insignia at the following:

*Dyfed*

Cardigan: Commercial Hotel, Mason Arms
Carmarthen: Black Horse, Boar's Head, Castle Hotel, Drover's Arms, Golden Lion Wheatsheaf
Cilgerran: Cardiff Arms
Ferryside: White Lion
Gorseinon: Station Hotel
Kidwelly: Anthony's Hotel, Boot and Shoe, Joiner's Arms, Mason's Arms, Miner's Arms, Plough and Harrow
Kilgetty: Kilgetty Arms, White Horse
Llanddarog: Butcher's Arms
Llandeilo: Tregeyb Arms
Llandyssul: Llwyndafydd Inn

Llangennech: Castle Inn, Farmer's Arms, Tinwork's Arms
Llanon: Red Lion
Nantgaredig: Salutation Inn
Narberth: Kirkland Arms
Newcastle Emlyn: Plough
Penygroes: Norton Arms
Pontardulais: Red Lion, Wheatsheaf
Pontyates: Rwyth Inn, Square and Compass
Pontyberem: Three Compasses
St Clears: Butcher's Arms, Penyrheol Hotel
Tumble: Gwendraeth Arms, Tumble Hotel
Whitland: Fisher's Arms

*West Glamorgan*

Cwmgors: New Star Inn
Loughor: Red Lion, Station Inn

Morriston (Swansea): Champion Brewer
Pontlliw (Swansea): Castle

**Plassey Brewery**
Independent Local Brewers
Eyton, Wrexham, Clwyd

The Plassey complex has a caravan site, restaurant, swimming pool, jewellery shop, stained-glass shop, needlework shop and a coffee bar. It also has an active brewery, the only independent one in North Wales.

When Marston's took over Border Breweries and closed the business down in 1984, brewer Alan Beresford arranged with farmer Tony Brookshaw to open a brewery in the old dairy buildings on the farm site. The five-barrel-or-so output is now overseen by Peter Ireland, who assumed brewing duties when Alan Beresford retired. In an area where there are many tied houses and little opportunity for a new brewery it is a tribute that Plassey had maintained its presence. With the imminent changes in the trade over the next few years, that resilience may well pay off.

The single bitter is very light and can be compared with Boddington's or Tanglefoot. A stronger ale has been brewed but the North Wales taste is for beers of modest gravity.

REAL ALE
Farmhouse Bitter (OG 1039) – a refreshing, pale, all-malt bitter

TIED HOUSE
Plassey: Treetops Bar

FREE TRADE
*Clwyd*
Rhewl, Llangollen: Sun Inn
Pontfadog, Glyn Ceiriog: Swan Inn

## Sam Powell
Independent Local Brewers
Newtown, Powys

The old mid-Wales Eagle Brewery served the area for seventy-eight years until it closed in 1958. Rather than concentrating on brewing, the company decided to turn its attention to distribution of national brands to the licensed trade.

It was not until 1981 that the art of brewing was revived in Newtown, in the name of the Powys Brewery. Recognising the need for a local real ale or two, brewer Stuart Roberts had established a new brewery on the Mochre Industrial Estate, across the road from the main warehouse. Sadly, his new enterprise folded within two years.

The Powell family stepped in at this point, installing the experienced Peter Ratcliffe as brewer. They operate under the banner 'Sam Powell – The Real Ale of Wales. First brewed 1880'. Twenty-five barrels are produced per week, mainly for the free trade. However, the family now has three tied houses as a retail base for its expanding operation.

REAL ALES
Sam Powell BB (OG 1035) – a fairly light balanced bitter
Sam Powell OB (OG 1038) – stronger and of fuller flavour
Samson (OG 1050) – a malty premium bitter

TIED HOUSES
*Powys*
Llanidloes: Trewythen Arms
Newtown: Eagles Hotel
Pontdolgoch: Mytton Arms

FREE TRADE
Outlets vary and can number around sixty in the summer
season. Try any of the following:

*Dyfed*
Aberaeron: Harbourmaster Hotel
Llangeitho: Three Horseshoes
Pisgah: Halfway Inn

*Powys*
Old Churchstoke: Oak Inn

*Shropshire*
Wentnor: Crown Inn

## Raisdale Sparging and Brewing Company
Home-Brew Hotel
Raisdale Road, Penarth, South Glamorgan

Brewing enthusiast Stephen Simpson-Wells runs one of Britain's
most intriguing mini-breweries at the Raisdale Hotel. In a shed
behind his mother's hotel he brews a range of real ales, mostly
for bottling, in equipment only slightly more sophisticated than
that used by the average home-brewer.

The term 'sparging' in the company's title emphasises the fact
that Stephen does use malted barley in his brews. However, he
also uses a proportion of malt extract. The technique of combining a mini-mash with added extract is familiar to home-brewers
but Stephen is the master of experiment. He will tell you that
his actual processes are still developing and are secret.

The small brewhouse has a row of plastic fermenting barrels,
a tiny mash tun, crates of bottles and cleaning equipment. There

is also a desk where he keeps his records for the perusal of HM Customs and Excise. Stephen is proud of the quality of his beers but you will have to book into the hotel in order to try them. Should you do so, a whole new world of Stanley's Steamhammer, Looby's Lust and O'Hooligan's Revolt will be available to you. As Stephen continues to experiment he is aiming for the strongest beer in the land, at around 16 per cent alcohol by volume, perhaps to be called 'Kegbuster'.

In the autumn of 1989 he began looking for new premises for his enterprising brewing operation and a move from the Raisdale Hotel is likely.

REAL ALE
Eight Bore Special (OG 1041) – a pale malty bitter

# CHAPTER THIRTEEN

# Scotland and Northern Ireland

**Belhaven Brewery Company Limited**
Regional Brewers
Belhaven, Dunbar, East Lothian

Beers have been brewed in Belhaven since at least the thirteenth century. Pure water from the Lammermuir aided the monks of that time in beginning a tradition of fine ales. Over the centuries Belhaven has had many admirers, said to include the emperor of Austria and Boswell ('the best small beer I have ever had').

The Belhaven Brewery began commercial production in 1719. It is about 28 miles from Edinburgh within the Royal Burgh of Dunbar, on the south of the entrance to the Firth of Forth. The vaulted cellars which those monks built are still present in the existing brewery. A certain John Johnstone owned the building when it began brewing for sale.

After a partial rebuild following a fire the business passed to an in-law, Ellis Dudgeon, in 1815 and began trading as Dudgeon and Company. Most of the outlets were local ones but some of the ales from Belhaven found their way out of the area via Dunbar harbour.

By 1837 the company's advertisements were claiming that the emperor of Austria had pronounced Belhaven Strong Ale 'the Burgundy of Scotland'. That heady brew is said to have been matured for at least a year before bottling. Certainly in his sixty-one years of control over the business Ellis Dudgeon did a great deal to establish the reputation of the company. He was succeeded by his son-in-law Alexander Hunter.

Having resisted the charge of the big brewers in the 1960s, the confidently independent firm was renamed the Belhaven Brewing Company Limited in 1973. Between 1976 and 1980 an expansion programme saw the volume of sales increase by no less than 40 per cent. The policy of providing a full range of draught beers had brought its rightful rewards. In 1988 HRH The Princess Royal opened an extension to allow yet more capacity.

However, Scotland's oldest independent brewery finally succumbed to the outside world, also in 1988. The brewery was purchased by Nazmu Virani's Control Securities for £7.5 million.

REAL ALES
60/- Light (OG 1031) – in fact a rather dark moderate ale
70/- Heavy (OG 1035) – a splendidly well-balanced bitter
80/- Export (OG 1041) – a rich premium ale
90/- Strong Ale (OG 1070) – a heady and dangerous strong ale

OUTLETS
Most of Belhaven's output finds its way into the free trade. The geographical spread is quite surprising. The following are a few scattered examples:

*Borders*
Coldstream: Commercial

*Central*
Drymen: Salmon Leap Inn
Stirling: Wallace

*Fife*
Elie: Ship Inn
St Andrews: Cellar Bar

*Grampian*
Aberdeen: Kirkgate Bar
Elgin: Thunderton House

*Lothian*
East Linton: Crown Hotel
Edinburgh: Bennet's Bar, Starbank Inn
Linlithgow: Four Marys

Belhaven Brewery

*Strathclyde*

Bishopton: Golf Inn
Cambuslang: Sefton Bar
Glasgow: Bon Accord,
  Ubiquitous Chip

Kilmarnock: Gordon's Lounge
Largs:Clachan
Paisley: Buddies
Renfrew: Ferry Inn

*Tayside*

Dundee: Shakespeare,
  Speedwell Bar

## Borve Brewhouse
Single-Pub and Free-Trade Brewers
Ruthven, Grampian

It was in March 1988 that the Hughes family decided to begin brewing at Ruthven, which is between Huntly and Keith. They had moved from the Isle of Lewis and purchased an old schoolhouse in delightful rural surroundings, with the notion that it would make the ideal site for a brewery and pub. The struggle to obtain the necessary planning permission was a protracted one. By the time that the authority had been obtained and the equipment installed over a year had elapsed. It was July 1989 before the first brew was mashed. Several weeks later the Borve Brewhouse Inn opened to the public.

Jimmy Hughes and his son Gregory have a full-mash brewery in a stone outbuilding next to the former schoolhouse. It has a five-barrel brew-length and two fermenting vessels. The ales are sold in the Borve Brewhouse and have appeared at beer festivals. Their route to the free trade is mainly through Dixie Taylor of the Ale Cellar in Aberdeen.

To have converted the schoolhouse into a home, a public house and a brewery is an achievement in itself. From this self-contained unit the success of the Hughes family seems assured, particularly when you realise that brewer Gregory has a master's degree in brewing from Heriot-Wall, Edinburgh. Borve, like Orkney, is a welcome addition to the Scottish real-ale scene and it is to be hoped that it will develop into a significant force in the local battle against keg beers.

REAL ALES
Borve Heavy (OG 1040) – a lightly hopped tasty ale
Borve Strong (OG 1085) – golden-brown rich and powerful

## Broughton Brewery Limited
Independent Local Brewers
Broughton, Biggar, Lanarkshire

'Let me exhort my countrymen to brew their ale from the softest water, the palest malt and the most fragrant hops . . .' wrote George Younger in 1779. When his descendant David Younger founded Broughton Brewery 200 years later, he brought with him seven generations of inbred skill from the most distinguished brewing family in Scotland. His grandfather's great-grandfather had first brought Scottish beer to world prominence with his Old Edinburgh Ale.

David's partner when he established Broughton was the less likely James Collins of the famous publishing family. Together they began this, the first of the 'new wave' of small breweries in Scotland, in the rolling Border hills. A small stream runs close by the brewery and the local water is as soft as George Younger could ever have wanted. Sheep bleat in this part of John Buchan country and you might be forgiven for thinking that this enterprise in such a lovely rural setting would be a sleepy affair.

In fact the calculated and businesslike policy has been one of steady expansion since 1979 and the partners' target has been achieved so convincingly that the term 'local brewers' used to describe Broughton Brewery may now be an under-statement of its strength. As well as a good range of cask-conditioned ales the brewery produces attractively packaged bottled beers and is the sole Scottish distributor for Theakston's Best Bitter and Old Peculier.

Greenmantle, the flagship ale, takes its name from John Buchan's sequel to *The Thirty-Nine Steps*, which concludes: 'Then I knew that the prophecy had been true, and that their prophet had not failed them. The long-looked-for revelation had come. Greenmantle had appeared at last for an awaiting people.'

REAL ALES
Greenmantle Ale (OG 1038) – a well-hopped sweet bitter
Broughton Special (OG 1038) – differs from Greenmantle in
  the piquancy from dry-hopping
Merlin's Ale (OG 1044) – a full-flavoured premium ale
Old Jock (OG 1070) – usually in bottle but the odd cask
  of this very strong ale can be found in winter

FREE-TRADE
Draught beers from Broughton are present in at least 150
outlets in Central and Southern Scotland. If it says 'Free House'
over the door, you have a good chance of finding Greenmantle
or Merlin there. A few of the brewery's regular customers are
listed below:

Almondbank: Almondbank
Inn
Bearsden: Burnbrae Hotel
Callander: Bridgend House
Canonbie: Riverside Inn
Castlecary: Castlecary House
Darvel: Loudounhill Inn
Dundee: Phoenix

Eaglesham: Cross Keys
Glasgow: Bon Accord, Victoria
Gretna: Solway Lodge
Isle of Arran: Cameronia Hotel
Moffat: Black Bull
Seamhill: Glenboyd Hotel
Troon: Lookout

## Caledonian Brewing Company Limited
Independent Local Brewers
Slateford Road, Edinburgh

The former Lorimer and Clark brewery was built in 1869 to
serve the Edinburgh area. It became part of the Vaux Group
during the rush to acquire Scottish breweries. After a few years
and to a great deal of local disappointment, Vaux decided to close
it down.

Fortunately, a management team stepped in to rescue the
fine beers. In 1987 the Caledonian Brewery became independent again. This was no ordinary brewery to be saved from the
bulldozer. It is one of the most impressive Victorian breweries in
Britain and the brewing process is one for the purist to gloat over.

There are no stainless-steel vessels, consoles or rows of dials
here. There is no penny-pinching either. Beer is brewed as it was
in Victorian times. These are the last direct-fired open coppers in
Britain. The emphasis is, quite simply, on quality. Only the best
malted barley, crystal malt, roasted malt, hop flowers, liquor and
yeast find their way into these beers.

The fermention of the beers is long, with a lengthy conditioning
in cask in the brewery cellars (where the temperature is cool
whatever the season). Caledonian Strong Ale is not allowed to
leave the cellars of this, the last fully working Victorian brewery in Scotland, until it has had two weeks in the fermentation

room and as long as is necessary in the cellars to bring it to its very best.

It is well worth the trouble to seek out Caledonian ales in the free trade.

REAL ALES
70/- (OG 1036) – a dark amber session beer
Porter (OG 1038) – dark from the character of roast barley
80/- (OG 1043) – rich, malty and well-hopped
Merman XXX (OG 1050) – strong premium beer from an
    1890 recipe
Strong Ale (OG 1075) – rounded and very strong, but the
    long maturation process avoids any cloying sweetness

FREE TRADE
The outlets for Caledonian are a changing (and expanding) scene. Try any of the following:

Aberdeen: Prince of Wales
Balerno: Marchbank Hotel
Edinburgh: Bannerman's Bar,
    Canny Mann's, Cramond
    Inn, Doric Tavern, Guildford
    Arms, Leslie's Bar, Malt
    Shovel, Minder's, Navaar
    House Hotel, Oxford Bar,
    Smithie's Ale House

Glasgow: Athena Greek
    Taverna, Bon Accord
Inverness: Muirtown Motel
Letham: Commercial Inn
Musselburgh: Volunteer Arms
Renfrew: Pickwick's

**Harviestoun Brewery**
Free-Trade Brewers
Dollarfield Farm, Dollar, Clackmannanshire

Down a farm track near the River Devon in a 200-year-old stone dairy you will find Ken Booker's home-made brewery. The splendid rural location provides an ideal home for one of Scotland's few remaining mini-breweries. Ken will tell you that it is the enormous initial capital expenditure which usually cripples new brewing ventures. He avoided this problem by assembling his own equipment. The hot wort may be cooled by his own creation of copper pipes running through a tank of cold water rather than by any fancy paraflow system, but Ken understands the economics of the business.

He worked as an area manager for Ford's in Edinburgh and when he opened Harviestoun he kept that job until he could judge the potential of his brewery. The village fish and chip shop was also in his ownership. In September 1988 he resigned from Ford's and in the summer of 1989 he sold the 'chippy'. He is now fully occupied as a brewer, working at Dollarfield Farm with a single assistant, Eric Harris.

It is a strange coincidence that when the floors of the lofty old dairy needed renewing in the 1950s, long before Ken's involvement, timber was acquired from Alloa Brewery for the job. In the building today is a ten-barrel-brew-length plant with two gas-fired coppers. Output is around seven barrels per week, but now that Ken is able to devote his full attention to the brewery this is likely to increase. 'It's hard work but I am optimistic,' he says, and you can only admire his skill and tenacity. His ambition is an output of twenty barrels per week.

The two beers from Harviestoun are gradually penetrating a difficult free trade. They are sold through agencies in Scotland and northern England and are often seen as guest beers. Look out for them at beer festivals, where they are always in great demand.

REAL ALES
Harviestoun 80/- (OG 1040) – a tasty well-rounded ale
Old Manor (OG 1050) – dark, rich and of good strength

FREE TRADE
*Central*
Stirling: Birds and Bees

*Clackmannanshire*
Dollar: Strathallan Hotel
Sauchie: Mansfield Arms

*Lothian*
Edinburgh: Guildford Arms

*Strathclyde*
Bishopton: Golf Inn
Castlecary: Castlecary House Hotel
Glasgow: Toll Booth

## Hilden Brewery
Free-Trade Brewers
Hilden House, Grand Street, Hilden, Lisburn, Country Antrim

Since the Down Royal Inn stopped producing real ales, Hilden has been left as the last bastion of traditional beers in Northern Ireland. Seamus and Ann Scullion are to be congratulated on their determination to overcome the difficulties which the trade presents for their enterprising business, established in 1981. Not only is there the problem of brand pressure from the major brewers, supported by heavy TV advertising, but there is the additional hazard of pubs without proper cellars. One of the regular outlets for Hilden has a cold room on the third floor rather than a cellar below.

Hilden House is an old mill house and the brewery is located in the mill stables across the courtyard. It is a stainless-steel plant of fifteen-barrel-brew-length and Seamus regularly turns out ten to fifteen barrels per week for the free trade. He also sells directly from the brewery and has several accounts with clubs.

Seamus is certainly an enterprising man. Functions are organised on the premises, so that parties can enjoy a barbecue washed down with Hilden Ale or Special Reserve, and most years there is a mini beer festival on the premises which enables the locals to sample beers from England and Scotland. The agency which supplies Seamus for these festivals, Legendary Yorkshire Heroes, also returns the compliment by selling Hilden in the free trade in the north of England. Look out for a chance to try Northern Ireland's only real ales.

REAL ALES
Hilden Ale (OG 1040) – a tasty light bitter
Special Reserve (OG 1040) – darker and fuller-flavoured

FREE TRADE
Balmoral: King's Head
Belfast: Botanic Inn, Linen Hall

**Maclay and Company Limited**
Independent Local Brewers
Thistle Brewery, Alloa

Alloa has been famous for its ales since the eighteenth century
and Maclay's has played a large part in consolidating that sound
reputation. The firm has largely remained in the hands of two
families since the brewery began in 1830.

In the year that King William IV ascended the throne,
James Maclay came as lessee to the Mill's Brewery after
learning something about the trade as an accountant at the
old Hutton Park Brewery. A native of Alloa, he brewed at
Mill's for several years until he resolved to build to his own
requirements. The Thistle Brewery was erected to his design
at the east end of the East Vennel, but the worry and effort
of the enterprise so affected James Maclay that he passed away
suddenly in late 1875.

The family continued the business until 1896, when it was
sold to Alexander Fraser. The new proprietor was an innovator.
His attention to the scientific side of the business brought new
production methods and he introduced a sales technique to be
admired. The buildings were extended on all sides to accommodate increasing demand. Through Fraser's efforts the solid
base for Maclay's was assured. It was one of only two Scottish
breweries to retain its independence during the takeover ram-
page which struck the country. 'Brewed in Alloa' is still a proud
label to carry.

REAL ALES
60/- Light (OG 1030) – a dark tasty beer of moderate strength
70/- Heavy (OG 1035) – the traditional hoppy Scottish bitter
80/- Export (OG 1040) – a full-flavoured premium ale
Porter (OG 1040) – a dark rich porter

TIED HOUSES

Airdrie: Claymore,
   Commonside Inn
Alloa: Thistle Bar
Alva: Cross Keys Inn
Arbroath: St Thomas' Bar
Clackmannan: County Hotel

Coatbridge: Forge Inn,
   Woodside Bar
Cummock: Thistle Inn
Dalmellington: Snug Bar
Dunfermline: Cartwheel, City
   Hotel, Well

East Whitburn: Gothenburg
Edinburgh: Southsider
Hamilton: George Bar
Inverkeithing: Volunteer
  Arms
Johnstone: Stand Bar
Kilwinning: Victoria Bar
Linlithgow: New Inn

Loanhead: County Bar
Menstrie: Hollytree Hotel
Ochiltree: Commercial Inn
Perth: Hal o' the Wind
Saltcoats: St Andrew's Bar
Stirling: Halfway House
Uddingston: Rowantree Inn

## Orkney Brewery
Independent Free-Trade Brewers
Quoyloo, Orkney

Britain's most northerly brewery is a remarkable recent addition to the assets of the industry. It was brought into being by Roger White, a civil engineer who simply decided one day that it would be a good idea to revive brewing on the island (which lapsed before the Second World War). Quoyloo is not far from the west coast of mainland Orkney and the setting for the brewery is delightfully rural. When Roger first applied for planning permission, he was offered a unit on an industrial estate. That was not to his taste. He held out and eventually was able to install a Peter Austin system in an old schoolhouse at Quoyloo.

The first mash was in April 1988 and Orkney Brewery has happily established itself since then. Roger uses stainless-steel equipment with a ten-barrel brew-length and two fermenters. No additives or sugars are included in his brews, which have a moderate hop content in order to meet the demands of the Scottish palate. The old school building has stone walls about 3 feet thick, which give him excellent temperature control for his fermentations. Raven Ale won First Prize at the Paisley Beer Festival in 1989.

Beer from Quoyloo is shipped from Stromness to the mainland and thence to beer agencies. Roger is steadily breaking down the keg domination in northern Scotland. Dixie Taylor sells Raven Ale in his Ale Cellar, Aberdeen, and also conveys it to an increasing number of free-trade outlets. 'Orkney is here to stay' says Roger and there can be little doubt about that.

In late 1989 he intends to launch a second real ale at the

Aberdeen Beer Festival. Skullsplitter, with an original gravity of around 1075, will be a dark and dangerous strong ale. The name commemorates the Viking Third Earl of Orkney, Thorfin Skullsplitter. Roger also intends to begin bottling his ales.

REAL ALE
Raven Ale (OG 1038) – malty and full-flavoured with a
    pronounced 'nose'

FREE TRADE
*Grampian*
Aberdeen: Blue Lamp,
    Prince of Wales

*Tayside*
Perth: Greyfriars

**Rose Street Brewery**
Home-Brew Pub
Rose Street, Edinburgh

A few of the major breweries have flirted with the real-ale revolution. When Allied's Scottish representative, Alloa of Clackmannanshire, decided to do so, it chose the White Cockade in Rose Street as its base for a home brewery.

Auld Reekie ales are produced on the premises for consumption on the premises much in the style of the old publican brewer. The difference is that they are not brewed in the traditional way. Instead of a full-mash system the brewer uses malt extract.

In many modern home-brew establishments the public can view the brewery, but the Rose Street establishment is unusual in that the operation takes place on the first floor. The normal weekly output is six barrels for the bars downstairs.

REAL ALES
Auld Reekie 80/- (OG 1043) – a full-flavoured malty ale
Auld Reekie 90/- (OG 1055) – a rich strong ale

## Traquair House
Renowned Independent Brewers
Innerleithen, Peeblesshire

Traquair House is a world-renowned unique brewery. It stands alone in its individuality and historic character. The house itself is the oldest inhabited home in Scotland. It was here that Alexander I signed a charter over 800 years ago and a testimony to its age is that the so-called 'modern wings' were in fact completed in 1680. The house is open to the public, normally at Easter and from May until the end of September – you can see the famous Bear Gates which have remained unopened since 1745 when Prince Charles Edward Stuart passed through them for the last time. You can also see the working brewery and sample its products.

No one knows exactly when brewing began at Traquair. When Mary, Queen of Scots, visited in 1566, she probably had a tipple – the brewery is known to have been in operation then. In 1739 a 200-gallon copper (at a cost of £8) was installed

Bear Gates, Traquair House

and this may well have provided refreshment for Bonnie Prince Charles when he called in 1745, perhaps feeling a warm glow as those gates were closed behind him.

Sadly, it was only a few years later that the brewery fell idle and the dust began to gather. For over 200 years it was a silent museum.

In 1952 the 20th Laird of Traquair, Peter Maxwell Stuart, opened Traquair to the public. In 1962 he dusted down the brewery, well in advance of CAMRA and the general resurgence of interest in real ales. Setting up the old equipment under the chapel of the house, he personally used the original tools and vessels to brew to an ancient family recipe. Traquair House Ale was reintroduced – a strong ale of immense character brewed to an original gravity of 1075.

The self-conditioning bottled ale was at first produced at the rate of only a few thousand bottles a year, mainly brewed in the winter because of lack of temperature control under the chapel. Demand increased, both at home and abroad, and by 1982 70,000 bottles were being produced annually. The Laird had to employ an assistant brewer in order to cope with the orders. Brewing takes about ten days and the ale is stored in casks for three to four months.

Traquair House Ale has a bottle life of around ten years. It is brewed only from barley malt, hops and yeast supplied by Belhaven Brewery. The smooth and delicious flavour is said to be attributable to the 200-year-old oak casks in which it is conditioned. Exports are to many countries, including Denmark, Far East countries, France, Holland and the United States.

For special occasions (such as the Laird's 200th brew in 1983) an even stronger commemorative ale is produced, usually with a mind-blowing original gravity in the range of 1090-8. To delight the more cautious drinker the Laird has in recent years added a cask-conditioned ale, which can be found in a few free-trade outlets and at beer festivals.

REAL ALES
Bear Ale (OG 1050) – a full-flavoured premium ale
Traquair House Ale (OG 1075) – the renowned smooth strong
   ale, usually in bottle but sometimes on draught

OUTLETS
Obviously Traquair House is the place to drink the beers. However, Bear Ale is becoming increasingly available in the

free trade and the following will usually be able to serve you with a pint:

*Borders*
Peebles: Cross Keys Inn

*Lothian*
Edinburgh: Malt Shovel,
    Minder's, Navaar House
Linlithgow: Four Marys

And south of the Border:

*Yorkshire*
Leeds: Ale House
York: Spread Eagle

CHAPTER FOURTEEN

# The Channel Islands

## The Guernsey Brewery Company (1920) Limited
Subsidiary Brewers
South Esplanade, St Peter Port, Guernsey

There cannot be a much better setting for a brewery than South Esplanade. The impressive four-storey frontage is within 15 yards of the sea, overlooking the boats in Havelet Bay. You can see Castle Cornet and the neighbouring islands from there. At one time it was even nearer to the sea, for the mid-nineteenth-century-built premises were almost on the beach before South Esplanade was built on reclaimed land.

John Le Patourel bought the original premises in 1845. He combined two houses and added a top storey as well as a brewery at the side and back. The London Brewery, as it was then called, was opened in 1856. After brewing for a number of years he ceased trading and the future of the brewery seemed uncertain. However, a military officer and a brewer from Abingdon purchased the business in 1895. Together they formed the Guernsey Brewery Company Limited.

The most traumatic period of the brewery's history was obviously during the German Occupation of the Channel Islands. Roy Higgs, who held a first-class diploma in brewing and came from his father's Lion Brewery in Reading, was the head brewer at the time. He was faced with immense difficulties but showed great initiative through the dark years from the time when the bombs fell on St Peter Port and the troops arrived. Although he had good stocks of hops and sugar, malt supplies were very limited. Gravities were reduced progressively and beer rationing was introduced. When it seemed likely that his limited supplies of malt would be requisitioned, he cleverly avoided this by making a baker's balm (a yeast/malt cake) with the help of a prominent baker.

Inevitably, despite these contrivances, the malt stocks became exhausted. Roy Higgs did not close the brewery but produced beer from invert sugar, and to prolong his brewing he even turned to the use of sugar beet and parsnips in increasing quantities. Eventually the use of sugar for brewing was banned and Roy was reduced to a non-alcoholic Hop Ale, using saccharine. It was not just the brewing process that was affected – the Germans commandeered the company's board room and offices in 1942. Roy Higgs was deported but he left his Hop Ale recipe behind to see the business through to better days.

After Liberation the brewery flourished again. Between 1947 and 1954 all of the equipment was renewed and more pubs were purchased. A purpose-built fermenting room was added. In 1985 at Burton-on-Trent, Guernsey Brewery IPA won the major award in UK Brewing, the Championship Trophy.

In 1977 the company had been sold to Bucktrout and Company Limited, but it had been allowed to continue in independent production of its beers. Bucktrout itself was sold to Ann Street Brewery, a Jersey-based company, in 1988. Seventy per cent of the output from the Guernsey Brewery is kegged these days but a mild and a bitter are still produced in the traditional manner. They are known locally as 'Pony Ales'.

REAL ALES

LBA Mild (OG 1037) – a medium dark sweet mild
Real Draught Bitter (OG 1045) – a balanced premium bitter
    with good hop content

TIED HOUSES

Besides the twenty pubs in and around St Peter Port, try any of the following on Guernsey:

Grandes Rocques: Wayside Cheer Hotel, Wayside Tavern
St Martin: Captain's Hotel, L'Auberge Divette, La Trelade Hotel
St Pierre du Bois: Longfrie Hotel
St Sampson: Hotel Houmet de Nord, Houmet Tavern, Pony Inn
St Sampson Harbour: English and Guernsey Arms
St Saviour: St Saviour's Hotel
Vazon: Vazon Bay Hotel

## R.W. Randall Limited
Independent Brewers
Vauxlaurens Brewery, St Julian's Avenue,
St Peter Port, Guernsey

It is believed that the Vauxlaurens Brewery had been in operation for over 200 years when R. H. Randall, a native of Jersey, purchased it in 1868. He ran the business until his death in 1899 and was succeeded by his eldest son, whose name the company now bears. As well as a brewery there was a mineral-water factory on the site, but R. W. Randall sold that to the Guernsey Aerated Water and Jam Company in 1921 so that he could concentrate on beer. He was joined by his two sons in the late 1920s and the business has been under the direct control of his descendents ever since.

When a private limited company was formed in 1929, care was taken that all of the shares were held by the family and that remains the case today. In 1950-2 a new brewhouse and bottling store were erected and at about that time the fourth generation of Randalls began joining the firm.

The beers are known on Guernsey as 'Bobby Ales'.

REAL ALES
Best Mild (OG 1037) – a dark heavy mild
Best Bitter (OG 1047) – hoppy and full-bodied

TIED HOUSES
Six of the company's outlets on Guernsey sell draught beer:

Castel: Rockmount Hotel
St Andrew's: Last Post
St Peter Port: Fermain Inn,
   Prince of Wales, St Jacques
St Sampson: London House

Most of Randall's real ale is sold on Guernsey, but if you are on Alderney try the Coronation Inn at St Anne. No Channel Islands draught ales are sold on Jersey but there are several outlets for Draught Bass.

# CHAPTER FIFTEEN

# The Giants of British Brewing

When the Government decided to take some sort of action following the 1989 Report of the Monopolies and Mergers Commission, over 32,000 pubs were held by just six major brewers. This factor made certain that beer drinkers had a very restricted choice in many areas of England, Scotland and Wales. It also created a state of affairs in which any aspiring free-trade brewer would find potential outlets for his beers, however splendid they might be, so restricted that he would be lucky to survive for any length of time.

The Big Six produce a large range of ales, from the most bland of mass-produced beers to some of the most delicious. Over the years they have been able to dictate taste and to concentrate their massive advertising budgets on keg beers and, in particular, lager. They have also been able to set the prices of their products with very little challenge from competitors. Although the situation may change slowly as a result of the relaxation of the tie, few of the new-wave brewers (whose products may well be superior) see much cause for optimism. The grip of the giants is likely to remain a tight one.

The members of this elite group of companies are considered below in descending order of size. The various real-ale breweries which they control are listed with the beers produced. Some of the finest breweries in the land have fallen into the hand of the Big Six. However, the several non-cask breweries, which manufacture only lagers and pasteurised beers, have been omitted.

## BASS

With an estate of around 7,300 public houses and restaurants, Bass is Britain's leading brewer. Its interests extend well beyond brewing, of course, but beers and pubs still account for over two thirds of the company's turnover. Producing around eight million barrels per year, Bass distributes around a fifth of the beer sold in Britain. The giant firm owns thirteen working breweries of which the following eight produce real ales:

*Bass Brewing, Station Street, Burton-upon-Trent, Staffordshire*
Draught Bass (OG 1044) – no longer a Burton Union ale
   but still a fine sweet premium bitter

*Bass Cannon, Rutland Road, Sheffield, South Yorkshire*
*(Part of Bass North)*
Stone's Best Bitter (OG 1038) – a refreshing hoppy bitter

*Bass Highgate, Sandymount Road, Walsall, Staffordshire*
*(Part of Bass, Mitchell's and Butler's)*
Highgate Mild (OG 1036) – a dark well-flavoured Midlands mild

*Bass Mitchell's and Butler's, Cape Hill, Birmingham*
M&B Mild (OG 1036) – a dark refreshing Midlands mild
Brew XI (OG 1040) – a distinctive sweetish bitter

*Bass Springfield, Grimstone Street, Wolverhampton,*
  *West Midlands*
*(Part of Bass, Mitchell's and Butler's)*
Springfield Bitter (OG 1030) – a very light clean-tasting bitter
Charrington IPA (OG 1039) – a standard session bitter for
  the South
Springfield Original (OG 1050) – a strong full-bodied bitter

*Bass Tadcaster, Wetherby Road, Tadcaster, North Yorkshire*
*(Part of Bass North)*
Bass Light (OG 1031) – the easy-drinking five-star light mild
Bass Mild XXXX (OG 1031) – a dark mild of good flavour
Bass Special (OG 1038) – a clean-tasting session bitter

*Tennent Heriot, Roseburn Terrace, Edinburgh, Scotland*
*(Part of Tennent Caledonian)*
Tennents 80/- (OG 1042) – a well-flavoured Scottish premium ale

*Welsh Brewers, Crawshay Street, Cardiff, South Glamorgan*
*(Part of Bass, Wales and West)*
Worthington PA (OG 1033) – a refreshing pale ale
Hancock's PA (OG 1033) – a pale ale of rounded character
Worthington M (OG 1033) – similar to PA
Worthington Dark (OG 1034) – a dark mild of good flavour
Worthington BB (OG 1037) – once brewed at Burton-upon-Trent,
    a fine session bitter
Hancock's HB (OG 1037) – a well-balanced distinctive bitter


## ALLIED BREWERIES

Close on the heels of Bass comes Allied Breweries, a subsidiary of the massive Allied Lyons Company, with around
6,600 public houses and a market share of over an eighth of
national beer sales. With twelve different breweries producing
real ale, Allied has the most comprehensive brewery network
of them all and covers wide areas of England, Scotland and
Wales. It is interesting to note, however, that those eleven
breweries produce a choice of only twenty-five ales between
them. The average number of cask-conditioned beers produced
by the Allied establishments is little more than two per brewery
and that meagre variety is likely to decrease. Even with this
restricted range of beers, the company showed a trading profit
of £200 million in 1989.
   The most familiar banners under which the ales are sold
are Ansell's, Ind Coope, Friary Meux and, of course, Tetley's. In
recent years there have been changes in the brewing pattern,
with the trend towards the removal of some regional beers in
favour of national products. There is one interesting member of
the family – Holt, Plant and Deakin, which supplies thirty-one
pubs in the Black Country with some interesting beers. The
home-brew outlets run under the Hall's Division are dealt with
separately in the regional chapters of this book.


*Alloa Brewery Company, Craigmillar, Edinburgh, Scotland*
Archibald Arrol's 70/- (OG 1037) – a well-hopped, clean-tasting
    bitter
Archibald Arrol's 80/- (OG 1042) – a premium-strength Scottish
    ale

*Ansell's, Aldridge Road, Perry Barr, Birmingham*
Ansell's Mild (OG 1036) – an excellent, rich, dark mild
Ansell's Bitter (OG 1037) – a standard Birmingham session
    bitter

*Friary Meux, Station Road, Godalming, Surrey*
Friary Meux Best (OG 1037) – a well-balanced session bitter

*Hall's (Oxford and West), Park End Street, Oxford, Oxfordshire*
Harvest Bitter (OG 1037) – a distinctive rich session bitter

*Holt, Plant and Deakin, Station Road, Oldbury, West Midlands*
See the separate entry in Chapter Nine.

*Ind Coope Benskin's, Station Road, Watford, Hertfordshire*
Benskin's Best (OG 1037) – a well-hopped standard bitter

*Ind Coope Burton, Station Street, Burton-upon-Trent,
Staffordshire*
ABC Bitter (OG 1037) – a refreshing session bitter brewed
    for the Aylesbury Brewing Company outlets
Burton Ale (OG 1047) – the flagship premium bitter: distinctive
    and of good flavour

*Plympton Brewery, Valley Road, Plympton, Plymouth, Devon*
Plympton Best (OG 1039) – a well-balanced bitter
Plympton Pride (OG 1045) – a full-flavoured premium bitter

*Taylor Walker, Muswell Hill, London N10*
Taylor Walker Best (OG 1037) – a balanced session bitter

*Joshua Tetley, Hunslet Road, Leeds, West Yorkshire*
Falstaff Best (OG 1032) – a rare, refreshing, light mild
Tetley Mild (OG 1032) – a rich dark mild
Tetley Bitter (OG 1035) – refreshing, with that familiar thick
    head so loved by Yorkshiremen

*Tetley Walker, Dallam Lane, Warrington, Cheshire*
Tetley Mild (OG 1032) – rich and dark, as good as the Leeds
    brew
Tetley Bitter (OG 1035) – hoppy and quite similar to Joshua's
    version

HPD Mild (OG 1036) – a dark mild brewed for Holt, Plant and Deakin
HPD Bitter (OG 1036) – a distinctive hoppy bitter for the Black Country

*Peter Walker, Duke Street, Liverpool, Merseyside*
Mild (OG 1032) – a well-flavoured dark mild
Bitter (OG 1033) – a light session bitter
Best Bitter (OG 1035) – a well-hopped clean-tasting bitter
Winter Warmer (OG 1060) – a dark strong ale

## WHITBREAD

Since the closure during 1988 of Chester's of Manchester and Wethered's of Marlow, Whitbread has reduced its breweries to six. There are two massive lager and keg factories among them, leaving just four traditional breweries to provide the real ales for the company's 6,000-odd tied houses. In 1989 an agreement was reached with Marston's which will mean that Pedigree Ale will become apparent in selected Whitbread houses.

Over the years Whitbread has closed down many breweries which it had acquired, sometimes retaining the names. For example, although the Flowers' Ales from the West Country Brewery bear little relationship to the original brews from Stratford-upon-Avon, the name and the image have been retained many years after the Stratford Brewery was demolished. Within the industry Whitbread is regarded as having a well-run operation. Recent emphasis within the group has been directed towards the very successful Beefeater restaurants and Whitbread has a major interest in the growing Pizza Hut chain. Together the brewing and restaurant interests account for about 85 per cent of the company's profits.

*Castle Eden Brewery, Hartlepool, Cleveland*
Castle Eden Ale (OG 1040) – an excellent, well-rounded and tasty premium bitter

*Fremlin's Brewery, Court Street, Faversham, Kent*
Fremlin's Bitter (OG 1035) – a refreshing session bitter
Pompey Royal (OG 1043) – a full-bodied premium bitter
Flowers' Original (OG 1044) – a distinctive premium bitter

*Whitbread Sheffield, Exchange Brewery, Sheffield, South Yorkshire*
Chester's Best Mild (OG 1032) – a dark mild of light flavour
Chester's Best Bitter (OG 1033) – a hoppy session bitter
Trophy (OG 1036) – a balanced standard bitter

*Whitbread West Country, Monson Avenue, Cheltenham, Gloucestershire*
West Country Pale Ale (OG 1030) – a light lunchtime session beer
Wethered Bitter (OG 1035) – a full-flavoured tasty standard bitter
Flowers' IPA (OG 1036) – a well-hopped and very drinkable session bitter
Strong Country Bitter (OG 1037) – a well-rounded bitter of average strength
Wethered SPA (OG 1040) – a full-flavoured premium bitter
Flowers' Original (OG 1044) – a distinctive premium bitter
Wethered Winter Royal (OG 1055) – a dark strong ale for cold nights

*Boddington's and Higson's – see Chapter Eleven.*

## GRAND METROPOLITAN

The old Watney Mann and Truman combine is now under the Grand Metropolitan umbrella, again brewing real ales from four main breweries. Also within the group are the Berni Inns chain and Clifton Inns, whose home-brew establishments are dealt with separately in this book. After disposing of a fair number of its less profitable pubs, the group now has approaching 5,500 tied houses. Besides the beer and restaurant trade, Grand Metropolitan had growing interests in food, such as Eden Vale and Green Giant, and in gaming and leisure. Beer accounts for less than 10 per cent of the combine's turnover.

The splendid Ruddle's Brewery in Rutland was purchased by Watney's in 1986 and is the company's flagship producer of real ales. Ruddle's was founded in Langham in 1858 and it seemed that the family firm had survived the takeover wave of the post-war period. Tony Ruddle seemed to have assured the company's independence when he made overtures to the grocery trade and began supplying his ales to famous supermarkets. However, the board rather over-reacted to this success and disposed of all of the company's public houses between 1977 and 1984. Ruddle's became vulnerable again and the founder's grandson eventually sold out in 1986. Although it is always sad to see the loss of independence of a well-loved regional, the absorption into Grand Metropolitan has at least meant that Ruddle's has become familiar as a handpumped ale rather than just as a beer in a supermarket trolley.

*Ruddle's Brewery, Langham, Oakham, Rutland, Leicestershire*
Best Bitter (OG 1037) – a well-rounded session bitter
County (OG 1050) – the renowned malty premium bitter

*Truman's Black Eagle Brewery, Brick Lane, London EI*
Best Bitter (OG 1044) – a sharp but well-balanced premium
  bitter

*Usher's Brewery, Parade House, Trowbridge, Wiltshire*
Best Bitter (OG 1036) – a rather sweet and very individual
  bitter

*Webster's Fountain Head Brewery, Ovenden Wood, Halifax, West Yorkshire*
Wilson's Mild (OG 1032) – a well-flavoured dark mild
Webster's Green Label (OG 1033) – a well-hopped light mild
Webster's Yorkshire Bitter (OG 1036) – a standard Yorkshire
  session bitter
Wilson's Original Bitter (OG 1036) – a well-rounded tasty
  session bitter
Webster's Choice (OG 1045) – a balanced premium bitter

## ELDERS IXL

The Courage/John Smith combine is now owned by the Australian giant Elders, the company which fought so hard in 1989 with its £1.6 billion bid for Scottish and Newcastle to reduce the Big Six to the Massive Five. The main claim to fame of Elders is that it produces Foster's Lager and Miller Lite. Although the company has various interests throughout the world, the Courage group is virtually its only stake in Britain. The 5,000 odd pubs are these days held by a separate company of which Elders has a half-share. Elders' slice of the British beer market approaches 10 per cent.

One of the reasons for Elders' bid for Scottish and Newcastle was a desire to increase brewing capacity. There are just two traditional breweries (the Reading Brewery produces no real ale) to serve the large tied estate. The John Smith Brewery in Tadcaster stands across the road from Sam Smith's, following the split in the family during the nineteenth century. For many years it turned out only keg beers (with the exception of the superb bottled Imperial Russian Stout), but today there is the single traditional version of John Smith Bitter.

The Courage Bristol Brewery probably had its origins in the late eighteenth century, though there are records going back much earlier. Courage gained quite a reputation at one time for closing down traditional breweries, but in recent years the Bristol Brewery has been extended and the production of real ales expanded.

*Courage Bristol Brewery, Counterslip, Bristol, Avon*
Bitter Ale (OG 1030) – a very light but tasty session bitter
Best Bitter (OG 1039) – the familiar well-malted bitter
Director's (OG 1046) – the flagship ale, a rich and powerful premium bitter

*John Smith, Tadcaster Brewery, Tadcaster, North Yorkshire*
John Smith Bitter (OG 1036) – a pleasant well-flavoured standard bitter

## SCOTTISH AND NEWCASTLE

The infant of the party, Scottish and Newcastle, controls less than half of the public houses of any of the others (around 2,300). Nevertheless, it sells over 10 per cent of the nation's ale (with beer sales of around £800 million per annum). One of the reasons for this, of course, is the popularity of the bottled pressurised Newcastle Brown.

Happily the company has pursued a policy of maintaining regional breweries rather than closing them down in recent years. Five breweries now operate under the Scottish and Newcastle banner, although some rationalisation is likely (particularly with regard to Matthew Brown). S&N also has interests in holiday camps (Pontin's), hotels (Thistle) and restaurants (Chandler's), but brewing and pubs still account for 85 per cent of its turnover.

Theakston's Masham

The company arose from a merger of William McEwan and William Younger in 1931, followed by the purchase of Newcastle Breweries in 1961. Several other breweries were added to the portfolio over the years. The most famous of them is Theakston's of Masham. A splendid old brewery situated in the North Yorkshire Dales, Theakston's still gives regular brewery trips and maintains a tap on the edge of the site. Lack of capacity has meant that the three Theakston beers have been brewed at various locations over the years. After an investment of £1 million the three beers are again all brewed at Masham (although Best Bitter is also brewed at Newcastle). A large proportion of the output from Masham finds its way into a widespread and appreciative free trade.

*Matthew Brown, Lion Brewery, Blackburn, Lancashire*
Mild (OG 1031) – a dark mild of good flavour
Bitter (OG 1036) – a sweetish session bitter

*Fountain Brewery, Fountainbridge, Edinburgh, Scotland*
McEwan 70/- (OG 1036) – a well-rounded session bitter
Younger Scotch (OG 1036) – the same ale under a different name
McEwan 80/- (OG 1042) – a full-flavoured premium ale
Younger IPA (OG 1042) – again, the same beer under a
　　different bar clip
Younger No.3 (OG 1043) – a darker premium ale of good full
　　flavour

*Home Brewery, Daybrook, Nottingham, Nottinghamshire*
Mild (OG 1036) – a dark and full-bodied mild
Bitter (OG 1038) – well-hopped, a distinctive Nottingham bitter

*Theakston, Wellgarth, Masham, North Yorkshire*
Best Bitter (OG 1037) – a light hoppy bitter
XB (OG 1044) – a premium bitter of fuller flavour
Old Peculiar (OG 1057) – the renowned rich strong ale

*Tyne Brewery, Gallowgate, Newcastle*
Theakston Best Bitter (OG 1037) – light and well-hopped

# *Index*